Vietnam

Conflict and Change in Indochina

Alan Pollock

OXFORD

UNIVERSITY PRESS

OXFORD

UNIVERSITY PRESS

253 Normanby Road, South Melbourne, Victoria 3205, Australia.

Oxford University Press is a department of the University of Oxford.
It furthers the University's objective of excellence in research, scholarship,
and education by publishing worldwide in

Oxford New York

Auckland Bangkok Buenos Aires Cape Town Chennai
Dar es Salaam Delhi Hong Kong Istanbul Karachi Kolkata
Kuala Lumpur Madrid Melbourne Mexico City Mumbai Nairobi
São Paulo Shanghai Singapore Taipei Tokyo Toronto

with an associated company in Berlin

OXFORD is a trade mark of Oxford University Press
in the UK and in certain other countries

National Library of Australia
Cataloguing-in-Publication data:

Pollock, Alan, 1954-,

Vietnam: conflict & change in Indochina.
New ed.
Bibliography.
Includes index.

ISBN 0 19 553755 6.

1. Vietnamese Conflict, 1961-1975. 2. Indochina – History –
1945-. 3. Indochina – Relations – Australia. 4. Australia –
Relations – Indochina. 5. Indochina – Relations – United States
6. United States – Relations – Indochina. 7. Vietnam – History –
1975-. I. Pollock, Alan, 1954-. Asian tragedy. II. Title. III.
Title: Asian tragedy.

959.053

Designed by Jennifer Johnston
Cover photograph by Brian Gilks
Maps and diagrams by Juli Kent
Typeset by Bandaid Productions, Melbourne
Printed through Bookpac Production Services, Singapore

*To my beautiful wife and daughters, Reyleen, Jessica and Natalie,
without whose help and patience the work would never have
been completed.*

CONTENTS

TIMELINE   iv

INTRODUCTION   v

  1   INDOCHINA: THE ISSUES TODAY   1

  2   INDOCHINA YESTERDAY   24

  3   FRANCE'S INDOCHINA WAR   38

  4   A NATION DIVIDED   50

  5   AMERICA PLUNGES IN   64

  6   AMERICA PULLS BACK   80

  7   CHOPPERS AND MEN IN BLACK PYJAMAS   91

  8   CAMBODIA AND LAOS   103

  9   REBELLION AT HOME   116

 10   ENDS AND BEGINNINGS   128

NOTES   145

CAST OF CHARACTERS   146

GLOSSARY   148

DOCUMENTARIES AND FILMS   149

BIBLIOGRAPHY   150

INDEX   152

ACKNOWLEDGMENTS   154

TIMELINE

43	Trung sisters lead revolt against Chinese rule
1802	Vietnam unified under Emperor Nguyen Anh
1883	France takes control of Vietnam
1887	French Indochinese Union created
1890	Ho Chi Minh born
1914	World War I breaks out
1917	Russian Revolution begins in October
1930	Indochinese Communist Party formed
1940	Japan occupies Indochina in World War II
1941	Ho Chi Minh forms Vietminh to fight for Vietnamese independence
1945	Ho proclaims Vietnamese independence after Japan defeated; French return to power in southern Vietnam
1946	War begins between French and Vietminh
1949	Laos and Cambodia given limited independence by France
1950	United States begins aiding France
1954	French defeated at Dien Bien Phu; Geneva Conference divides Vietnam into North and South Vietnam
1955	Ngo Dinh Diem elected President of South Vietnam
1957	Vietcong action starts in South Vietnam
1961	US President John Kennedy increases aid and advisers to South Vietnam and Laos
1963	Diem overthrown in coup; President Kennedy assassinated
1964	Tonkin Gulf Resolution gives US President Lyndon Baynes Johnson wide-ranging powers to wage war in South-East Asia
1965	First US and Australian combat troops arrive in Vietnam
1968	Communist Tet offensive
1969	US forces begin to withdraw
1970	Prince Sihanouk overthrown in coup
1972	Gough Whitlam becomes Prime Minister in Australia and withdraws remaining troops
1973	Cease-fire negotiated in Vietnam; last US troops leave Vietnam; coalition government in Laos
1974	US President Richard Nixon resigns over Watergate scandal
1975	Communist takeovers in Vietnam, Laos and Cambodia
1979	Pol Pot defeated by Vietnamese army; China invades Vietnam
1986	Vietnamese leaders adopt policy of Doi Moi, moving away from a centralised economy
1989	Vietnamese troops withdraw from Cambodia
1991	UN-sponsored peace plan signed by Cambodian factions
1993	United Nations-supervised election in Cambodia
1994	United States ends trade embargo against Vietnam

INTRODUCTION

Vietnam: Conflict and Change in Indochina looks primarily at the conflicts that have beset the countries of Indochina (Vietnam, Cambodia and Laos) since the end of World War II. The narrative begins by looking at current issues in Indochina: changes and developments in the countries of the region today, and the struggles of Indochinese refugees and the veterans of the Vietnam War to overcome the scars of that war. Attention is then directed to the roots of the conflict, to Indochina's early history and traditions and to French colonial control, beginning in the nineteenth century. The succeeding chapters view Vietnam's attempt to seize independence and the successive conflicts which have wracked the region as a result — war against the French and the Americans, civil wars and wars between the nations of Indochina themselves.

The Vietnam Wars which dominate this history have caused great controversy in Australia and America ever since the 1960s. Few if any issues in American and Australian politics have caused more furore than Vietnam. Hundreds of thousands of men and women around the world were motivated to take an active political stand on the issue and to protest at the suffering in Vietnam. The Vietnam War reached millions via newspapers and television, indelibly leaving its mark on what has been called the 'Vietnam generation'.

Conflict in Indochina is not a closed issue; not something that is finished and forgotten. Certainly the end of the Vietnam War in 1975 did not stop the arguments about the rights and wrongs of the Australian and US commitment. Former US President Ronald Reagan called Vietnam 'a noble cause'; writer Neil Sheahan characterised it as 'a war without heroes'; another ex-US president, Richard Nixon, believed the US 'won the war but lost the peace'. And the conflict is not over — fighting continues in Cambodia; and all of Indochina is still struggling to emerge from the shadow of thirty years of torment. Overseas, hundreds of thousands of soldiers who fought on the battlefields of Indochina still bear the physical and psychological scars of war, and the hundreds of thousands of refugees who fled Indochina are still trying to rebuild their shattered lives and families. Australia has accepted thousands of Indochinese refugees and has in its midst thousands of veterans of Vietnam, many still attempting to recover from their own agony of involvement. Until recently Australia had soldiers in Cambodia as part of a United Nations peacekeeping force helping to bring stability to that troubled nation. Australian businesses are involved throughout Indochina in building a new economic future for the region.

The study of Conflict and Change in Indochina raises an enormous number of problems and issues which students should deliberate upon, investigate and come to their own conclusions about. Just a few of these problems and issues include: revolutionary and counter-revolutionary forces in Indochina; communism and democracy in Indochina; the changing face of modern warfare; war and peace in Indochina; why America and Australia failed in Vietnam; and the future for Indochina. Many of these concerns are raised in the text or in the activities at the end of each chapter — there are undoubtedly many, many more.

Vietnam: Conflict and Change in Indochina is a very practical text for history teachers and students. It offers a clear, detailed narrative supported by extensive quotations, maps, illustrations, tables, diagrams and photographs. Throughout each chapter there are document studies which will help students develop skills of comprehension and interpretation. The questions that are placed throughout each chapter have several important functions. Some are designed to encourage students to reflect on what they have just read; some require students to make value judgments about others' actions and about their own beliefs. Some of the questions require students to analyse arguments and/or source materials; others are formulated to stimulate further enquiry and research. Activities are provided at the end of each chapter to help students understand the historical information and develop a wide range of learning skills. Teachers should select only those activities they think appropriate. The activities are intended as suggestions, not as fully delineated lessons. Each activities section contains a selection of research topics — they represent a set of suggested areas only. For that reason the topics are wide-ranging; it is up to teachers or students to select a particular topic and to narrow it down into a suitable research theme. A number of appendices complete the book and add to its practicality: a bibliography, a glossary and a cast of the major characters involved.

Vietnam: Conflict and Change in Indochina is not designed to be a student's only source of information; rather, it pushes students towards other sources and opinions through the questions raised by the narrative, sources and the provided activities. Students and teachers should realise that the text relies heavily on the work of Western historians and the sources available to them, chiefly because of the difficulty in obtaining large amounts of Indochinese material. If students and teachers have access to other such sources they should take full advantage of the opportunity.

As Conflict in Indochina is a Modern World Study, students should keep abreast of current events in Indochina by watching the media closely. Newspaper and magazine articles and news and current affairs programs on radio and television provide important and up-to-date material on a topic which is changing from day to day.

1 INDOCHINA: THE ISSUES TODAY

WHERE IS INDOCHINA?

Indochina lies to the north-west of Australia. The map below gives an indication of the distance and direction involved. It also shows that Indochina lies between the two large and populous countries of India and China from where the area gains its name.

Indochina is in South-East Asia, which contains some of the fastest growing economies in the world. The countries of Indochina, Vietnam, Laos and Cambodia do not share this growing prosperity because of the events that will be explained in this history, but there is hope for the future, provided the area can return to peace and stability.

The Asian continent has been wracked by upheavals and disorder since the end of World War II, but Indochina has suffered the longest, and has experienced the greatest damage.

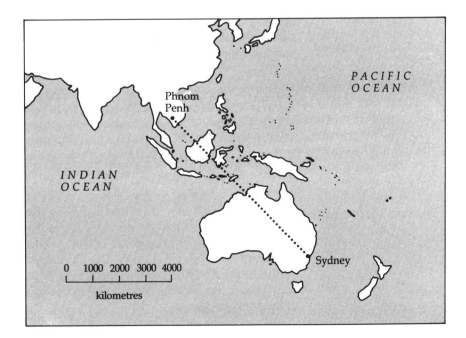

Fig 1.1 The relationship of South-East Asia to Australia. Phnom Penh, capital of Cambodia, is 7031 km from Sydney.

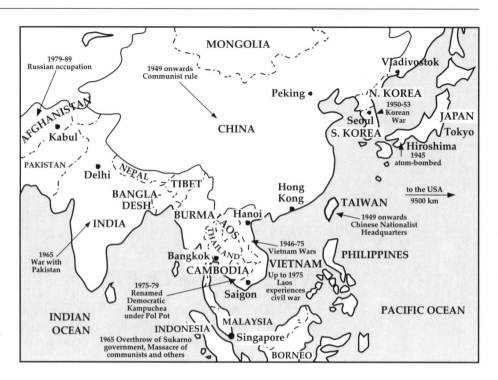

Fig 1.2 Asia has been the scene of continual upheaval, political and social since 1945.

Indochina today is still full of danger, turbulence and change. The region is attempting to recover from the enormous damage done over the last fifty years, during which time the Vietnamese people experienced almost continuous fighting and bloodshed. The conflict was magnified by the direct and indirect involvement of overseas powers, including the United States and France. Laos and Cambodia have also suffered from civil wars and from the Vietnam War which spilled over into their territories.

THE COUNTRIES OF INDOCHINA

Vietnam

Geographically, Vietnam is small, long and narrow. During the years 1954 to 1975 the country was divided into North and South Vietnam. Today the country is unified — the Democratic Socialist Republic of Vietnam.

Vietnam has been described as having the appearance of a farmer who is carrying two baskets of rice, each at the end of a wooden pole. The baskets represent the deltas of the Mekong and Red Rivers in the south and north of the country. The capital of Vietnam is Hanoi, at the mouth of the Red River in the north. Ho Chi Minh City (formerly known as Saigon) is the most important city in the south and lies at the mouth of the Mekong River.

Fig 1.3 Indochina: Vietnam, Cambodia (Kampuchea) and Laos.

Cambodia

Cambodia lies to the east of Vietnam and to the south of Laos. Until 1970, Cambodia successfully avoided most of the suffering and bloodshed experienced by Vietnam and Laos. However, after a military coup in 1970 and a change of government, the country experienced torment few countries have had to endure.

Cambodia is round in shape, with mountains to the north, west and east. The nation's capital, Phnom Penh, is located in the south of the country. In the east, Cambodia is divided from Vietnam by low hills, forming a valley through which the Mekong River flows. Cambodia's territory today is only a small reflection of the powerful empire that existed 1000 years ago. In the recent past Cambodia has had a number of different names. During the period 1970–75, the country was known as the Khmer Republic; between 1975 and 1979 the nation was called Democratic Kampuchea; during the period 1979–89 it was called the People's Republic of Kampuchea. Today it is simply called Cambodia.

Vietnam's coat of arms. The cog-wheel and the rice indicate the importance of agriculture and industry.

Democratic Socialist Republic of Vietnam[1]

Area	330 341 square kilometres
Population	64.3 million (1989)
Government	Communist
Language	Chiefly Vietnamese
Religion	Mostly Buddhist
Currency	Dong
Economy	Agriculture, rice, coffee, spices, timber, rubber, handicrafts, coal and other minerals, some light manufacturing
Geographic features	Long coastline and mountain chain, Mekong and Red River deltas
National symbols	Unicorn, tortoise, phoenix and dragon

Cambodia[2]

Area	181 035 square kilometres
Population	8.2 million (1990)
Government	Multi-party democracy
Language	Khmer
Religion	Chiefly Buddhist
Currency	Riel
Economy	Rubber, rice, pepper, maize, livestock, fish products
Geographical features	Cardomon and Elephant Mountain Ranges, Tonle Sap Lake
National symbols	The symbol of the temples of Angkor Wat has always represented Khmer civilisation

Laos

The history of Laos has been strongly influenced by the proximity of Vietnam and their common border. After Laos was granted independence following World War II, the country was torn apart by a civil war which lasted until 1975 when the Lao communist movement, the Pathet Lao, came to power.

Laos is also a long and narrow country. It is mostly mountainous, and two-thirds of the country are covered by forests. The capital, Vientiane, lies in the north-west. Laos is completely landlocked by its five neighbours: Vietnam, Cambodia, Thailand, China and Burma (Myanmar).

Lao People's Democratic Republic[3]	
Area	236 804 square kilometres
Population	4.2 million (1991)
Government	Communist
Language	Lao
Religion	Chiefly Buddhist and Animist
Currency	Kip
Economy	Mostly agricultural, rice, coffee, timber, hydro-electricity
Geographic features	Annamite Mountain Ranges, Plain of Jars, Mekong River, climate is tropical/monsoonal
National symbols	Before becoming a communist state in 1975, the national symbol was a three-headed white elephant standing on a five-step pedestal under a parasol against a red background. The elephant represents an ancient Lao kingdom, the parasol represents the monarchy, and the steps the five principles of Buddhism

Indochina's major occupation is the growing of rice.

Indochina has a tropical, monsoonal climate. The coolest part of the year is between November and February while the hottest lasts from March to May. At the end of this period the monsoon begins to move in, bringing heavy rains.

WHAT IS INDOCHINA LIKE TODAY?

Due to its much larger size and strength, Vietnam has traditionally dominated Indochina. It has one of the largest (2 million on the active and reserve lists), well-trained and experienced armies in the world.

Evidence of Vietnam's dominance lies in Vietnam's influence on the development of communist movements in Laos and Cambodia, and more recently in the invasion and occupation of Cambodia in 1979. By September 1989, however, Vietnam had withdrawn its troops from Cambodia and is now more intent on solving its own problems. In 1995, as this book went to press, the coalition government of Cambodia was struggling to maintain control of the country in a civil war against the dreaded Khmer Rouge.

Vietnam and Laos signed a 25-year treaty of friendship and cooperation in 1977. Vietnam was a major source of aid for Laos and maintained a large army presence there at the request of the government. All this changed with the collapse of communism in Eastern Europe in the late 1980s. This forced the Vietnamese to abandon both their long-standing alliance with the Soviet Union and their special interest in the countries of Indochina. The Vietnamese were forced to concentrate on their own survival and therefore worked hard to improve relations with China, USA and the ASEAN nations. Thus, today Vietnam is not a major source of aid for Laos nor does it maintain a military force in that nation.

■ What might happen in Cambodia in the future?

What changes have been made in Indochina?

Along with other communist nations around the world in the late 1980s, communist Vietnam, Cambodia and Laos took steps to expose their economies to market forces by introducing a measure of free enterprise. Like the USSR, Poland, Hungary and China, Vietnam found that her economy was neither producing enough commodities nor being efficient enough under highly centralised, state-directed communist control. In simple terms, communism was failing to produce the standard of living that capitalism was producing. As journalist, Colin Leinster has written:

> Thirteen years after a North Vietnamese tank rolled through the gates of Saigon's Independence Palace, Vietnam's Communist rulers are openly waving the economic equivalent of a white flag . . . Party General Secretary Nguyen Van Linh, 74, has begun acknowledging that a strong dose of capitalism is essential to revive Vietnam's moribund economy.[4]

The economy of Vietnam was close to collapse during the 1980s. Vietnam's problems included: inflation running at between 700 and 1000 per cent; unemployment in the major cities of 20 per cent; few Vietnamese factories operating at more than half capacity; the country's infrastructure (roads, railways, bridges, ports etc.) needing billions of dollars worth of rebuilding; a poorly educated population; and little access to modern technology.

■ Will communism remain a force in Indochina?

The Vietnamese government's response was to introduce the policy of Doi Moi or Renovation in 1986. This meant a movement towards a market economy where private business is encouraged along with foreign investment. Communist control has not been relinquished, however: there are no free elections and the press is firmly controlled by the government.

CURRENT DIRECTIONS IN INDOCHINA

The enormous problems in Indochina have not been solved overnight, but with the changes discussed above and the lifting of the US trade embargo in 1994 (which allowed a huge rush of overseas investment into Vietnam), the possibility of greater prosperity exists in the future.

Even in 1989 there were signs of improvement. *The Far Eastern Economic Review* of April 1989 reported: 'The prospects for trade, aid and inward investment are beginning to look brighter . . .' and that there had been a:

> sudden upsurge in economic activity, 1000s of small private enterprises and shops selling a greater variety of imported and locally produced goods have sprung up in Hanoi and Ho Chi Minh City since last year.[5]

In 1994 Vietnam's economy was growing at an average of 8 per cent, inflation was down to 17 per cent and rice production and exports in general were booming. The end of the US embargo on foreign aid and investment means that foreign businesses will be lining up to be involved in the Vietnamese economy. Many people in Vietnam are certainly more prosperous than before, but Vietnam is still a very poor nation with a myriad of economic and social problems to confront in the future.

Source 1.1   The end of the embargo

US lifts trade embargo on Vietnam

WASHINGTON, Friday: The United States President, Mr Bill Clinton, yesterday lifted the 19-year trade embargo on Vietnam in a move estimated to unleash the equivalent of about $A5.7 billion worth of business deals for US companies.

But Mr Clinton, ever mindful of the intense opposition to his decision from prisoner-of-war and missing-in-action lobby groups, warned that the move was reversible if the Vietnam Government ceased co-operating over returning the remains of US soldiers.

And he claimed that "trade questions did not enter into this decision . . . I never had a briefing on it and we never had a discussion about it".

Although recent opinion polls show a slim majority of Americans favour ending the ban, veterans groups claimed the President had broken his word to the families of those missing in action in order to satisfy business interests.

More than 2200 US servicemen are still listed as missing in various areas of South-East Asia, including 1647 in Vietnam.

Australia has been one of many countries taking advantage of the prohibition on US investment in Vietnam — a situation that has left scores of US firms watching helplessly as their competitors in Japan, France and elsewhere snapped up lucrative contracts in the increasingly liberal Vietnamese economy.

Such major US firms as Caterpillar Inc, Mobil, General Electric and the major airlines are poised to leap into what they hope will be lucrative infrastructure, energy and transport sectors in Vietnam.

Ms Ann Mills Griffiths, the sister of a missing soldier and executive director of the National League of Families of American Prisoners and Missing in South-East Asia, said the President had "clearly broken his promise" to keep full pressure on Hanoi to resolve the MIA issue.

Announcing his decision in the White House, Mr Clinton said he was lifting the embargo because "I am absolutely convinced it offers the best way to resolve the fate of those who remain missing and about whom we are not sure".

Pilita Clark,
Sydney Morning Herald,
5 February 1994

Questions

1 What does the lifting of the embargo mean?

2 Comment on Clinton's statement that trade questions did not enter into this decision.

3 What concerns does the veterans lobby have?

4 Why were major US firms so keen to have the embargo lifted?

Source 1.2   Hanoi wins the peace

Hanoi looks to growth as it finally wins the peace

The lifting of the United States' trade embargo against Vietnam yesterday symbolised the acceptance of the end of the war by the US side, 19 years after communist tanks rolled into Saigon to occupy the Presidential Palace.

For the Communist Party-controlled Vietnamese Government, the lifting of the embargo marks the re-entry of Vietnam into the international community. The nation that won the Vietnam War only to become a virtual pariah in the eyes of all but the former Soviet Bloc has now re-established diplomatic ties across the international political spectrum with China, the European nations and Australia.

Although the US has not for-mally normalised diplomatic ties, the end of the embargo is seen as the first step.

From a practical point of view, the private US investment and aid which is expected to flow into Vietnam — and the international aid which will be available with US co-operation within bodies such as the World Bank and the International Monetary Fund — will make the long-overdue reconstruction of the nation possible.

Although Vietnam abandoned the disastrous Soviet-style centralised economic system in 1986, its efforts to stimulate economic growth through the creation of a market economy have been only moderately successful, largely because the Government is desperately short of cash and has been unable to rebuild much of the infrastructure ruined during the war. Every business venture in Vietnam has been hampered by appalling transport links and difficult communication.

"For the Vietnamese, the war ended in 1975 but the life which followed in the Soviet orbit was pretty miserable and terribly poor," said one diplomat. "In reality, the end of the embargo marks the end of the war and for the first time there is real cause for optimism that the country will be rebuilt."

Louise Williams,
Sydney Morning Herald,
5 February 1994

Questions

1 What will the lifting of the US investment and aid embargo mean to the Vietnamese economy?

2 Explain the statement: 'the end of the embargo marks the end of the war'.

Laos and Cambodia are both following similar economic paths to Vietnam. In both countries the private sector (small businesses producing for the local market or trading overseas) has been encouraged in an attempt to fuel economic recovery. Some success was recorded by the *Far Eastern Economic Review* of February 1988: 'more liberal economic policies, introduced in 1986, have led to a minor economic boom and a measure of prosperity in Phnom Penh'.[6] By 1993 Laos had lowered its inflation rate to below 15 per cent with growth almost reaching 9 per cent while per capita incomes have more than doubled in the last five years.

The vice-president of the Asian Development Bank, William Thompson said in Sydney in December 1993:

> This (the Mekong Region) is where two of the fastest-growing economies in the world, China and Thailand, intersect with the virtually untouched natural resources of Laos, Burma, Vietnam and Cambodia. We regard the outlook for Indochina as very positive.[7]

Source 1.3   Economic change in Laos

The Lao learning curve

The silent dusty exhibition halls of the "Museum of the Revolution" overlook a grassy vacant block where a hand-painted billboard announces the next chapter in the history of the ruling Communist Party of Laos. Here, the sign says, a new five-star hotel and shopping arcade will rise, amidst the muddle of peeling French colonial villas and frangipani trees, the Chinese-style shop houses and the concrete Soviet flats of the capital, Vientiane.

Already life has changed dramatically under one of the last Communist Party-run governments in the world. The austere Soviet-inspired economic policies have been replaced by market forces, filling Vientiane with consumer goods and an air of liberty which contrasts sharply to the days of re-education camps and production co-operatives.

Economic growth this year is expected to reach 7 per cent and, with inflation back to single digits from almost 90 per cent, Laos may be close to achieving the difficult marriage

of economic liberalisation and single-party political rule.

But, behind the bright, bustling market-places lies a long history of secrecy and social and political control. As in neighbouring Vietnam, many of the men and women who won the war against Western imperialism retain political control.

The "westernisation" of the Lao people's social values is still greatly feared and a question remains as to how many nightclubs and idle youths drag-racing motor bikes will be tolerated in the name of economic growth.

Laos is listed by the United Nations as one of the world's least-developed countries with an annual average income of $US220. In 1991, it faced potential catastrophe when it lost both its ideological big brother and main aid donor with the collapse of the Soviet Union. But, like Vietnam, the Lao Communist Party leadership set out to buy its own survival with growth. As one Lao official said: "We cannot afford the kind of roller-coaster crisis in which you say that things have to get

worse before they get better. Things just have to get better."

The State Bank stopped printing money to cover the budget deficit and cut loans to unprofitable State enterprises; thousands of Government employees were stood down and hundreds of licences were issued to foreign investors to make up for the sudden loss of Soviet capital . . .

But, market-driven economic growth is seen as a mechanism with which to raise the credibility of the ruling party, not a new ideology for the nation. The Government believes new influences must be strictly controlled and few observers can be certain what this might mean.

Early next year an Australian-built bridge across the Mekong will directly link Thailand and Laos for the first time. Thailand's freewheeling capitalists are already widely blamed for the return of brothels and drugs to Vientiane, which was forcibly cleared of prostitutes, pimps and addicts in 1975. Thai television, which beams its popular soaps into Laos, is undermining earnest attempts to retain conservative family values.

Economic development has clearly widened the gap between Vientiane and the isolated villages of subsistence farmers in much of the rest of the country, as well as between city entrepreneurs and the poorly paid Government workers. But, the Government's fears are not about the poor, said one official, who admitted that crime and violence were rising.

"Being poor doesn't make you into a thief. Most poor people are very good people. It is a question of social values as a whole and we can see already that values are changing."

Louise Williams,
Sydney Morning Herald,
25 October 1993

Questions

1 How has life changed dramatically in Laos?

2 'The "westernisation" of the Lao people's social values is still greatly feared.' Why, and to what extent, has this happened?

Cambodia has by far the greatest difficulties as the country is still not at peace. For over a decade (from 1979), resistance forces (particularly the Khmer Rouge) fought a civil war against the Vietnamese occupying forces and the Vietnamese-backed communist government of Cambodia.

The Vietnamese forces were withdrawn in 1989 and a peace plan was agreed upon by all the resistance factions in 1991. Multi-party elections were held in 1993, resulting in a coalition government formed by FUNCINPEC, a royalist party, and the Cambodian People's Party (CPP), which had controlled the previous communist government. (The CPP has, however, abandoned communism and has pledged to allow a free market economy and a multi-party democracy.)

■ Will Cambodia's future be as black as its recent past?

But the war continues between the new government and the Khmer Rouge who opted out of the UN-sponsored peace process and refused to lay down its arms. The Khmer Rouge, while small in numbers, is well-armed, tightly organised and has the finances to keep the war going indefinitely. Whilst in power (1975–79) the Khmer Rouge were responsible for the deaths of an estimated 2 million of their fellow Cambodians. The nation is balanced on a knife's edge.

Cambodian refugee camp. Millions of Cambodians were forced to flee their country in the 1970s, 1980s and 1990s.

Source 1.4   Continuing division in Cambodia

Sihanouk losing hope for peace?

PHNOM PENH: King Norodom Sihanouk has expressed "despair" at fading hopes of unifying Cambodia and the "silence" of the Khmer Rouge guerilla faction on his cease-fire proposal.

"From the side of the Cambodian Government, they agree with this cease-fire, but the Khmer Rouge remain silent in this regard," the ailing 71-year-old monarch said in a letter to the United Nations Secretary-General, Dr Boutros Boutros-Ghali, dated May 25.

A roundtable peace summit between the coalition Government and Khmer Rouge is scheduled to be held at King Sihanouk's North Korean residence from tomorrow to Tuesday, but he conceded prospects for reconciliation appear dim.

He said Cambodia was "unfortunately divided into two parts, one of which is composed of government zones and the other of "Khmer Rouge autonomous zones". He said the chances of ending Cambodia's partitioning were slim.

"It's a problem that, over the long term, threatens the very existence of Cambodia, which saddens me so much and which plunges me into despair," he said.

The Khmer Rouge, which has inflicted two major military defeats on government forces, has agreed to send a seven-man delegation to the talks at Pyongyang.

The Maoist-inspired insurgents are held responsible for the deaths of a million Cambodians during a reign of terror in the 1970s when they governed Cambodia. They continue to wage guerilla war to back demands for an advisory role in government.

Earlier, Cambodia's Second Prime Minister, Mr Hun Sen, predicted the peace talks had a "point one per cent" chance of success.

King Sihanouk had called on both warring parties to declare a cease-fire on June 15 and sign a national unification agreement after the peace talks. The Khmer Rouge has insisted that the talks be unconditional.

King Sihanouk's peace plan also calls for establishment of a cease-fire commission to be supervised by neutral generals.

Mark Dodd,
Sydney Morning Herald,
27 May 1994

Questions

1 Who are the warring parties in Cambodia?
2 How is Cambodia effectively partitioned?
3 Why is Sihanouk losing hope?
4 What is happening in Cambodia today?

AMERICAN AND AUSTRALIAN VIETNAM VETERANS

Many of the Australian and American soldiers who fought in the Vietnam War have had problems in adjusting to life back in society. Several reasons have been put forward to explain this. US soldiers in Vietnam were the first Americans not to emerge victorious from a war. Australian and US soldiers were also considerably younger than their predecessors in Korea and WWII. Because of helicopter mobility and modern medical methods, many soldiers returned home with crippling injuries or severe disfigurements. Another reason is that drugs were cheap and widely available in Vietnam.

Many veterans were also exposed to dangerous chemicals in the defoliation campaigns which may have led to serious medical problems. From 1962 until 1971, millions of litres of herbicide were sprayed on South

Vietnamese forests in an attempt to take away the cover of the Vietcong guerilla fighters. The region most heavily sprayed was the area where the Australians operated. Agent Orange was the name given to the most common herbicide used. It contains dioxin which is known to cause cancer and birth defects in unborn children.

The Vietnam veterans were often welcomed home with contempt and hostility rather than parades and flag waving. Some were accused of being baby killers and were spat at by anti-war protesters. The Returned & Services League (RSL) failed to provide much help and government agencies were unsympathetic. In the USA it is estimated that 700 000 veterans are suffering or have suffered from some form of 'post-traumatic stress disorder' (the modern name for battle fatigue).

Source 1.5   Coming home from Vietnam

I landed at Travis Air Force Base in California. I did the traditional things, kiss the ground when I got off the plane, and all that. I was so happy that I had survived. And I had a thirty-day leave. It was March 1967.

I didn't spend any money in Vietnam, so I had a lot of money. My brother was living in Berkeley at the time. So I figured I would take a cab to visit my brother before I went back to Philadelphia to see my family. As I'm riding down Telegraph Avenue I told the cab driver that I wanted to walk. It was sunny and beautiful, all these bright colors and people. And the cab driver said, 'Are you sure you want to get out here?' Well, of course, I didn't know what was going on. I got out of the cab. I was in my Class A uniform.

I was spit on. This gang of guys walking behind me threw peanuts at me. I went into a bar and phoned my brother. I almost didn't make it out of there. The real shock of coming back was in that bar. These guys weren't going to let me out. They wanted to kick my ass. Calling, 'You kill any women? You kill any kids?'

These guys were long-haired, long-bearded. And my brother and Nicky and about five other guys came and busted into the bar. There was a big hassle and I stopped them from fighting. I just wanted to get out. My brother drove me to his home and told me what the score was because I didn't understand. I just didn't know.

We went out to a dance that night. All I had was my Class A uniform. And boy, it was such a shock. People looking at me like, 'You scum'. They'd walk by and spit on the ground. And I got this tremendous feeling that I had done something wrong. It was like I wasn't supposed to have survived.

Frank McCarthy,
quoted in A. Santoli,
To Bear Any Burden, p.111

Questions

1 How did people react to the soldier returning from Vietnam?
2 Would all people have reacted in this way?
3 Why were so many reactions negative?
4 How would the welcome the soldier received have affected him at the time and in the future?

In the 1980s the Vietnam veterans began to receive some of the recognition they deserved. In 1982 in the USA the Vietnam War Memorial was unveiled in Washington before a crowd of 150 000. In 1987 in Australia, Vietnam veterans proudly led the Anzac Day March and in October of the same year, a 'Welcome Home' March was held in Sydney. In 1994 a Vietnam Memorial was unveiled in Canberra by Prime Minister

Paul Keating. Gradually the public has accepted the debt owed to those who fought in Vietnam. In the 1994 budget, the Labor government earmarked 20 million dollars to be spent on the treatment of post-traumatic stress disorder amongst Australian Vietnam veterans. On a trip to Vietnam in 1994, the first by an Australian Prime Minister since the war ended, Paul Keating spoke about the need for a memorial in Vietnam. He said:

> . . . those who died in Vietnam died with the same faith in Australia, with the same courage, the same willingness to lay down their lives for their country as those who died in other wars . . . In the future, Australian Prime Ministers will come to Vietnam regularly, and when they do, like me, they will remember those who suffered and died in that terrible conflict of the '60s and '70s. And I confidently expect that, in due course, they will be able to remember them at a suitable memorial.[8]

Source 1.6   I was only nineteen

Mum and Dad and Denny saw the passing out parade at Puckapunyal.
(It was a long march from cadets.)
The sixth Battalion was the next to tour and it was me who drew the card.
We did Canungra and Shoalwater before we left.
And Townsville lined the footpaths as we marched down to the quay.
This clipping from the paper shows us young and strong and clean,
And there's me in me slouch hat with me S.L.R. and greens.
God help me, I was only nineteen.
From Vung Tau riding Chinooks to the dust at Nui Dat
I've been in and out of choppers now for months.
But we made our tents a home. V.B. and pinups on the lockers,
And an Asia orange sunset through the scrub.
And can you tell me doctor, why I still can't get to sleep?
The night-time's just a jungle dark and a barking M.16?
And what's this rash that comes and goes, can you tell me what it means?
God help me, I was only nineteen.
A four week operation any step can mean your last one
On two legs, it was a war within yourself.
But you wouldn't let your mates down 'til they had you dusted off.
So you closed your eyes and thought about something else,
And then someone yelled out 'Contact!' and the bloke behind me swore.
We hooked in there for hours, then a god-almighty roar.
And Frankie kicked a mine the day that mankind kicked the moon.
God help me, he was going home in June.
I can still see Frankie drinking tinnies in the Grand Hotel
On a thirty-six hour rec. leave in Vung Tau.
And I can still hear Frankie lying screaming in the jungle,
'Till the morphine came and killed the bloody row.
And the Anzac legends didn't mention mud and blood and tears,
And the stories that my Father told me never seemed quite real.
I caught some pieces in my back that I didn't even feel.
God help me, I was only nineteen.
And can you tell me doctor, why I still can't get to sleep?
Any why the Channel 7 chopper chills me to my feet?
And what's this rash that comes and goes, can you tell me what it means?
God help me, I was only nineteen.

Song by John Schumann

Questions

1 Why does the song repeat 'God help me, I was only nineteen'?
2 What are the following: SLR, Chinooks, VB, M16, rec. leave, Nui Dat, 'Contact'?
3 How has the war affected the digger in the song?

Agent Orange — What has it done?

Veteran organisations in the US and Australia still strongly argue that Vietnam vets have not received sufficient aid from governments to meet their special needs and hardships. Australian veteran groups are especially bitter about the failure of governments to compensate veterans for the damage done to them and their families by exposure to chemical defoliants like Agent Orange. By 1980 veterans were reporting various disabilities but were receiving little or no help from governments or the RSL. In 1985 the Evatt Royal Commission on the effects of chemical agents on Australian personnel in Vietnam declared that there was not enough evidence to prove that Agent Orange had caused harm to servicemen. The Commission has been criticised since by leading academics for a lack of scientific understanding and for drawing a number of unwarranted conclusions. NSW Vietnam Veterans' Association President Tim McCombe described the Commission as 'a conspiracy to save the government money'. The Commission did state that the different nature of the war had been particularly stressful for the soldiers involved and that this could have caused psychological problems back in society and that therefore the veterans were entitled to Repatriation benefits.

In America successful court action by veterans has forced seven chemical companies to set up a multi-million-dollar fund to help veterans and their families. Soldiers who served in Vietnam receive compensation for three diseases linked to dioxin, an ingredient in Agent Orange. And in 1993 the US Department of Veterans' Affairs added two more diseases caused by exposure to Agent Orange to those for which veterans could receive compensation. Tim McCombe commented: 'This is the final nail in the credibility of the Evatt Royal Commission.'

■ Do you think the veterans should have to fight to be compensated?

Source 1.7 Agent Orange breakthrough

Govt finally faces medical facts

The Federal Government has finally surrendered to medical evidence that chemical defoliants including Agent Orange are responsible for some cancers and other maladies suffered by about 600 Australian Vietnam veterans.

The veterans will now be eligible for compensation and medical benefits for their wartime exposure to the herbicides, which will cost the Government an estimated $3 million.

However, the costs could rise if more of the 50,000 Australians who served in Vietnam develop these cancers in the future.

The wives of veterans who have died of these diseases will also be eligible for war widows' pensions.

The Federal Government

announced yesterday it had accepted the report of an independent medical committee which found there was sufficient evidence to link the herbicides to a range of diseases.

These are chlorachne, soft tissue sarcoma, porphyria cutanea tarda, non-Hodgkin's lymphoma, Hodgkin's disease, multiple myeloma, leukaemia and cancer of the lung, larnyx and trachea.

The Government had already accepted the link between the herbicides and some of these conditions.

Professor Robert MacLennan of the Queensland Institute of Medical Research and Professor Peter Smith of the Royal Children's Hospital in Melbourne were commissioned last year to examine a 1993 US National Academy of Sciences report that found exposure to herbicide had caused cancers in US Vietnam veterans.

They endorsed the US findings and had also accepted there was a link between herbicide exposure and leukaemia.

The Minister for Veterans' Affairs, Mr Sciacca, said that the report would be a landmark for veterans.

"I welcome the committee's findings on what has long been a matter of considerable contention amongst Vietnam veterans," he said. "It is my expectation that this report and subsequent action by the Government, will address the continuing concerns of many

Vietnam veterans who were exposed to herbicides during their war service.

"While the Australian report came up with a similar outcome to the US report, it was appropriate that our indepen-

A HISTORY OF AGENT ORANGE

1962	The spraying of defoliants on Vietnam begins
1965	Australian 1st Battalion arrives in Vietnam
1967	American Botanist Arthur Galston of Yale queries long term effects of herbicides on Vietnam's environment
1970	Swedish report that 2, 4, 5, T and 2,4-D may cause cancer
1971	Spraying ends
1977	Veterans' Administration in US discovers illness among Vietnam veterans who blame exposure to Agent Orange
1979	Defence Minister Mr Jim Killen claims no Australian troops exposed to Agent Orange
1979	Three Vietnam veterans claim illness caused by exposure to herbicides
1982	Senate inquiry rejects claims
1983 to 1985	Evatt Commission conducted: Agent Orange not guilty
1985 to 1993	Claims continued to be pressed, with Government resisting
1989	Conference in Canberra reassesses Evatt commission and makes damning statements on its methodology and findings
1993	Opening up of Vietnam reveals large numbers of deformed children and evidence that links these with Agent Orange
1994	A number of other cancers added to the list of those which entitle Vietnam veterans to compensation
1994	Questions of genetic damage on children and grandchildren of veterans still unanswered

dent expert medical specialists reviewed the material before any action was taken."

Veterans have been frustrated in their drawn-out campaign for compensation, particularly after the controversial findings of the 1985 Evatt royal commission which cleared Agent Orange.

The medical evidence is now clearly in their favour but some veterans are bitter about the Government's tardiness in accepting these findings.

A Canberra Vietnam veteran, Mr Mike Boland, said yesterday that there was a common thread in the battle for compensation of the nuclear testing veterans, survivors from the HMAS Voyager sinking and the servicemen exposed to the defoliants.

"In each case the Government has taken the stand right from the word go that they would fight like mad to avoid paying compensation," he said.

"The common denominator is the unaccountability of the bureaucracy."

Between 1962 and 1971, the US military sprayed about 72 million litres of herbicide including more than 42 million litres of Agent Orange on the jungles of Vietnam in a bid to deny the North Vietnamese and Vietcong troops the cover they needed to wage a guerilla war.

Ironically, many veterans have pointed out that the rapid jungle regrowth was so thick and vigorous than it provided better concealment that the original foliage.

Mr Sciacca said the Australian report had been referred to the Repatriation Medical Authority, which would develop a system for veterans to lodge claims.

David Lague,
Sydney Morning Herald,
8 October 1994

Questions

1 Why did the Federal Government finally decide to compensate the veterans?

2 What exactly did the government decide to do?

THE REFUGEE PROBLEM

Since 1975 almost 2 million Indochinese have fled their countries. By 1987 a total of almost 700 000 Indochinese refugees had arrived in Thailand by land and sea. Over 118 000 were still in Thai refugee camps at that time. By 1988, Australia was the fourth largest recipient of Indochinese migrants — (116 997) — behind the United States (714 782), China (284 000) and Canada (121 182).

The refugees have fled for many reasons. Some have left because of their fear of communism (particularly its rigid social control and the abolition of private enterprise). Many have fled because they had been identified with the losing side in Vietnam, Laos or Cambodia. The Hmong people of the mountains of Laos, for example, escaped to Thailand primarily because they had been recruited by the US to fight the Pathet Lao. The losing sides in Indochina were often treated very cruelly in re-education or labour camps.

Thousands of Chinese living in Vietnam fled after 1975 when the communist government began to actively discriminate against them. In Cambodia, thousands escaped from the terror of Pol Pot's government and later from the invading Vietnamese army. Perhaps the majority left simply to look for a better life and a better chance for their children away from the poverty of Indochina.

The majority of Indochinese refugees fled their shattered homes to a country on or near their borders, a nation of first asylum, such as Thailand, Malaysia or Hong Kong before resettling in a third country such as Australia, Canada, Britain or the USA. However, many thousands of 'boat people' travelled much further. Travelling to Indonesia and Australia, refugees have endured nightmarish voyages of thousands of kilometres in small, overcrowded, leaky boats, always at the mercy of the weather, pirates and corrupt officials.

The nations of first asylum have found it difficult to provide adequate facilities for the refugees. In 1989, Hong Kong had nineteen different refugee camps containing over 50 000 boat people and refugees. In the late 1980s many of these nations objected to the continuing influx of Indochinese refugees, which places great strains on their economies. They have publicly questioned whether the majority of the more recent arrivals are genuine refugees fleeing persecution or simply people leaving to find better economic conditions for their families.

The major resettlement nations like the US and Australia have also become less willing to take large numbers of refugees, particularly with the impact of recession in the early 1990s. About 300 boat people, most of them Cambodian, were being held in detention centres in Australia in 1994

■ Do the nations who fought in Vietnam have a moral obligation to take more refugees?

awaiting court decisions on their applications to be recognised as refugees. The government had detained them because they arrived in Australia illegally. Some have been locked up for almost four years. By May 1994, only forty Cambodian refugees remained in detention in Australia. About a third of the 300 had been granted refugee status, and 149 repatriated back to Cambodia with the promise that if they stayed a year then they would be eligible to migrate to Australia.

Source 1.8   Hung's story

Hung is twenty-seven years old and comes from central Viet-nam. Prior to the change of government in 1975, he lived in Saigon, the capital of former South Viet-nam, where he was a university student.

The arrival of the new regime brought many changes.

Hung and fellow students were soon required to spend periods of one month in special labour camps in the country. Eventually, students whose parents had held positions in the defeated government were sent out of the universities. They were considered to be of no use to the new government. By this time, Hung had decided to leave the country, realising that there would be no place for him in the new society.

Returning to where his family lived in central Viet-nam, Hung developed a plan of escape in collaboration with three old high school friends. After considerable negotiation a boat was purchased. Hung revealed the plan to his parents the night before the intended day of departure. Although his father was against the scheme, there was little he could do to prevent it. The following day, as planned, the boat left without incident. After a day at sea, the boat was rescued by an Indonesian vessel and the twenty passengers were eventually transported to a refugee camp near Jakarta.

Hung was prepared to seek resettlement in any country that would accept him. Eight months passed before he was accepted for resettlement in Australia, a country he knew nothing of.

Once in Australia, Hung commenced English classes while living in one of the migrant hostels in Melbourne. Although 'fluent' in 'broken English', the process of understanding the new environment required many months.

Shortly after his arrival, an Australian couple visited the hostel and provided explanations for many of the unknowns Hung was faced with. It wasn't long before this same family assisted Hung to move out of the hostel and secure both accommodation and employment as a tram conductor.

In 1979, he was able to return to part-time study at university and thus have his qualifications recognised by completing the final two years of a degree already finished in Vietnam.

In 1981, Hung's five brothers and two sisters arrived in Australia. They had made the sea journey to one of the larger Vietnamese refugee camps situated on Pulau Bidong Island, Malaysia.

Soon after, Hung rented a house large enough to accommodate his family aged between seven and twenty-seven. His role as 'parent' involved many new responsibilities. Having already been in Australia for three years, he was now fully conversant with the way of life and thus able to introduce his brothers and sisters to their new country, with minimal assistance from others.

Although concerned with their progress at school, Hung realised that his younger brothers and sisters needed a lot of time to watch television and play with school friends, and thus gain an insight into life in Australia through their own experience. Late in 1982, Hung received news that his parents and three cousins had arrived in a refugee camp in Indonesia. Once again, a sponsorship form was lodged with the Department of Immigration and Ethnic Affairs and early in 1983, the whole family was reunited.

Six years had elapsed since the day Hung had left Viet-nam. Another house was required to accommodate the large extended family.

As observed by many of Hung's friends, his was a lucky family to be reunited in Australia. For many, the dream of family reunion is second only to that of one day going back to Viet-nam.

The family was very happy to be together again. However, life was not without its usual problems. Hung's father was concerned that his children were not receiving enough discipline. He often gave them additional homework to do when he considered that the schools hadn't set enough. Hung understood his father's concern and that he hadn't been in Australia long enough to realise that life was, in many ways, very different from Viet-nam. However, the traditional relationship between father and son prevented Hung from explaining such matters.

In Viet-nam, Hung would have consulted his grandfather who would in turn use his position as father to influence his son. The grandparents had, however, remained in Viet-nam. For persons of their age, the adjustment to life in Australia would be too great. This friction between father and son remains unresolved. Hung also resented his father's wish to choose a wife for him . . . Life in Australia, although presenting new and often difficult challenges, is without the problems left behind. Even Hung's father, who recently stated '. . . we are free to speak, but I don't speak the language', realises that the opportunities for his children are much better in Australia. Hung is philosophical about the future: '. . . for sure I will go back to visit and maybe there is hope to return for good . . . but I know I would be disappointed; things change, and we change, but . . . got to have a dream.'

Phillip Benoun et al.,
The Peoples from Indochina, pp. 20-22

Questions

1 What are your feelings about and reactions to Hung's life story?
2 Which do you think were the most difficult problems Hung faced in settling into life in Australia?
3 If you were Hung would you be interested in returning to Vietnam?

Source 1.9   I feel like an animal in a cage

I am one of the Cambodian boat people who have never known what peace, freedom, or human rights are. I have never known what it is like to have love and affection from my father. He was killed when I was two years old. I lived with my mother, my sisters and brother without a father. All of us lived through very rough and hard times during the Pol Pot regime. We did not have much food to eat. We ate only watery porridge. Luckily we are still alive.

We hoped that the new regime which was governed by Hun Sen would bring freedom, prosperity and respect human rights. But our hopes were like smoke. It came and went so quickly: the regime's concern was their power and their money. I went to school like other children. I was supposed to be treated like other children. Unfortunately, I did not receive the same treatment because my mother is a widow. They also looked down on me because I did not have a father to serve the regime.

Those who were lazy and didn't study still received good results. They always received a good mark. It was because their father or relatives worked for the government or they bribed the teachers. The daytime teachers knew only money. If someone gave them money they would treat them better. I always wondered when this bribery and corruption would end. We were powerless and could not do anything. Our family was classified as ethnic Chinese (N:351). I was hurt badly.

I wondered when I could avoid this oppressive regime. I had struggled to stay for 10 years until my mother received the news that there was a fishing boat wanting to flee Cambodia seeking peace and freedom. My mother then sent my sister, my brother-in-law and me to the boat. Our separation began. My tears started to fall.

I left Kampong Som province and went into the jungle for one day. It seemed my life was blown by the wind and without destination. I looked around me. There were people hiding and waiting to escape. I ate lunch and dinner in the jungle regardless of how the rice tasted. I was lucky to have it at all.

When I was on the boat I was shocked. I thought about why I played with my life on the sea. I did not know what to do because if I returned I would be killed. So I took a risk and trusted my destiny. From the boat I could not see anything except the sky and big waves. We arrived in Singapore about three days later. We asked the Singaporean authorities to let our boats land on their shore, but they refused. Our boat had run out of food and fuel to continue our journey. We were lucky the Singapore army supplied us with fuel and food.

There wasn't enough food because there were too many of us on the boat. It was very hot during the daytime and there wasn't enough shade to cover us from the sun. I was in the front of the boat. I was sitting in the hot sun during the daytime and soaked with salty water at night-time. All my body was covered by salt. We did not take a bath or clean our bodies until we arrived in Australia, which was more than 20 days later.

When I put foot on Australian soil I felt I was born again. I couldn't believe that we had made it to Australia. I was very happy and full of hope that I would have a peaceful life, freedom and a bright future. But my hope did not last very long. It disappeared shortly after our arrival. We were transferred to Springvale Migrant Enterprise Hostel in Melbourne. We were guarded by five or six of the uniformed officers. I learnt later that they were from the Australian Protective Service. I had to report three times a day and was prohibited to walk out of the hostel. When I first arrived at the hostel, there were a lot of Cambodians who came to visit us. They came to see in case their relatives, from whom they had been separated for a long time, were among the boat people.

I was very excited when I met my brother. He came to Australia in 1982. I wanted to live with him but sadly I was not able to because the immigration authorities wouldn't allow us to reunite. I have a feeling that the department tried to separate our family. Our living was very harsh in the centre. We were not allowed to leave the hostel and the rules were as strict as in gaol.

One thing that terrified me was that one day at about 6 am while I was sleeping someone knocked on the door. When I opened the door there were three people. One of them was a Cambodian interpreter; the other two were from Immigration. They told me that I was being transferred to another place in Sydney. We had to pack all of our clothes and belongings within an hour. I couldn't do anything at the time. My body was shaky and numb. I didn't trust the department and was fearful that they were going to send us back to Cambodia. I knew that I was powerless. My tears fell non-stop.

I begged the Immigration officer to make a phone call to my brother but they didn't listen. In August 1991 I was transferred to Westbridge Migrant Detention Centre [Villawood]. My first bad feeling when I arrived at Westbridge Centre was when I saw the double fence with barbed wire on the top. I knew that it was the end of my dream for peace and freedom. I have risked my life trying to escape from an oppressive and corrupt country. Now, I end up in a heartless and inhuman country; the country that treated us worse than their pets; the country that gave us no freedom.

I heard a lot before I came that Australia is a humanitarian country. People were kind and had open hands to help other people such as refugees. Now, I know the reality. I have been kept in the centre with double fences like an animal in a cage. I am hurt badly. I have suffered too much since I was born.

I am 17 years old now, but my future is still in a very dark cave. A story which is well known to a lot of Cambodian people is "the water is full of hungry crocodiles. On the land there are hungry tigers. At the same time the mouse is eating the string that is holding you." So which way do I have to go? My only hope now is to beg the Australian people and Minister for Immigration to allow us to stay so that I can experience the peace and freedom which I have been waiting for the past 17 years. Please help me.

Kim Leang Thai's story told by
Helen Signy,
Sydney Morning Herald,
5 November 1993

Questions

1 Why did Kim Leang Thai want to escape from Hun Sen's Cambodia?

2 Outline Kim's experience as a boat person coming to Australia.

3 Comment on Kim's treatment in Australia. Do you think the boat people have been treated fairly?

4 Why do you think the Australian government would want to send the Cambodian boat people back?

Kim Leang Thai, a refugee behind the wire in Australia.

ATTITUDES AND POLICIES OF OTHER COUNTRIES TOWARDS VIETNAM

People's Republic of China

China is Vietnam's traditional enemy. They have clashed for over a thousand years. Up until the early 1990s China supported the Khmer Rouge with arms and supplies against the Vietnamese-backed Cambodian government. China itself invaded Vietnam in 1979, in support of the Khmer Rouge.

China has opened its economy up to market forces and to international investment and is experiencing (especially in Southern China) a boom in economic growth. China brutally rejected requests from its own citizens for greater independence in political matters in the Tiananmen Square massacre in June 1989. This attitude to increased social freedom remains firmly in place. In May 1994, the Chinese President stated that the government's actions at Tiananmen Square had been proven right because of the five years of stability the nation had enjoyed since. Stability, he said, was the key to economic development. China now sees Vietnam as a potential area for economic expansion and relations have accordingly become much closer.

Russia

Up to the collapse of the Soviet Union in 1991, the former USSR was Vietnam's major communist ally and its biggest supplier of aid, amounting to billions of dollars yearly. The USSR had maintained a large and strategically important naval base on the east coast of Vietnam at Cam Ranh Bay. President Gorbachev began major political and economic reforms in the USSR in the 1980s which led to the ending of the communist system

US President Bill Clinton lifted the Vietnamese embargo in February, 1994.

and the breakup of the Soviet empire. Along with this historical development came the ending of the Cold War and tensions with the US. Of course, aid to Vietnam and other past communist allies has ended; in fact, Russia today has severe economic problems and is heavily reliant on aid from the US and other developed nations.

United States of America

Until 1994, the US did not supply aid to Vietnam and, like China, but it had supported Vietnam's opponents in Kampuchea in the 1980s. But with President Clinton's lifting of the embargo on aid and financial assistance in 1994, international aid is again flowing and US companies are desperate for a stake in a rich but undeveloped market. Over 800 000 refugees from Indochina have settled in the United States since the end of the Vietnam War in 1975. The US's embargo was intended to punish Vietnam for the humiliation in the Vietnam War. The US also used its power and influence to stop other countries trading with and supplying financial aid to Vietnam. Since the withdrawal of Vietnamese troops from Cambodia, the settlement of the issue of US prisoners of war and those missing in action, and, most importantly, the ending of the Cold War, the US has at last been able to begin to reverse its punitive policy towards Vietnam.

Australia

Australia did not provide aid officially to Vietnam until recently, although a great deal of aid has been given to Indochina through non-government organisations like Care Australia. Over 150 000 Indochinese refugees have found a home in Australia. Australia has become eager to invest in the Asian region. Many Australian companies like BHP and Telecom are actively involved in business ventures in the rapidly expanding Vietnamese economy. Australia's Foreign Minister, Gareth Evans, was responsible for initiating the United Nations plan which has seen free elections and a new government in Cambodia in 1993. Australian troops played an important part in the UN peacekeeping force which supervised the ceasefire and the elections. Australian companies have helped build the Friendship Bridge across the Mekong River between Laos and Thailand, which will serve as a vital transport link in the Indochina region.

Association of South-East Asian Nations (ASEAN)

ASEAN includes Indonesia, Malaysia, Singapore, Thailand and the Philippines. ASEAN has been wary of the expansionist (that is, expanding its influence into other nations) motives of Vietnam but the withdrawal of Vietnam from Cambodia has seen a change in the group's approach. ASEAN itself is intent on expanding its trading base and seeks trade with and to aid in development awakening Vietnam, Cambodia and Laos. All ASEAN countries have refugee camps containing thousands of Indochinese. Thailand, which borders on Cambodia, bears the brunt of the refugee problem.

WHAT ARE COMMUNISM AND CAPITALISM?

An important pair of concepts in Conflict in Indochina are the political philosophies of communism and capitalism. The Vietnam War was fought, according to many of the participants at least, to stop the spread of communism, so it is vital to understand the two conflicting systems.

The German philosopher, Karl Marx, outlined the theory of communism last century and argued that it would replace capitalism. Communist governments usually come to power by a violent revolution.

Only one political party is allowed in a communist country, the Communist Party. China and Cuba are examples of communist nations. Since the collapse of communism in the USSR and Eastern Europe there are only a few surviving communist nations. Most of those like China, Vietnam and Laos, have restructured their economies to allow capitalist-style businesses and profits.

Mikhail Gorbachev, ex-President of the USSR, who initiated revolutionary change in the communist world.

In communist countries:
- the working class (traditionally manual labourers) has taken power from the capitalists (owners of big business);
- goods and services are produced under the control of the government for the benefit of all;
- there are no profits for a few individuals.

NOTE: It should be pointed out in regard to the three points above that communism in theory is often different from communism in practice. In reality, many communist regimes have given little power to the workers and a great deal of power to party officials. Corruption and inequality have flourished in communist nations as they have elsewhere.

In capitalist countries:
- the majority of the economy is owned by private individuals. Money is invested to make a profit;
- sections of the economy, even in capitalist countries like Australia or the United States, are owned and run by the government;
- in most advanced capitalist countries there is substantial freedom of expression, including the right to elect a government of your choice and a free press (not subject to government control or manipulation).

The end of the Cold War and the disappearance of communist dictatorships in Eastern Europe means to some extent that the words above are obsolete. In the USSR in the late 1980s President Mikhail Gorbachev introduced policies of *glasnost* (greater openness and freedom in society, for example, newspapers had the right to criticise government policies) and *perestroika* (the restructuring of the economy into a free market system). Subsequently, communist governments were overthrown, and capitalism began to be reintroduced across Eastern Europe and beyond, so the old truths have faded. Nevertheless, the above points held true for the period of time that this history covers and there are still nations like Vietnam, Laos and China which are communist one-party states despite changes to their economies.

Activities

Key words

Define these important terms:

Indochina	*perestroika*	FUNCINPEC
independence	refugees	Khmer Rouge
communist	civil war	post-traumatic stress
capitalist	inflation	disorder
republic	embargo	Agent Orange
Doi Moi	coup	nations of first asylum
revolution	ASEAN	
glasnost	infrastructure	

Research topics

1 Gorbachev, *glasnost* and *perestroika*.
2 The Mekong River valley.
3 Indochinese refugees in Australia.
4 The Agent Orange debate.
5 The nations of Indochina at the time of study (this is essential as students must be aware of the very latest developments in Indochina).

What if you were . . .?

1 You are an Australian Vietnam veteran. Write a letter of protest to a member of parliament concerning the lack of assistance available to you.
2 You are a Vietnamese politician outlining the changes that have been made in Vietnam since the late 1980s.
3 You are a Indochinese refugee. Write a letter to your family in the home country.

Review questions

1 What is Vietnam's position in Indochina today?
2 Outline the differences between capitalism and communism.
3 How do other world nations view Vietnam today?
4 Describe briefly the three countries of Indochina today — include aspects like their size, population and geography.
5 What major social and economic changes are taking place in Indochina today?
6 What are the most significant dilemmas that the nations of Indochina will face in the late 1990s?
7 Why have so many Vietnam veterans had difficulty settling back into society?
8 Why have so many refugees fled Indochina and what problems have they experienced in starting new lives in their adopted countries?

What would you say?

1 A speech on the countries of Indochina today.
2 A Vietnam veteran speaking to a group of high school history students on his experiences in the Indochinese conflicts and on returning home from the war.
3 A talk by a young refugee from Indochina to a group of students on his/her life, particularly the escape from Indochina and settling down in Australia. (Or, if possible, an interview with an Indochinese refugee.)

2 INDOCHINA YESTERDAY

EARLY HISTORY OF INDOCHINA

Vietnam

Northern Vietnam was first occupied by Indonesian peoples in the Bronze Age (c. 3000-2000 BC). The Chinese invaded the area in about 111 BC and it was part of that Empire until AD 939. This 1000 years of Chinese domination was marked by frequent attempts at rebellion and the assimilation (taking in) of much of Chinese culture. The Trung sisters led the first successful revolt in AD 43 but committed suicide (in aristocratic fashion by throwing themselves into a river) two years later when the Chinese army put down the revolt. Today, the Trung sisters remain national heroes. Further occasional fighting against the Chinese continued up to the 1400s.

The history of Vietnam is characterised by a great ability in warfare and continual determined resistance to foreign domination. Another dominant theme has been Vietnamese expansion and settlement south from the Red River Delta through central Vietnam and into the Mekong Valley. This southern expansion took over 450 years between the fourteenth and eighteenth centuries.

In the 1500s, Vietnam experienced a civil war between powerful families (the Trinhs and the Nguyens). Conflict continued for 200 years with Vietnam divided at approximately the same place it was in 1954 (at the 17th parallel). It was not until 1802 that the whole of Vietnam, as we know it today, was unified for the first time under Emperor Gia Long (this was the name he took as emperor; formerly he was known as Nguyen Anh). From 1802 to 1862, Vietnam had one government, a centralised administration ruled from the city of Hué by an emperor. The Vietnamese emperor governed through a hierarchy of mandarins — scholarly administrators, who achieved their positions solely by success in examinations on the writings of Confucius, the great Chinese philosopher. By 1883, the whole of Vietnam had been taken over by a French nation eager to increase its imperial possessions.

Source 2.1 Vietnamese heroes

It took the Vietnamese a millennium of revolt and sacrifice to win their independence from China in AD 938. During the next near millennium, from 938 until the arrival of the French in the 1850s, every new dynasty that came to power in China invaded Vietnam. The recurrent necessity to drive out big invaders from the north, and incessant warfare with less menacing neighbours in the course of their expansion southward down the Indochinese Peninsula, lent a martial cast to Vietnamese culture. Chinese civilisation, as it developed in later centuries, did not admire the soldier. China produced the intellectual who was also a man of action — the Confucian mandarin-governor. He was a figure worthy of emulation because of his learning and the ethical standards of his conduct. The warrior was regarded as an inferior human being, to be tolerated when it was necessary, but never to be admired. There was nothing intrinsically good in his art of war. This Chinese ideal underwent a mutation in Vietnamese society. The Vietnamese ideal became the intellectual and man of action who was also a great soldier, a mandarin-warrior. The Vietnamese had few gentle heroes like Lincoln. Their heroes, as a foreigner might notice after studying the porcelain figurines on shelves and tables in Vietnamese homes, were men on horseback or elephants, clad in armor, swords in hand. The same held true for their legendary women heroes, the Trung Sisters, who drowned themselves in AD 43 rather than submit after their rebel army was defeated by the Chinese. Physical courage was highly prized for its own sake in Vietnamese culture. Le Loi, the mandarin who overthrew two decades of Chinese domination in a nine-year war in the fifteenth century and consequently founded a new dynasty, made an observation that was often repeated: "We have been weak and we have been strong, but at no time have we lacked heroes."

The wars with the big power to the north also led the Vietnamese to elaborate a particular idea as the central concept of their military thought. The concept is that an ostensibly weaker force, properly handled, can defeat a stronger one. This idea is hardly unique to universal military thought, but in Vietnamese doctrine it became the main arch. Vietnamese military teaching emphasized historically that to bring this concept to fruition, the more powerful enemy had to be worn down by protracted warfare. The Vietnamese forces had to employ hit-and-run tactics, delaying actions, and the ravages of ambush and harassment by guerrilla bands. The enemy had to be lured into wasting his energy in the rain forests and mountains and other formidable terrain of the country, while the Vietnamese used the same terrain as shelter in which to build their strength. Finally, when the enemy was sufficiently drained and confused, he was to be finished off by sudden shock offensives delivered with flexible maneuver and maximum surprise and deception. The most famous of the early Vietnamese generals, Tran Hung Dao, used this strategy to destroy the Mongols.

Neil Sheehan,
A Bright Shining Lie
pp. 159-60

Questions

1 Why was there a 'martial cast to Vietnamese culture'?
2 Explain the contrast between Vietnamese and Chinese heroes.
3 Explain the quote by Le Loi.
4 What does this passage suggest about the likely success of foreign intervention in Vietnam?

Laos

From about AD 750, a number of kings ruled in the territory of present-day Laos. For a time, the region was under Cambodian control. By 1353, these separate kingdoms were united as one country known as Lan Xang. In the 1600s, Lan Xang flourished culturally and economically and expanded into parts of Vietnam and Cambodia, southern Burma and northern Thailand. In 1694, after an internal power struggle, Lan Xang split into three separate territories. This weakened the Lao kingdom and, for the next 200 years, armies from Thailand and Vietnam invaded Laos and occupied much of Lao territory.

By the late 1800s, a great part of Laos was dominated by Thailand and only the intervention of the French saved Laos from disappearing as a nation.

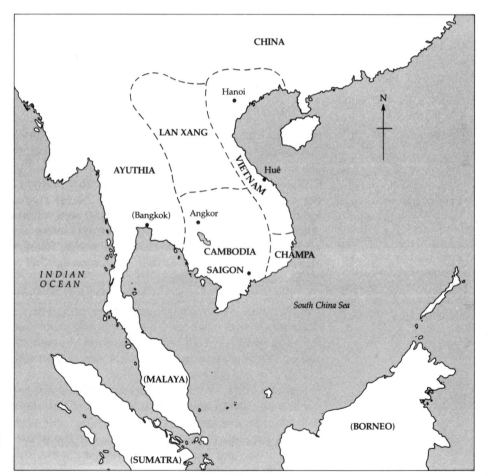

Fig 2.1 Vietnam and her neighbours, AD 1500.

Cambodia

The people of Cambodia trace their ancestry to a Hindu people called the Khmers. The earliest known state in Cambodia was Funan, an empire that existed in the early centuries AD and comprised southern Cambodia and the

■ What might Indochina have been like in the late 1800s without French intervention?

Mekong Delta of South Vietnam. Funan was a prosperous trading nation.

In the 800s, a Khmer king, Yasovarman I, founded a state around the city of Angkor in central Cambodia. Angkor became the centre of a Khmer empire which expanded into parts of Thailand and Vietnam by the end of the ninth century. At its height the empire of Angkor extended to Champa (central Vietnam) in the east.

Between 1300 and 1800, the Khmer state diminished rapidly in size after constant attacks by armies from Thailand and Vietnam. By the middle of the 1400s, the Khmer kings left the city of Angkor and retreated to the Mekong. In the years 1700-60, under pressure from invading Vietnamese troops, Cambodia was forced to give up the region which now forms the Mekong Delta area of southern Vietnam.

In 1861, the Cambodian ruler, King Norodom (1859–1904), was forced to seek the help and protection of the French in order to prevent the country from falling completely under the domination of its neighbours.

Part of the temple complex of Angkor Wat.

Source 2.2   Cambodia's history repeated as tragedy

In the early 19th century Thailand and Viet Nam were the most powerful states in mainland Southeast Asia. Lying between them, Cambodia was a pitifully weak kingdom. Its ruler [paid] tribute to both Bangkok and Hue [the capitals of Thailand and Vietnam] and rival factions within the Cambodian royal family sought support from these two major power centres. The Cambodian king who reigned from 1806 to 1834, Ang Chan, was backed by the Vietnamese. His brothers placed their hopes in association with the Thais. When King Ang Chan died in 1834, the Vietnamese emperor, Minh Mang, was not prepared to risk the possibility of a hostile government coming to power in Cambodia. His army invaded and occupied most of modern Kampuchea, set the Princess Ang Mey to reign powerlessly on the throne, and attempted to "Vietnamise" the country.

It was the Vietnamese determination to transform Cambodia that was so bitterly resented. Vietnamese administrative patterns were introduced. Cambodian officials were required to adopt Vietnamese official dress. And the Cambodian Buddhist church, a basic symbol of national identity, came under attack.

In reaction to this Vietnamese attack on Cambodia's existence, a major rebellion supported by the Thais broke out in the early 1840s. The Vietnamese were expelled, and Cambodia continued to survive precariously as a mutually useful buffer state between Thailand and Vietnam. The institution of a French "protectorate" over Cambodia in 1864 saved the kingdom from what seemed to be the imminent probability of absorption at the hands of its stronger neighbours.

M. Osborne, quoted in E. Graff & H. Hammond, *Southeast Asia*, p. 139

Questions

1 Compare relations between Indochinese countries in the nineteenth century to relations today.

2 How has history repeated itself in Indochina according to this source?

3 What does it mean to 'Vietnamise' the country? How would the Cambodians feel about this?

INDOCHINESE SOCIETY

Each of the countries of Indochina has a different culture from the others. Nevertheless, there are many similarities. The majority of Indochinese live in villages, making their living from agriculture — chiefly from growing rice. Family life is very important to the Indochinese: the family is the chief social unit.

Many religions have been worshipped in Indochina over the centuries. Although Vietnam, Cambodia and Laos are or have been until recently, communist nations and are therefore by definition atheistic, the old religions are still very powerful and popular in practice. The most popular is Buddhism but there are many more, including Animism, Islam, Hinduism, Christianity and Ancestor worship. The Chinese philosophies, Taoism and Confucianism, are also important in Indochinese thought.

■ How is Indochinese society different from the society in which you live?

Literature is also very important to the Indochinese people. The Confucian tradition in Vietnam in particular gives the knowledge and study of literary works great significance in their society.

The long period of rule by the Chinese in Vietnam had the effect of creating a Chinese culture among the Vietnamese. Chinese religion, education, government and methods of agriculture were introduced into Vietnam. By contrast, Cambodia and Laos derived their culture chiefly from India. For example, Vietnam adopted the Chinese style of writing in ideographs, whereas the rest of Indochina utilised the alphabetical systems of India.

FRENCH COLONISATION OF INDOCHINA

The race for empire

In the nineteenth century, France, like other European nations, invested a great deal of time, money and national honour in building an empire by acquiring overseas colonies. Imperialism (the gaining of colonies) was justified on a number of grounds. Great Britain believed that its empire, so large that 'the sun never set' on it, was part of the 'white man's burden' in bringing civilised society to those less developed areas of the world. Similarly, France justified its accumulation of colonies on its '*mission civilisatrice*' (bringing civilisation to underdeveloped nations). J.A. Hobson, a British economist, gave imperialism rather baser motives. He believed it was chiefly about securing favourable investment markets.[1] There is no doubt that France and the other European empire builders wished to gain a profit from the raw materials, the cheap labour and the compliant import market that a colony represented.

Fig. 2.2 French Indochina.

By 1907, most of the continent of Africa had been colonised by the European powers. Asia had also been divided up into 'spheres of influence' and outposts of empire.

NOTE: Vietnam's dominant role in Indochina today and yesterday is mirrored by its position in this narrative. The greater part of the chapters and their contents concerns the history of Vietnam, particularly the Vietnam Wars. The histories of Laos and Cambodia revolve around the Vietnam Wars, thus Vietnam is the prime focus of the text. There will be a separate chapter on Cambodia and Laos, but the rest will focus heavily on Vietnam.

How did France take over?

France's initial contact with Vietnam was through Catholic missionaries in the early 1600s. By the middle of the nineteenth century, Vietnamese leaders were concerned by the popularity of Catholicism among their people and also by the possibility that the Catholic missionaries were acting as a vanguard for French imperialism. As a result, they began to persecute Catholic priests and their followers. Vietnamese Catholics had their left cheeks branded with the word 'infidel' (meaning non-believer) as well as having their property confiscated. Many were expelled from Vietnam or executed.

In 1893, the countries of Vietnam, Cambodia and Laos became the French Indochinese Union.

Young Bao Dai with his mother, Tu Cung, in 1921. Bao Dai became emperor in 1925 at the age of twelve.

French rule

As soon as France took over Indochina the traditional social order was disrupted. The old rulers, the monarchs and aristocrats of Vietnam, Laos and Cambodia, were made to look powerless before the modern might of an industrialised nation. The emperor and his officials continued to administer internal affairs, but overall authority lay with the French who ran customs and public works. It was less disruptive for the French to leave the Vietnamese in charge of day-to-day affairs than for them to take total control.

The greatest disruption to the social order was economic. The self-sufficient agriculture of the village, with peasants producing crops for their own use, was replaced by a market economy where goods were produced for sale and profit. As a result, most villagers were deprived of their land and became wage earners working on large plantations, mines and factories owned by the French or rich Indochinese. (Seventy per cent of Vietnam's peasants became landless villagers.)

French Indochina was rich in rice, rubber, minerals and silk and the export and sale of these products was immensely profitable for France. In

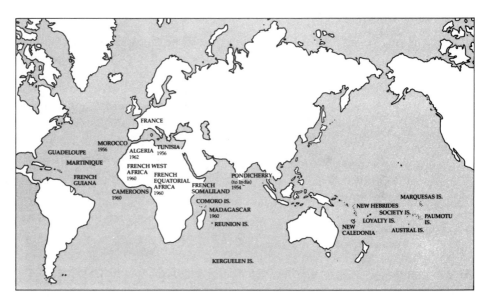

Fig 2.3 The French Empire in 1946. The years indicate when independence was achieved.

return, the peoples of Indochina received some of the benefits of modern civilisation: improved roads, canals and railways, contemporary medicine, some Western schooling, and the beginnings of industrialisation.

However, the economy was serving the needs of the French, not the Vietnamese. Rice, the staple food of the nation, was scarcely available for local consumption because much of it was exported overseas. The Indochinese became second-rate citizens in their own land. The French dominated all major positions in government and administration (the few Vietnamese who rose to high ranks in government were paid considerably less than their French colleagues). French culture and French goods, education and language superseded Indochinese cultures that had developed over thousands of years.

What were the costs of imperialism?

The costs of imperialism were high. Despite the increased production achieved by modern methods of agriculture and the larger scale of the plantations, many peasants starved because most production was exported. Coal mines and rubber plantations earned massive export income, yet thousands of native 'coolies' (poorly paid, unskilled labourers) died, working under inhumane conditions. At one rubber plantation in Vietnam, 12 000 of 45 000 local workers died of malaria, malnutrition and dysentery between 1871 and 1944. One Vietnamese writer commented that 'the workers were fertilisers for the rubber trees as their corpses were buried under the trees'.[2]

Worst of all for many proud Vietnamese were the French arrogance and the inability of the Indochinese population to express themselves on economic, social or political policy. Phan Chu Trinh, a Minister at the Imperial Court, communicated this feeling of impotence in a letter of warning to the French Governor in the early 1900s:

> In your eyes we are savages, dumb brutes, incapable of distinguishing between good and evil. Some of us, employed by you, still preserve a certain dignity . . . and it is sadness and shame that fills our hearts when we contemplate our humiliation.[3]

■ How do you think the Vietnamese would have reacted to this French dominance?

In addition to these hardships, French prices and taxes were much higher than they had been under Indochinese governments and they continued to grow at an unmerciful rate throughout the period of French rule. These burdens weighed most heavily on the poorer peasants. A number of new taxes were added (on salt and alcohol) when it became clear near the turn of the century that France was not making a profit out of Indochina. In fact, alcohol became a highly profitable state monopoly, as did the sale of opium, which was not widely used in Indochina before the French arrived. The French built their own opium refinery and increased consumption of the drug immensely. Of course, the local inhabitants were not consulted at all when these decisions were made. Vietnamese citizens had many reasons for advocating a return to an independent and free Vietnam.

MOVEMENTS FOR INDEPENDENCE

There was always resistance to French rule in Vietnam. The Vietnamese have a long history of rebellion and they made no exception in the case of French colonialism. Vietnamese resistance started as early as 1859 after the French had taken Saigon. They used guerrilla tactics ('hit and run' tactics which would also be used a century later) and were supplied with food, refuge and new recruits by a sympathetic population. The French commander circulated the following account in 1862:

> We have had enormous difficulties in enforcing our authority . . . Rebel bands disturb the country everywhere. They appear from nowhere in large numbers, destroy everything and then disappear into nowhere.[4]

Rebellions continued to erupt as the proud and nationalistic Vietnamese refused to bow to the French invaders. In 1885, the Vietnamese emperor, Han Nghi, began a revolt to rid his country of the French invaders. The revolt lasted only two years and all but two of the emperor's followers were executed. Of the others, one died in the fighting and the other strangled himself to death at the shame of defeat. In 1914, a group of Vietnamese formed the Association for the Restoration of Vietnam. Their aim was to restore the traditional aristocratic government while leaving Vietnam as part of the French Empire. Some Vietnamese government officials sympathised with their ideas, as did Emperor Duy Tan. There was a rebellion in 1916 but it was quickly suppressed by the French Foreign Legion who ruthlessly and efficiently ended any opposition.

Few concessions to self-government were allowed by the French even after thousands of Indochinese fought in Europe on the Western Front with the French in World War I. Many who returned from France to Vietnam carried with them some of the democratic or communist ideas so prevalent in Europe just after World War I.

Several political parties were formed in the 1920s. The most popular was the Nationalist Party of Vietnam, which was started in 1927, and led an uprising in 1930 against French authority at Yen Bay in Tonkin. Again it was ruthlessly suppressed and the Nationalist Party was all but destroyed. Many of the leaders were executed and the rest fled from Vietnam or into hiding. In general, the French ruled Vietnam by a combination of ruthless military repression and severely limited political freedom.

Moves for a less repressive regime by the young Emperor Bao Dai (who became emperor in 1925 at the age of twelve) in the 1930s, supported by a provincial governor named Ngo Dinh Diem, were also discouraged by the French authorities. The resistance soon learnt that peaceful reform under the French was impossible and this added to the popularity of the groups advocating extremist solutions, notably the communists. The Indochinese Communist Party (dominated by the Vietnamese) was formed in 1930 and quickly gained support. As a consequence of the French refusal to allow peaceful reform and the French suppression of the Nationalists (the communists' major rival), the communists had assumed the leadership of the independence movement by the middle of the 1930s.

Events outside Vietnam also encouraged movements towards independence. The Great Depression of the 1930s created severe economic hardships in Vietnam and thousands of discontented workers were increasingly likely to rebel against the government. The examples of the Chinese Revolution of 1911 and the Russian Revolution of 1917 encouraged the desire for national freedom. At the same time, Japan's defeat of a European power, Tsarist Russia, in 1905 and its subsequent industrial and military development destroyed the image of white European invincibility.

The French also contributed to their own downfall. Although French schooling reached only a minority of Vietnamese (only one in five Vietnamese boys was attending school in 1940), a small middle class was created and educated in French colleges. Here the future revolutionaries who would set in motion the removal of France from Indochina learnt the principles behind the French revolution and democracy. They would learn about 'liberty, equality, fraternity', principles which the French obviously believed did not apply to Indochina.

Source 2.3   An anti-communist alternative

There was no anti-Communist alternative in Vietnam. The French and the shortcomings of the non-Communist nationalists cleared the way for the Communists to lead the struggle for independence back in the 1930s. The French political police in Indochina, the Sûreté Générale, decimated the largest non-Communist nationalist party, the Vietnam Kuomintang, modeled on the Chinese party, after an uncoordinated uprising in 1930. Its leaders were sent to the guillotine. The survivors fled to China. The non-Communists failed to rebuild their movements in the face of French repression because most of them were urban elitists who lacked the interest in social change necessary to marshal a following. The communists were also badly hurt by a similarly ill-conceived rebellion in 1930 and 1931, organizing peasant soviets for the Foreign Legion to crush. A second peasant revolt fomented in the Mekong Delta in November 1940 was suppressed by the insecure Vichy authorities with unusual ferocity. The Communists recovered and learned, because their concern with social goals always took them back to the bottom, where there was discontent on which to build.

Neil Sheehan,
A Bright Shining Lie, p. 171

Questions

1 Why was there no anti-communist alternative in Vietnam according to Sheehan?

2 What was the weakness of the Vietnamese nationalists in comparison to the communists?

3 What methods would the French have used to suppress these political parties?

Ho Chi Minh, Vietnamese nationalist and communist leader, founder of present-day Vietnam.

Who was Ho Chi Minh?

The man who would lead Vietnam's fight for independence, the head of the communist movement and one of the greatest revolutionaries of our times was born in 1890, named Nguyen Sin Cung. (Ho Chi Minh, meaning 'Bringer of Light', was an alias he adopted in the 1940s.) He was the youngest son of a district magistrate who was dismissed for nationalist activity.

At the age of twenty-one, Ho left Vietnam (not to return for thirty years) and set out on a journey to the United States, Great Britain and France. In France he became involved in radical politics and was one of the founding members of the French Communist Party (1920). He was attracted to the communists because they alone supported the independence of colonial countries. From France he went to Moscow in the newly formed USSR and learnt communist and revolutionary theory. Over the next two decades he put this knowledge to good use, travelling through Europe and Asia fostering revolution.

In Hong Kong in 1930, Ho unified the existing communist groupings in Vietnam into the Indochinese Communist Party. Its chief political aim was the independence of Vietnam by the revolutionary action of the workers.

After the outbreak of World War II in 1939 and the defeat of France by Hitler's Germany and Japan's occupation of Indochina in 1941, Ho realised that the time was right for Vietnam to begin in earnest its fight for independence. In 1941, he travelled to Vietnam for the first time in thirty years and formed a national front of patriots to fight against the Japanese and the French.

The national coalition was named the Viet Nam Doc Lap Dong Minh Hoi (meaning the Revolutionary League for the Independence of Vietnam), better known as the Vietminh. Ho associated the Vietminh with the Allies (the major countries fighting against Germany, Italy and Japan — chiefly the USA, USSR and Great Britain), expecting them to defeat the Japanese, oust the French from Vietnam and grant the nation its independence. By 1945, the communists had come to dominate the Vietminh.

Ho was to be disappointed because the Allies instead supported France's wish to return to power in Indochina, despite the fact that Ho had proclaimed an independent Vietnam on 2 September 1945. The USA in particular was conscious of the need to build a strong and stable western Europe — hence the need to assist France. Despite this setback and others, Ho continued to lead the fight against the French and later on against the Americans until his death in 1969. Ho was President of North Vietnam from 1946 until his death.

Source 2.4   Declaration of Independence of the Republic of Vietnam, 2 September 1945 – speech by Ho Chi Minh

"All men are created equal. They are endowed by their Creator with certain inalienable rights, among these are Life, Liberty, and the Pursuit of Happiness."

This immortal statement was made in the Declaration of Independence of the United States of America in 1776...The Declaration of the Rights of Man and the Citizen of the French Revolution in 1791 also states: "All men are born free and with equal rights, and must always be free and have equal rights." . . .

Nevertheless for more than eighty years, the French imperialists deceitfully raising the standard of Liberty, Equality, and Fraternity, have violated our fatherland and oppressed our fellow citizens. They have acted contrarily to the ideals of humanity and justice.

In the province of politics, they have deprived our people of every liberty.

They have enforced inhuman laws: to ruin our unity and national consciousness. They have carried out three different policies in the north, the center and the south of Viet-nam.

They have founded more prisons than schools. They have mercilessly slain our patriots; they have deluged our revolutionary areas with innocent blood. They have fettered public opinion; they have promoted illiteracy.

To weaken our race they have forced us to use their manufactured opium and alcohol.

In the province of economics, they have stripped our fellow citizens of everything they possessed, impoverishing the individual and devastating the land.

They have robbed us of our rice fields, our mines, our forests, our raw materials. They have monopolized the printing of banknotes, the import and export trade, they have invented numbers of unlawful taxes, reducing our people, especially our country folk, to a state of extreme poverty.

They have stood in the way of our businessmen and stifled all their undertakings: they have extorted our working classes in a most savage way.

In the autumn of the year 1940, when the Japanese fascists violated Indochina's territory to get one more foothold in their fight against the

Allies, the French imperialists fell on their knees and surrendered, handing over our country to the Japanese, adding Japanese fetters to the French ones. From that day on, the Vietnamese people suffered hardships yet unknown in the history of mankind. The result of this double oppression was terrific: from Quangtri to the northern border two million people were starved to death in the early months of 1945.

. . . we declare to the world that Vietnam . . . has in fact become a free and independent country.

Claude A. Buss,
Southeast Asia and the World Today, pp. 154-5

Questions

1 Why might Ho start the Declaration of Vietnam's Independence with the words from the American Declaration of Independence?

2 According to Ho, what are five of the crimes the French committed against the Vietnamese?

3 How reliable is this as evidence about French behaviour in Vietnam?

Activities

Key words

Define these important terms:

Empire
Buddhism
Khmer
imperialism

mission civilisatrice
colony
industrialisation
subsistence

repression
independence
revolutionary
Lan Xang

Research topics

1 Vietnamese rebellion against Chinese rule.

2 Education in French Indochina.

3 The principles of Buddhism.

What if you were . . .?

1 You are a member of a middle class Vietnamese family. Write a letter of complaint regarding French rule to a high ranking French government official.

2 You are a Vietnamese who believes that Vietnam should be free of foreign rule. Design a propaganda leaflet or poster advocating Vietnamese independence.

Review questions

1 What were the most significant events in the early history of Indochina?
2 How and why did the French acquire Indochina?
3 Describe the positive and negative features of French rule in Indochina.
4 Why did the Vietnamese rebel against the French?
5 Outline the history of Vietnamese resistance to French rule up to the 1940s.
6 What part did Ho Chi Minh play in Vietnam's independence movement?

What would you say?

1 Explain the early history of Indochina in a conversation with a friend who is also studying Indochina.
2 Give a speech by a member of the independence movement to a group of peasants, persuading them that it is time for the French to leave Vietnam.

3 FRANCE'S INDOCHINA WAR

WHAT HAPPENED IN INDOCHINA DURING WORLD WAR II?

Indochina's involvement in World War II began when Japan took over Vietnam, Cambodia and Laos in May 1940. Indochina was important to the Japanese war strategy because of its plentiful supplies of rubber, coal and rice.

At the same time in Europe, France was being overrun by the war machine of Hitler's Germany and a pro-German government had been installed in France at Vichy. France's Vichy government co-operated with Germany's ally, Japan, by allowing Japanese troops to occupy Indochina. The French remained in nominal control of the government, but behind the scenes, real control lay with the Japanese. Japan had free use of Vietnamese ports, railways, roads and airfields to help their war effort. Only in March 1945 did the Japanese forces overthrow the French government. They seized control of the country and, in dismantling the French security system, they gave the Vietminh the opportunity to build up their numbers and power throughout the countryside (the Japanese were interested only in controlling the cities).

Vietminh guerrillas, the men and women of the national organisation that Ho Chi Minh had set up in 1941, were the only real resistance to the Japanese army in Indochina during World War II. This resistance was acknowledged by America's Office of Strategic Services (OSS), the forerunner of the Central Intelligence Agency (CIA), which is responsible for the security of the United States overseas. The OSS supplied the guerrilla army with arms and supplies in return for the Vietminh continuing to fight the Japanese and helping with the rescue of downed US airmen.

■ Do you think the Vietminh would have later expected support from America?

The Japanese caused terrible damage to Vietnam. By forcing villagers to grow crops other than the staple rice for the benefit of their war machine, they brought about a famine which killed more than 2 million Vietnamese in the later part of World War II.

The Vietminh continued their fight against the French also, working to turn discontent with the war and poor economic conditions into increased nationalist feeling. During 1942 and 1943, Vietminh strength grew slowly despite French attempts at repression. By late 1944, the Vietminh were sufficiently confident to attack two small French outposts successfully. The war and the Japanese occupation accelerated the movement for Vietnamese nationalism and independence.

The August Revolution

In August 1945, the USA dropped two atomic bombs on the Japanese cities of Hiroshima and Nagasaki, after which the Japanese soon surrendered. World War II was over. The Vietminh seized this opportunity to organise uprisings across the country and on 2 September 1945, they entered the northern capital of Hanoi and their leader Ho Chi Minh announced the independence of Vietnam. In what the communists have called the August Revolution, the Vietminh moved into villages across the country, taking control and conducting trials of villagers they accused of treason — mostly landlords who had sided with the Japanese and the French. Usually, if found guilty, the accused were executed, often on the spot. The French were widely unpopular and the Vietminh were mostly seen as liberators.

Source 3.1   Vietminh summons to fight the Japanese, March 1945

Compatriots!

The fascist Japanese continue to despoil us: they have just seized more than 600 *mau* of rice paddies pertaining to the villages of the provinces of Phuc-Yen.

Tens of thousands of peasants have been evicted from their villages and their houses. Gardens and rice fields have been occupied by the Japanese.

Thousands of families are without hearths and wander about haphazardly.

Compatriots! such is your lot.

Do not lament uselessly. Everyone, arm yourselves with clubs, spears, knives, expel the Japanese brigands and recover control of your rice paddies and homes.

The [American] bombs pour down wherever the Japanese are. To avoid [being in] so dang-erous an area, oust the undesirable hosts.

Compatriots who live close to the Japanese, hide well your rice, your pigs, your chickens; don't let them take these things.

Our blood boils
Our stomach is empty
Our belongings are plundered
Our hearths are destroyed

It is the Japanese who are responsible for all these disasters. There is only one way for us to save our lives; it is to prepare with all our compatriots to chase out the Japanese birds of prey.

Everyone, rise against the Japanese fascists, the seizers of lands.

Long live Vietnam Independence!

Allan B. Cole (ed.), *Conflict in Indo-china and International, Repercussions*, p. 16 *

Questions

1 What has prompted the summons?
2 Summarise the appeal being made in this document.
3 Which particular part of the Vietnamese population is being addressed?
4 Do you think the summons would have worked? Would you have risen against the Japanese in response?
5 Does the summons mention communism? Why not?

* *Source 3.1* The original source is: République démocratique du Viet-nam, Bureau de Paris, *Le Mouvement antifascist Vietnamien, Recueil de Témoignages françcais et étrangers*, Paris, October 1947.

DID THE FRENCH RETURN?

■ Why do you think French pride would have been low at this time?

Despite the action of the Vietminh and despite its defeat in World War II (including the damage done to the land and its citizens), France was unwilling to give up its colonial possessions. The loss of Indochina, one of the 'jewels in the crown' of France's overseas empire, was considered too much of a blow to shattered French prestige.

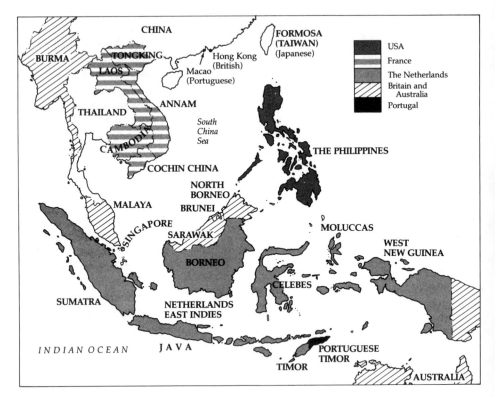

Fig 3.1 European possessions in South-East Asia in 1939.

Bao Dai, the emperor of Vietnam who had remained on the throne under the French and the Japanese, realised the difficulties that the French would have in returning to Vietnam and he warned the French president, Charles DeGaulle, on 18 August 1945 in these terms:

> You have suffered too much during four deadly years not to understand that the Vietnamese people . . . can no longer support any foreign domination . . .
>
> Even if you were to arrive to re-establish a French administration here, it would no longer be obeyed; each village would be a nest of resistance, every former friend an enemy . . .[1]

Ho's government in the north appealed to the Allied victors of World War II to support the cause of Vietnamese independence but without success. The Great Powers (USA, USSR and Great Britain) decided at the Potsdam Conference in the German Democratic Republic in July 1945 that the French should return to their dominant position in Indochina. (This support for continued French rule was in contrast to the Great Powers' rhetoric, which stated that they were fighting for the independence of all nations. They supported France because they were concerned with creating a stable Europe after the terrible destruction of the war.) The decision also specified that British troops in the south and Nationalist Chinese troops in the north would accept the surrender of the Japanese. In the south of Vietnam, the British under General Gracey actively assisted the French in reasserting their authority. On 23 September, French soldiers ousted the Vietminh forces from Saigon using weapons supplied to them by the British. The attempted reconquest of Indochina had begun.

■ Did the French have a right to return to Indochina?

When did France's Indochinese War begin?

Negotiations between the French and the northern communists over the future of Vietnam continued throughout 1946. By March, a compromise had been reached. The northern communists agreed to allow 25 000 French troops to stay in Vietnam for five years after which they would gradually withdraw and Vietnam would be recognised as a state within the French Union. It was not the full independence that Vietnam wanted, but as far as Ho was concerned, it meant that the Nationalist Chinese troops could now leave the north. Vietnamese history told Ho of the danger of Chinese troops on Vietnamese soil and he saw them as a greater threat than the French.

■ Why was Ho so concerned about the Chinese?

The compromise did not last long. War broke out in October 1946, when in a show of strength French troops moved to take over customs houses in Haiphong, an important northern port city and trading centre. The Vietminh resisted the French attacks, and French ships and planes subsequently bombed the city, killing an estimated 6000 Vietnamese. The Vietminh continued to resist and launched a rebellion in Hanoi in December 1946, but their forces were driven out after seven days of bloodshed. The first Indochinese war had begun.

Who were the Vietminh?

■ Who do you think would have been expected to win the war? Why?

The first Indochinese war was fought between the Vietminh and the French Union army, which consisted of French, Vietnamese, Algerians, Moroccans (other members of the French Empire) and mercenaries. The Vietminh army had been founded only in the early 1940s by Ho's military commander, Vo Nguyen Giap, but by the end of 1946, it had become an army of 60 000 men based largely in northern Vietnam. The Vietminh used guerrilla tactics, choosing their targets carefully, making sure they had the advantages in numbers and surprise, and escaping immediately the attack was finished. Vietminh units avoided large scale confrontations in the open with the French troops who were better equipped and possessed superior firepower.

Who was winning the war?

The war dragged on (as it would for the Americans in later years) through the late 1940s and into the 1950s. The French forces were unable to deliver a crippling blow to an enemy they often could not locate. A military stalemate developed, with the French in charge of the major cities and the Vietminh in control of the countryside. Both sides were heavily reliant on

■ Why would these countries fund a war in a small Asian nation?

other nations for arms and other equipment. The USA increasingly funded the French war effort and the Chinese and Soviet Union communists supplied the Vietminh.

Troops of the French Foreign Legion operating south of Saigon.

Table 3.1 **French military expenditure in Indochina 1945-52[2]**
(in million francs)

Year		Year	
1945	3 200	1949	130 000
1946	27 000	1950	201 000
1947	53 310	1951	313 000
1948	89 700	1952	435 000 (estimate)

General Giap

General Vo Nguyen Giap was responsible for building the Vietminh from a small, ragtag group of guerrillas in the early 1940s to a large formidable army capable of defeating a major European power in the 1950s. Giap was one of the 20th century's greatest soldiers. Like the majority of the leaders of the Vietnamese revolution, he came from a well-educated (in French schools), middle-class background. At school and university he came into contact with Vietnamese nationalist ideas and later joined the Communist Party. Giap had particular reason to hate the French — his wife was arrested for nationalist activities, and both she and their young son died in French gaols.

WHAT IS REVOLUTIONARY WAR?

Giap's Vietminh army adopted the strategy of a revolutionary or people's war that was used so effectively by Mao Zedong's communists in their defeat of the Chinese nationalist armies during the Chinese Revolution in the 1940s. With their small numbers and primitive weaponry, the Vietminh could not hope to stand up to the French on an equal footing, but the strategy of people's war and the emphasis on guerrilla warfare techniques gave them the necessary breathing space to build up their forces into a large modern army.

Revolutionary war was waged by the Vietnamese (led by the Vietnamese communists) against the French colonialists and the society they had created in Vietnam. Ho Chi Minh, the communist leader, called on all Vietnamese to fight for their nations freedom:

> All Vietnamese regardless of sex, age, creed, political tendency and nationality must stand up to fight the French colonialists and save the country. Let those who have guns use guns, those who have swords use swords, and those who have no swords use picks, hoes or sticks.[3]

■ Do you think many Vietnamese would have sympathised with the Vietminh?

■ Do Vietminh aims sound communist or nationalist?

The communist-led Vietminh fought a war based around the peasantry. Their aim was to liberate Vietnam by winning over the villages and the peasantry to their cause. Vietminh propaganda stressed the injustices of the French system. The Vietminh especially promised to distribute land equally among the peasants in contrast to the situation under the French where only a rich few were able to own land. Making the peasantry aware of the possibility of real economic independence was an important priority in the revolutionary war.

Most importantly, the war was for national independence. The Vietminh argued that which was only by removing the French and its colonial system, which was designed for the benefit of the French and a minority of rich Vietnamese, could Vietnam be truly free and independent. Vietnam should be governed by Vietnamese and not by foreigners whose sole purpose was to exploit the native population.

Revolutionary war in theory contains three stages (in practice these stages are seldom separate):

1 The enemy has control of the major centres of population and the lines of communication. The revolutionary movement builds up support and strength and fights a guerrilla campaign against the enemy (attacking in small groups, causing damage especially to supplies and lines of communication — roads, bridges, railway lines, etc.).

2 A stalemate position. The revolutionary force has established strongholds throughout the countryside and the enemy is incapable of removing them. The enemy, however, still controls the major population centres. Guerrilla warfare continues.

3 The stage when the revolutionaries go on the offensive because their leaders consider they have superiority in numbers.

■ How is revolutionary warfare different from other types of warfare?

Revolutionary warfare takes place over many years. Many battles can be lost and yet the war can still be won. The strategy is designed to wear down the opponent. The most important battle rages in each village where the guerrilla firstly undermines the enemy's authority by a campaign of

Mao Zedong.

■ Why did the Vietminh take so much care to win over the peasants?

terror and assassination and then constructs a superior rival administration which collects taxes and delivers justice fairly and equally. Hence, the major task of the Vietminh was to outgovern the French rather than to merely defeat them in battle.

Mao and revolutionary war

Mao Zedong (leader of Chinese communists) said that 'the guerrilla must be of the people just as fish is of the sea':[4] Mao insisted that his Chinese troops treated the peasants fairly. Giap gave his men similar rules. The following are the eight reminders on how to behave to the people, the code of conduct strictly adhered to and enforced by the Vietminh:

1 Be polite.
2 Be fair.
3 Return anything borrowed.
4 Pay for anything damaged.
5 Do not bully.
6 Do not damage crops.
7 Do not flirt with women.
8 Do not ill-treat prisoners.

In contrast, the French Union soldiers often treated the villagers poorly, taking food and drink, ill treating both peasants and prisoners.

WHY WAS THE USA INVOLVED?

Those Americans in Vietnam during World War II were favourably disposed to the Vietminh. Major Patti of the OSS who had worked with Ho and the Vietminh in those years did not see Ho as a potential enemy of the USA. This is Patti's description of Ho:

> Ho Chi Minh did not strike me as a starry-eyed revolutionary . . . I saw that his ultimate goal was to gain American support for the cause of a free Vietnam and felt that desire presented no conflict with American policy.[5]

Franklin Roosevelt, President of the USA since 1932, perceived no conflict either. He was opposed to France returning to power in Indochina, and proposed that Indochina be placed under a trusteeship for a limited period leading to self-government. Yet the wider interests of US foreign policy took precedence. The USA wished France to play an important part in building a stable and strong western Europe to counterbalance the perceived threat of Soviet dominance in the east. Therefore, the USA decided to provide support and financial aid for France in reclaiming Indochina.

■ Do you think the domino theory made sense?

After 1949 and the Communist Revolution in China, US support for France became ever firmer. Support for the French against the communist Vietminh became part of the containment policy as proclaimed by Roosevelt's successor as President, Harry Truman. The need for the USA to contain the spread of communism was bolstered by the 'domino theory' which stated that if one domino (or country) fell to communism, then other dominoes (or countries) would also fall. It was therefore necessary to stop Vietnam from becoming communist otherwise nations like Laos, Cambodia, Thailand and Burma would follow.

■ What similarities do you see between the Chinese Communist Revolution, the Korean War and the Vietnam Wars?

The Korean War (see summary below) also increased American fears of communism and strengthened the government's resolve to help France in Indochina. A speech by Vice-President Nixon in 1953 sums up the domino theory and why America was supporting France in Indochina.

Source 3.2   Speech by Vice-President Nixon, 23 December 1953

Let us turn now to another area of the world — Indo China. And many of you ask this question: Why is the United States spending hundreds of millions of dollars supporting the forces of the French Union in the fight against communism in Indo-China? . . . If Indochina falls, Thailand is put in an almost impossible position. The same is true of Malaya with its rubber and tin. The same is true of Indonesia. If this whole part of Southeast Asia goes under Communist domina-tion or Communist influence, Japan, who trades and must trade with this area in order to exist, must inevitably be orientated towards the Communist regime. That indicates to you and to all of us why it is vitally important that Indochina not go behind the Iron Curtain.

Allan B. Cole (ed.) *Conflict in Indo-China and International Repercussions*, p. 171*

Questions

1 According to Nixon, what would happen in Asia if the domino theory became reality?
2 Has the domino theory proved accurate?
3 What arguments can be used against the domino theory?

* *Source 3.2* The original source is: Address on television and radio, 23 December 1953, State Department *Bulletin*, XXX, No. 758 (4 January 1954), p. 12.

Communist Revolution in China

Under the leadership of Jiang Kai-Shek, the Chinese Nationalist Party was the strongest force in China during the 1920s. The Communist Party emerged as a threat during that decade but, in 1927, Jiang nearly destroyed them in a ruthless purge.

Japan launched a full scale invasion of China in 1937. Much of Jiang's army was destroyed in the fighting and the communists under Mao Zedong became the only effective resistance against the Japanese. After World War II, a civil war broke out between the Nationalists backed by large American aid and the communists. The communists had the support of the peasants and triumphed in 1949.

Fig 3.2 North and South Korea.

■ Would you have supported the war if you had been French in 1953?

Korean War

North Korean communist troops invaded South Korea on 25 June 1953 and pushed the South Korean army back to the southern tip of the country. United Nations troops landed and succeeded in driving the North Korean army back to its northern border with China. At this stage China became involved and the United Nations forces were driven back. The war ended when a settlement was negotiated and Korea was divided at roughly the same position as before. Both North and South Korea suffered devastating damage and needed large amounts of aid to recover.

THE WAR BY 1953

By the middle of 1953, the war in Indochina was going very badly for the French. Without a massive injection of men and matériel, victory was beyond them. The voters back in France were tired of a war thousands of miles away that was draining the nation's money and young men. Despite massive US aid to the French Union forces, the Vietminh were becoming more powerful and taking over more territory. By 1953, 74 000 French had been killed and another 190 000 were still in Indochina making little headway.

The new commander in Indochina, General Henri Navarre, decided on a bold stroke to at least try and secure an advantageous political settlement to the war. The place he chose for this risky venture was Dien Bien Phu. The local people called this place the 'arena of the gods'.

Why Dien Bien Phu?

Navarre had two reasons for choosing to fight at Dien Bien Phu. One was to relieve the threat to Laos (Vietminh forces were strongest in the north and posed a direct threat to Laos) and the other was to tempt the Vietminh into an open battle where French firepower could dominate.

In late 1953, French paratroopers took the small village of Dien Bien Phu and established a strong, fortified garrison. The bait was set. Giap accepted the challenge and in an amazing feat of effort and organisation, 50 000 Vietnamese peasant porters, surviving on only very small rations of rice, managed to pull or carry across rugged mountains 200 pieces of artillery and 25 000 shells as well as food and other supplies for 40 000 Vietminh soldiers.

By March 1954, the French were completely taken by surprise and the garrison at Dien Bien Phu was surrounded, outnumbered and outgunned. Giap's forces soon destroyed the airfield at Dien Bien Phu, rendering the garrison totally isolated from outside aid. Dien Bien Phu was taken on 7 May after fifty-five days of siege. Of the original 16 000 defenders, 3 000 died. Over one-half of these survivors died on the march to captivity or in prison camps after the end of the war. Dien Bien Phu spelt the end of the French in Vietnam. Significantly, a nationalist movement in a small Asian nation had defeated one of the leading nations in Europe. In addition, the Vietminh had been placed in a very strong position for the coming peace conference.

In the nine years of the First Indochina War, the armies of the French Union had lost almost 90 000 killed or missing, while Vietminh losses have been estimated at more than 200 000.

A popular Ho Chi Minh with students in Hanoi.

THE GENEVA CONFERENCE

The day after the Vietminh flag (a red background with a gold star) was flown over Dien Bien Phu, an international conference opened at Geneva in Switzerland to try and produce a lasting settlement to the Indochinese conflict. Nine nations or groups were represented: the Vietminh, the Republic of Vietnam (Bao Dai's French Vietnam), Cambodia, Laos, USA, Great Britain, France, China and USSR.

The future

The Geneva Conference did not end the conflict. It produced a military truce. The participants (with the exception of the Republic of Vietnam and the USA who subscribed to none of the arrangements) gave only a verbal endorsement of the agreements. The signs were there that the future for Vietnam held prospects of more war and more death.

Tragically the signs were correct — the suffering was far from finished.

The Geneva Agreements
1 A cease-fire.
2 French troops to withdraw.
3 Vietnam divided into North and South Vietnam at the 17th parallel.
4 Laos and Cambodia established as independent states.
5 National elections to be held in two years throughout Indochina.
6 No foreign bases.
7 Freedom of movement between the North and South Vietnam for 300 days.

Source 3.3   Final Declaration of the Geneva Conference

(6) The conference recognises that the essential purpose of the agreement relating to Vietnam is to settle military questions with a view to ending hostilities, and that the military demarcation line should not in any way be interpreted as constituting a political or territorial boundary. It expresses its conviction that the execution of the provisions set out in the present declaration and in the agreement on the cessation of the hostilities creates the necessary basis for the achievement in the near future of a political settlement in Vietnam.

(7) The conference declares that, so far as Vietnam is concerned, the settlement of political problems, effected on the basis of respect for the principles of independence, unity and territorial integrity, shall permit the Vietnamese people to enjoy the fundamental freedoms, guaranteed by democratic institutions, established as a result of free general elections by secret ballot. To ensure that sufficient progress in the restoration of peace has been made, and that all the necessary conditions obtain for free expression of the national will, general elections shall be made in July, 1956, under the supervision of an International Commission composed of representatives of the member States of the International Supervisory Commission, referred to in the agreements on the cessation of hostilities. Consultations will be held on this subject between the competent representative authorities of the two zones from July, 1955, onwards.

quoted in D. J. Sagar, *Major Politcal Events in Indochina, 1945–90, Facts on File,* p. 189

Source 3.4   US Declaration at Geneva

In connection with the statement in the declaration concerning free elections in Vietnam, my Government wishes to make clear its position, which it has expressed in a declaration made in Washington on June 29, 1954 as follows:

'In the case of nations now divided against their will, we shall continue to seek to achieve unity through free elections, supervised by the UN, to ensure that they are conducted fairly.'

quoted in D. J. Sagar, *Major Political Events in Indochina, 1945–90, Facts on File,* p. 190

Questions

1 What is the primary purpose of the Geneva Agreement in relation to Vietnam?

2 How are the political problems of Vietnam to be solved?

3 Is it envisaged that Vietnam is to be permanently divided into two zones? Give evidence for your answer.

4 According to the US Declaration, what is the US's position on nations which are divided against their will?

Activities

Key words
Define these important terms:

Office of Strategic Services (OSS)	guerrilla war	trusteeship
	revolutionary war	containment policy
August Revolution	terror	domino theory

Research topics
1 Giap or Bao Dai.
2 The methods of guerrilla war.

What if you were...?
1 You are President Roosevelt in 1945. Write a memo to a cabinet member explaining your policy on Indochina.
2 As General Giap, write your diary entries on the battle of Dien Bien Phu.

Review questions
1 Describe the events leading up to the declaration of Vietnam's independence.
2 Why did the French return to Indochina and what problems did they have in reasserting their authority?
3 Account for the Allies' decision not to support an independent Vietnam at the end of World War II.
4 What were the tactics of the Vietminh in the First Indochinese War?
5 Examine the methods used by the Vietminh in attempting to win over the peasantry in the war against the French.
6 To what extent did the Chinese Revolution of 1949 and the Korean War affect the First Indochinese War?

What would you say?
1 A lecture by general Giap to his officers on how to fight a revolutionary war.
2 A speech by Ho Chi Minh to the United Nations on why Vietnamese independence should be supported.

4 A NATION DIVIDED

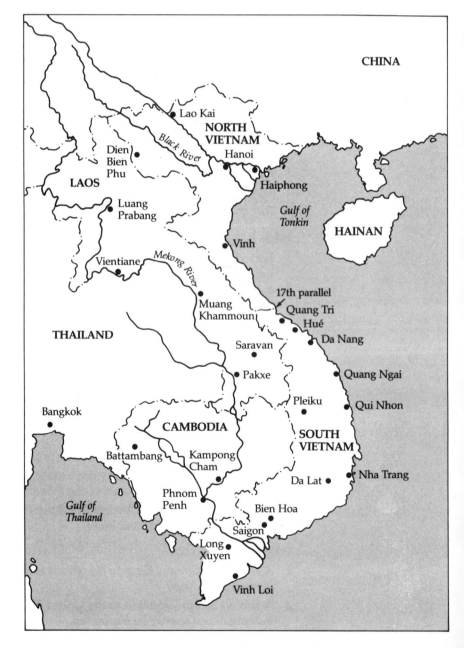

Fig. 4.1 Indochina after the Geneva Conference of 1954. Note that Vietnam is divided at the seventeenth parallel.

CHINA

Lao Kai

NORTH VIETNAM

Black River

Dien Bien Phu

Hanoi

LAOS

Haiphong

Gulf of Tonkin

HAINAN

Luang Prabang

Vinh

Vientiane

Mekong River

Muang Khammoun

17th parallel

Quang Tri

Hué

THAILAND

Saravan

Da Nang

Pakxe

Quang Ngai

Pleiku

Qui Nhon

Bangkok

CAMBODIA

SOUTH VIETNAM

Battambang

Kampong Cham

Da Lat

Nha Trang

Gulf of Thailand

Phnom Penh

Bien Hoa

Saigon

Long Xuyen

Vinh Loi

TEMPORARY DIVISION

By the Geneva Conference Agreements of 1954, Vietnam was partitioned (divided) into two nations: North Vietnam and South Vietnam. Geneva's foreign diplomats did not desire the division to be permanent and specified that national elections had to be held in two years time, after which the country would become one. This did not happen: South Vietnam became a separate political entity, supported by its powerful ally, the USA, in opposition to a communist North Vietnam ruled by Ho Chi Minh. As you read this chapter, consider whether or not this development was inevitable.

Source 4.1 Pham Van Dong on the Geneva Agreements, 21 July 1954

The Geneva Conference is concluded with the signing of the agreement which put an end to the hostilities in Indochina.

This is a great victory for the people of the Democratic Republic of Vietnam and the people of other Indochinese countries, for the people of France and all the peoples of Asia, a great victory for all peace-loving people.

It is a great victory for peace . . .

The signing of peace in Indochina on the basis of the recognition of the national rights of the Indochinese peoples is a victory for all oppressed people who raise high the banner of struggle for national independence and democratic liberties.

On behalf of the people and the Government of the Democratic Republic of Vietnam, the delegation of the Democratic Republic of Vietnam expresses its thanks to all the powers participating in this conference, and all the peace-loving peoples and governments far or near who have contributed to the achievement of peace for which our people have struggled with heroism for eight years.

A big step has been taken. More steps remain to be taken. We have to build up a stable and lasting peace in Indochina by settling the political questions, of which the most important is the achievement of the national unification of our people by means of elections, that is to say by peaceful and democratic means.

At the same time, we have to build up our country, which has been ravaged by prolonged war, continue and intensify the carrying out of democratic liberties, including freedom of opinion and belief, develop the country's economy and culture in order to raise the standard of the material and spiritual life of our people.

To accomplish these tasks, which already present themselves, we shall need the sympathy, support and assistance of our friends. We shall need the cooperation of peoples of South-east Asia and all the rest of Asia on the basis of mutual respect for sovereignty and territorial integrity, non-aggression and non-interference in each other's internal affairs, equality and mutual benefit, peaceful coexistence, and we shall need good relations with all countries of the world.

With France in particular, a country famous for its glorious tradition of liberty, the Democratic Republic of Vietnam ardently desires to form ties of confidence and friendship, which are indispensable to the restoration of peace in Indochina and the settlement of all related questions. We stand for the establishment of economic and cultural relations with France on the basis of equality and mutual benefit.

We need peace to achieve the unification of our country and to enable us to work for our national reconstruction. We shall faithfully and strictly carry out all terms of agreements which we have signed. We hope that the other parties concerned will do the same. We all need to maintain and consolidate the peace which has just been achieved.

Our thoughts go out to people of our country, who have shown such great patriotism and courage during the war and will exhibit the same patriotism and courage in the time of peace that has just begun. The conference has fixed a date for our unification. This unity we shall make and win as we have won peace.

No force in the world, internal or external, will turn us aside from our road to unity by peace and democracy. This will be the crowning achievement of our national independence.

People of Vietnam! Compatriots of the South, victory is ours! The independence and unity of our land is in our hands. The people who love

peace and justice throughout the world are of the same mind as we. Remember President Ho Chi Minh's words: The struggle is hard, but it is we who will win final victory.
    Long live peace!

Long live the unity of our Motherland!

Allan B. Cole (ed.)
Conflict in Indo-China and International Repercussions,
pp. 160-1*

Questions

1 What are the two major tasks for Vietnam now that the war is over, according to Pham Van Dong?
2 What barriers were there in Indochina to a lasting peace?
3 Could a lasting peace have been built in Indochina by political means as Pham believed?

* *Source 4.1* The original source is: New China News Agency, Peking, 23 July 1954.

THE SOUTH

The French knew they were finished in Vietnam after Dien Bien Phu and intended to keep to the terms of the Geneva agreements and leave within the year. In the south, their colony was replaced by the Republic of Vietnam (South Vietnam) ruled by Emperor Bao Dai.

In June 1954, Bao Dai chose Ngo Dinh Diem as his Prime Minister and head of government. Diem was a strict Catholic and fervent nationalist who had been in exile overseas for many years. He had been Bao Dai's Minister for the Interior in the emperor's ill-fated attempt at reform in the 1930s (see chapter 3).

How did Diem establish South Vietnam?

Diem's task as Prime Minister was a daunting one. The south was hopelessly divided, politically chaotic and, after nine years of warfare, enormous destruction had been inflicted on the nation's agricultural base. In addition, there were nearly 1 million Vietnamese from the north who needed to be resettled after moving south in the 300-day period of free movement. And perhaps the biggest problem was the existence of three private armies or sects which controlled substantial areas of the new state. The new government needed to exercise its authority over them in order to achieve credibility and to survive.

Who were the sects?

The Vietminh had never been as powerful in the south as it was in central and northern Vietnam partly because of three strong factions that opposed them in the region. The three factions were: the Binh Xuyen, a criminal organisation; and the Hoa Hao and the Cao Dai, both religious sects. Each had large private armies and were seen by Diem as obstacles to creating a unified government in South Vietnam under his leadership.

Diem defeated the sects using a combination of bribery and force. He offered the Cao Dai and the Hoa Hao a bribe of about US$12 million (only part of an enormous aid package from America) with the promise that their armies would be able to integrate into the national army at a later date. With the religious sects silent he declared war on the Binh Xuyen after cancelling the bargain they had struck with Bao Dai. The emperor had allowed the Binh Xuyen free rein in Saigon (including control of the police force) in return for money to fund his extravagant lifestyle. Bao Dai spent most of his time as emperor on the French Riviera indulging in wine, women and song. He would be ousted as emperor in 1955 when defeated by Diem in a national referendum.

In late April 1955, Diem's national army drove the Binh Xuyen out of Saigon and turned its attention to the armies of the sects. By early 1956, the Cao Dai and the Hoa Hao were beaten — the Cao Dai pope had escaped to Cambodia and a leading Hoa Hao was publicly guillotined. The sects were beaten but the areas they had controlled became problems for the South Vietnamese government because remnants of the sects' armies continued to fight the government and many others joined the communists.

■ Could Diem have beaten the sects and avoided their remnants joining the communists?

The Vietnamese Sects

Cao Dai The Cao Dai or 'High Church' sect was formed in 1919 by Ngo Van Chieu as a synthesis of Christianity, Buddhism and other religions. Amongst its 'saints' were Jesus Christ, Buddha, Joan of Arc and Victor Hugo. The sect soon turned political and after collaborating with the Japanese and later with the Viet Minh, they allied with the French in 1946, although a portion of the sect continued to support the Viet Minh. The Cao Daist army was originally armed by the Japanese but later received financial support from the French. By the mid-1950s the army, led by General Nguyen Thanh Phoung, was about 30 000 strong and controlled a large area around Tay Ninh, a region situated some 50 miles (80 kilometres) northwest of Saigon. The sect, led by 'Pope' Pham Cong Tac, claimed some 2 million adherents.

Hoa Hao Hoa Hao, founded in the southern village of the same name in 1939 by Huynh Phu So, proclaimed a simplified version of Buddhism. As with the Cao Dai, the sect rapidly entered the political arena and built up its own private armed forces. It collaborated in turn with the Japanese and the Viet Minh, but the majority joined the French in 1947. Huynh Phu So was subsequently assassinated by the Viet Minh and the leadership passed into the hands of General Tran Van Soai, who commanded the loyalty of some 30 000 troops. General Soai controlled an area west of Saigon, extending to the Cambodian border, with a population of about 1 million.

Binh-Xuyen Anything but a religious body, the Binh-Xuyen is nevertheless usually classed as one of the three major 'sects'. It started out as a group of bandits operating from the village of Binh-Xuyen (near Saigon) which supported the Viet Minh for a while before being granted control by the French of a zone east of Saigon in 1948. By the mid-1950s its forces numbered about 15 000 men commanded by General Le Van Hien. General Hien came to an arrangement with Bao Dai in 1954 through which Binh-Xuyen secured control of the capital's police force as well as a monopoly of the city's highly lucrative gaming houses, opium dens and brothels.[1]

Were national elections held?

The Geneva Accords had specified national elections in two years. Discussions on the nature of these elections were to begin in mid-1955. Diem refused even to hold the discussions. He announced on 16 July 1955:

> We are not bound in any way by those agreements signed against the will of the Vietnamese people . . . We shall not miss any opportunity which should permit the unification of our homeland in freedom, but it is out of the question for us to consider any proposal from the Vietminh if proof is not given that they put the superior interests of the National Community above those of communism.[2]

■ Do you think Diem's attitude to elections was justified?

North Vietnam protested but there was no support from the countries that had participated at Geneva. Soon the US government announced their public support of Diem's policy on national elections.

Source 4.2   Diem on national elections, 16 July 1955

Countrymen:

The National Government has emphasized time and time again the price it has paid for the defence of the unity of the country and of true democracy. We did not sign the Geneva Agreements. We are not bound in any way by these agreements, signed against the will of the Vietnamese people. Our policy is a policy of peace, but nothing will lead us astray from our goal: the unity of our country — a unity in freedom and not in slavery.

Serving the cause of our nation more than ever, we will struggle for the reunification of our homeland. We do not reject the principle of free elections as peaceful and democratic means to achieve that unity. Although elections constitute one of the bases of true democracy, they will be meaningful only on the condition that they are absolutely free.

Faced now with a regime of oppression as practiced by the Viet Minh, we remain sceptical concerning the possibility of fulfilling the conditions of free elections in the North. We shall not miss any opportunity which would permit the unification of our homeland in freedom, but it is out of the question for us to consider any proposal from the Viet Minh if proof is not given that they put the superior interests of the National Community above those of communism, if they do not cease violating their obligations as they have done by preventing our countrymen of the North from going South or by recently attacking, together with the communist Pathet Lao, the friendly state of Laos.

The mission falls to us, the Nationalists, to accomplish the reunification of our country in conditions that are most democratic and most effective to guarantee our independence. The Free World is with us. Of this we are certain. I am confident that I am a faithful interpreter of our state of mind when I affirm solemnly our will to resist communism.

To those who live above the 17th parallel, I ask them to have confidence. With the agreement and the backing of the Free World, the National Government will bring you independence in freedom.

Allan B. Cole (ed.)
Conflict in Indo-China and International Repercussions,
pp. 226-7*

Questions

1 What arguments does Diem use against the holding of national elections?
2 Why, according to Diem, are free elections in the north to be treated sceptically?
3 Does Diem indicate any of his aims and attitudes by making such a statement? If so, what are they?

* *Source 4.2* The original source is: Embassy of Vietnam, Press and Information Service, Vol 1, No. 18, 22 July 1955, Washington D.C.

What was Diem's record on land reform?

Eighty-five per cent of the population of both Vietnams lived in the countryside and relied on agriculture for their livelihood. Land was the most important issue socially, economically and politically for the majority of Vietnamese. To win the support of the mass of the population, it was essential to implement land reform (a fairer distribution of land amongst the community).

During the First Indochinese War, the Vietminh had seized land from French plantation owners and rich Vietnamese landlords and distributed it among tenant farmers and landless peasants. Soon after coming to power, Diem reversed this process of redistribution because he did not want to lose support of the big landowners. Diem did effect land reform but under his policy little land was redistributed and then mainly to northern Catholic refugees and not to southern farmers (in 1960 45 per cent of land was owned by 2 per cent of the people). Diem's land reform failed to win him widespread support among the peasantry.

THE NORTH

Ho and his communist colleagues in charge of North Vietnam (Democratic Republic of Vietnam) did not have the same problems as in the south. Ho's problems were economic. Most of the fighting in the First Indochinese War had been in the north where the greatest damage to productive capacity was inflicted. Perhaps even more damaging was North Vietnam's division from South Vietnam which cut the north off from its major supplier of food. For centuries the rice bowl of the Mekong Valley in the south had fed the northern population.

What was the communist record on land reform?

In the early years after partition, 1954–56, the problems faced by the communist government were made worse by a land reform program that ran out of control and inflicted terrible suffering on the population. Communist theory stated that land must be taken from the greedy landlords and distributed among the landless peasants. The communist leadership dictated that 5 per cent of the rural population were landlords and needed to be punished. People's Agricultural Tribunals were set up and thousands of small and large landowners were tried and executed. Many of those killed were not landlords but victims of over-enthusiastic cadres (party officials and group leaders) or victims of other peasants who had accused them to avoid accusation themselves. Precise figures are unknown but it is clear that thousands died and thousands more were sent to labour camps.

So land reform in the north was initially a terrible failure. In August 1956, Ho admitted that there had been 'errors' and promised that the government would compensate the victims. Giap commented:

> . . . we executed too many honest people . . . and seeing enemies everywhere, resorted to terror, which became far too widespread . . . Worse still, torture came to be regarded as a normal practice.[3]

After this time, the land reform program was implemented more responsibly and agriculture began to improve. Unlike the case in the south, the power of the landlords was broken and land was divided among the peasants equally. However, this was a communist system and the peasants did not own their land; all land was owned by the communist state.

THE ANTI-COMMUNIST CAMPAIGN

Not all Vietminh soldiers had retreated to the north as the Geneva Agreements prescribed. Some 8000–10 000 military and civilian cadres remained behind in the south at Ho Chi Minh's instruction. They were told to stay hidden and prepare for a future uprising and at the same time to encourage popular demand for the all-national elections in 1956. Most of these cadres were party members and came from all levels of Vietnamese society and they were located in all parts of the south.

Many other remnants of the Vietminh survived in the south. South Vietnam was full of men and women who had helped in the resistance against the French under the banner of the Vietminh. They had fought as guerrilla soldiers or as administrators in Vietminh local government or as guides, messengers or spies. There were also the relatives of the 100 000 who had gone to North Vietnam or the relatives of those who had died fighting the French. The majority of these men and women were not communists but had joined the Vietminh because they wished to see a Vietnam that was truly independent, with the French driven out of their country.

In the summer of 1955 President Diem launched what was called the Denunciation of the Communists campaign. Diem was concerned about the 8000–10 000 cadres, the 'stay-behinds' as they were nicknamed, inciting revolution and civil unrest. Yet his campaign was aimed at all ex-Vietminh and therefore its target included thousands of others who were not communists. All those who had opposed the French were suspected of communist sympathies and disloyalty to the government. Thousands of Vietnamese were killed as a result and perhaps 50 000 arrested and sent to labour camps (the exact numbers are not known because no accurate records were kept and the government was understandably not keen to publicise what it was doing).

The widespread terror and fear generated by the anti-communist campaign built up enormous hostility towards Diem's regime. Diem did not understand that he was in fact punishing many of the heroes of the resistance war against the French: most Vietnamese considered the Vietminh as patriotic heroes. But Diem and his family were interested only in their own survival and were intent on rooting out and repressing any opposition.

Who were the Vietcong?

As history has frequently shown, a policy of repression encourages rather than eliminates the opposition. The southern communists suffered great losses in the anti-communist campaign but, instead of fading into the shadows as Diem had hoped they would, they decided to fight back: they began to provoke the very revolution that Diem feared. A history of the period written by the communists, captured in 1966, explains why:

> In opposing such an enemy, simple political struggle was not possible. It was necessary to use armed struggle . . . The enemy would not allow us any peace.[4]

The communists found a population that was full of animosity towards Diem's government and full of recruits for a new resistance war. Amongst the new recruits were ex-Vietminh being harassed by the secret police and army, ex-members of the Cao Dai, Hoa Hao and Binh Xuyen ready to settle old scores, and many peasants upset at the injustice of land reform and troubled by a government which appeared as foreign and repressive as the French before them.

In 1957, the southern communist leaders began a campaign of counter-terror in the villages. Police, village chiefs (who were appointees of the Diem government), teachers and other representatives of the government at village level were murdered or abducted. The aim was to undermine the authority of the Saigon regime. By 1958, the war had expanded into a full scale guerrilla war.

The new guerrillas were called 'Vietcong' by the Saigon administration and by the Americans. It was an insulting term, being short for Vietnamese communists, in an attempt to label all resistance as communist. Like the Vietminh before them, the Vietcong (VC) adopted 'hit and run' tactics, built up their strength through the recruitment of new members, and set up a rival administration at village level. Also like the Vietminh, the VC concentrated on winning the battle for 'the hearts and minds of the peasantry', observing closely Mao's rules for dealing favourably and fairly with the local population. VC numbers and liberated areas began to grow. In December

1960, a National Liberation Front (NLF) was formed, representing various political groupings opposed to the South Vietnam government. The NLF and its military wing, the VC guerrilla army, were organised and led by the communists who took their orders from the government in Hanoi.

■ Could the south have avoided a guerrilla war?

> ### Ten Point Program of the NLF
>
> (1) To overthrow the disguised colonial regime of the US imperialism and the dictatorial Ngo Dinh Diem administration — lackey of the US — and to form a national democratic coalition administration. (2) To bring into being a broad and progressive democracy. (3) To build an independent and sovereign economy, improve the people's living conditions. (4) To carry out land-rent reduction and advance toward the settlement of the agrarian problem so as to ensure land to the tillers. (5) To build a national and democratic education and culture. (6) To build an army to defend the Fatherland and the people. (7) To guarantee the right of equality between nationalities, and between men and women; to protect the legitimate rights of foreign residents in Vietnam and Vietnamese living abroad. (8) To carry out a foreign policy of peace and neutrality. (9) To establish normal relations between the two zones and advance toward peaceful reunification of the Fatherland. (10) To oppose aggressive war, actively defend world peace.[5]

Source 4.3   The National Liberation Front

I returned to Vietnam from university studies in France in 1955. I saw that the nonrealization of the Geneva Accords would lead to war between the North and South. But I stayed away from political acts and worked in a private bank in Saigon.

Watching the political evolution of my country, I saw that the Diem government made many fundamental errors: First, it was a government of one family. Second, Diem suppressed many patriots who participated in the war against the French. Third, he put the Christian religion above the interest of the nation. I am personally not a Buddhist, but eighty percent of the Vietnamese population are Confucian or Buddhist.

From 1958 some resistance was formed, which led to the formation of the National Liberation Front in December 1960 in Tay Ninh Province, near the Cambodian border. I had been contacted by former resistance members and others who were unhappy with the Diem regime. I belonged to a well-known family in the South. I had relations in every stratum of society. I had been the comptroller of a large bank, and later became Director General of the Sugar Company of Vietnam and secretary-general of the Self-Determination Movement.

The mobilisation committee for the National Liberation Front was formed by intellectuals: the architect Huynh Tan Phat; the doctor Phung Van Cung; the lawyer Trinh Dinh Thao; myself; and others. We were all mostly educated in France. Our idea of independence came from what we saw in free countries in the West. Whereas Ho Chi Minh and the Communists in the liberation front were formed by the Soviet Comintern under Lenin and Stalin.

I was not Communist. I joined the resistance movement believing that Ho Chi Minh, Pham Van Dong, and the Vietnamese Communist Party were patriotic and would place the national interest above personal and ideological desires. I believed that we would consolidate our divided nation and begin the task of reconstruction. I believed the people of Vietnam would find peace, well-being, and freedom once the war ended. Because of love for my country, I gave up my family, everything, for this dream.

I would not listen when my father warned me, "In return for your service, the Communists will not even give you a part of what you have now. Worse, they will betray you and persecute you all of your life."

But I was adamant, because the North Vietnamese insisted that they never wanted to impose Communism on the South. We were, in fact, dependent on the North Vietnamese for weapons, communications, and especially for our propaganda network. And our movement was reinforced by troops coming from North Vietnam.

Beginning in 1959, the northerners came down through Laos and Cambodia on the Ho Chi Minh Trail. Many of these soldiers remained posted along the trail to protect the flow of arms and munitions coming from the North.

> Truong Nhu Tang, founding member,
> National Liberation Front, South Vietnam,
> 1960-76, quoted in
> A. Santoli, *To Bear Any Burden*, pp. 76-7

Questions

1 Outline Truong's criticism of the Diem government.
2 What was Truong's political background?
3 Did the communists deceive Truong?

President Diem (right) and US President Eisenhower.

DID US SUPPORT CONTINUE?

Chapter 3 mentioned the extent of American support for the French position in Indochina. Washington had funded 80 per cent of the French war effort. President Eisenhower, Truman's successor, would not involve American armed forces directly. When the French were trapped at Dien Bien Phu, their government pleaded for American air support. Eisenhower refused to be drawn any further into the conflict, however, without the backing of other allied nations. Yet Eisenhower's administration did support South Vietnam with massive amounts of aid, the majority of which was channelled into the military and the security forces.

Diem and South Vietnam would have struggled to survive without American military and economic aid. This is illustrated by considering the amount of US aid given to South Vietnam during 1952–66.

President John F. Kennedy.

Kennedy

In 1961, John Kennedy became President of the USA (1961–63) and pledged to continue the policy of supporting nations against the threat of communism. In his inaugural address in January 1961 he gave this warning:

> Let every nation know, whether it wishes us well or ill, that we shall pay any price, bear any burden, meet any hardship, support any friend, oppose any foe, to assure the survival and success of liberty.[6]

■ Who is this warning aimed at?

With such speeches and increased aid in money and men, Kennedy 'raised the stakes' in Vietnam. By the end of his time in office the USA had more than 16 000 American advisers in South Vietnam training the Army of the Republic of Vietnam (ARVN) in American military techniques. Many others were helping the government forces by showing them how to provide the peasantry with improved hygiene, agriculture and education. The idea was to increase support for the South Vietnamese government among the villages.

Despite these tactics and the massive American aid, however, the VC numbers continued to increase. By November 1961, the VC fighting forces had grown from the 2000 fighters that had been left after Diem's ruthless anti-communist campaign in 1957, to 16 000.

Regardless of American weapons and money (many US weapons ended up in the hands of the guerrillas anyway), the VC were winning the support of the villagers. South Vietnam's government and the Americans assisting them were too often seen by villagers as foreigners or their representatives: it was the VC who were seen to be Vietnamese fighting for Vietnamese independence.

■ Was it unavoidable that the VC would be seen in this nationalistic light?

The US military response to the deteriorating position in South Vietnam was to apply more military force. The Joint Chiefs of Staff (heads of the Army, Navy and Air Force) wanted six US divisions — 200 000 men — to be sent immediately to South Vietnam. Kennedy responded with caution and refused to send in US ground forces. Under Kennedy, the US commitment remained at an advisory level.

■ Why didn't Kennedy send in troops?

Table 4.1 US Economic and military aid to South Vietnam (millions of dollars)[7]

Fiscal Year	US Economic Aid	US Military Aid	Total US Economic and Military Aid
1953–57	823.3	277.8	1101.1
1958	188.7	53.2	241.9
1959	207.1	41.9	249.0
1960	180.3	70.9	251.2
1961	144.1	65.0	209.1
1962	142.9	144.0	286.9
1963	186.0	190.0	376.0
1964	216.1	186.9	403.0
1965	268.2	274.7	542.9
1966	729.2	170.8	900.0
Total, 1953–66	**$3085.9**	**$1475.2**	**$4561.1**

THE END OF DIEM

By the early 1960s, the Diem regime was collapsing. It had failed to win over the mass of the peasantry and had become very unpopular: it had failed to implement a genuine land reform package; its anti-communist program had affected many innocent civilians; its corruption and the program of 'strategic hamlets' had forcibly uprooted most of the population of South Vietnam.

What were strategic hamlets?

A significant cause of the dissatisfaction with the South Vietnamese government was the strategic hamlets program (also called fortified hamlets). The theory behind the strategic hamlets program was that the isolation of the VC from the villages of South Vietnam would deny them the supplies and recruits necessary for their survival. This was to be achieved by moving the villages away from the VC and then fortifying each village with guns and barbed wire to prevent the VC from coming back. By September 1962, the Saigon government claimed to have established strategic hamlets for one-third of the country's population.

But the removal of entire villages was often done very cruelly and caused great distress to the peasants. For the Vietnamese, the land is an integral part of their identity. Families had often farmed in the same area for hundreds of years and did not wish to have to start all over again in, to them, a foreign place. Furthermore, the graves of their ancestors, which formed an important part of their religious worship, were located near the village and could not be taken with them. The strategic hamlets were hugely unpopular and alienated entire villages of peasants, many of whom went over to the VC.

The Buddhist crisis

On 8 May 1963, a company of the Saigon government's Civil Guards opened fire on a group of Buddhists protesting against a new law which forbade the flying of the Buddhist flag on Buddha's birthday. The ban was the idea of the President's elder brother, Thuc, the Catholic Archbishop of Hué. The Buddhists had been forced to contend with persecution from the Catholic Diems since 1955.

During the subsequent weeks, the Buddhists' protests grew and became the rallying point for discontent with the South Vietnamese government. Diem's response was typically repressive: he tried to crush the revolt in the same way as he had crushed the Cao Dai and the Hoa Hao.

The Buddhists responded in a way the government did not expect. On 11 June 1963, Quang Duc, a 73-year-old monk seated himself in the lotus position on a Saigon road and, after being dowsed with petrol, burnt himself to death in protest at Diem's religious persecution. The photographs of the suicide stunned the world; and six more monks committed suicide publicly. The USA called for negotiations with the Buddhists. The Ngos (Diem, his brother Nhu and Nhu's wife) were indifferent to world opinion. Mme Nhu said she hoped there would be more 'barbecues' and Nhu, head of the secret police, responded in August with cruel raids on Buddhist pagodas throughout the country.

Even members of Diem's government were outraged at this response. South Vietnam's Foreign Minister resigned and shaved his head like a Buddhist monk in protest; the UN Ambassador, Mme Nhu's father, also resigned. Students, from universities and high schools, rioted across the nation. The riots were put down and the protests were ignored but, throughout the latter part of 1963, opposition to the Diem regime intensified to nearly boiling point.

A Buddhist monk commits suicide in protest at the Diem regime's persecution of his religion.

US patience with Diem, who had consistently ignored American advice on negotiations, began to run out. Many in Kennedy's administration now believed that the war could not be won with the Diems in power. The new US Ambassador to Vietnam, Henry Cabot Lodge, who arrived in Vietnam in September 1963, was among these. At Lodge's prompting, the US government imposed a freeze on loans to South Vietnam and threatened to withdraw military aid.

Encouraged by the American moves, a coup against the government was organised by the leading generals of the Saigon army. It was carried out successfully on 1 November 1963, and Diem and Nhu were shot and killed in the fighting. There was rejoicing in the streets of Saigon as the first in a succession of military governments came to power.

Activities

Key words
Define these important terms:

anarchy	land reform	National Liberation
partition	People's Agricultural	Front
Cao Dai	Tribunal	strategic hamlet
Hoa Hao	cadres	adviser
Binh Xuyen	'stay-behinds'	
referendum	Vietcong	

Research topics
1 One of the sects: the Cao Dai, Hoa Hao, Binh Xuyen.
2 The foreign policy of either Eisenhower or Kennedy as US President.
3 The Buddhist Revolt in South Vietnam.

What if you were . . ?
1 You are a Vietnamese villager who has been moved to a strategic hamlet in the early 1960s. Write down your thoughts on the change.
2 You are a reporter with Ngo Dinh Diem in October 1963. Write an article about your interview with him on his record as leader of South Vietnam.

Review questions
1 Evaluate Diem's period as President of South Vietnam.
2 Compare and contrast land reform in North and South Vietnam.
3 Why did the USA become involved in Vietnam in the 1950s?
4 What was US involvement in South Vietnam under Presidents Eisenhower and Kennedy? Were there any notable differences?
5 Who were the VC and why did they grow in strength?
6 Account for the failure of the Diem government in South Vietnam.

What would you say?
1 A northern communist leader speaking in a radio broadcast on why there should be national elections for Vietnam.
2 American adviser to the South Vietnamese government giving a talk after returning to the US about his role and the situation in the south in the early 1960s.

5 AMERICA PLUNGES IN

John F. Kennedy's involvement with the Vietnam War ended tragically in Dallas, Texas, when he was assassinated on 22 November 1963 while campaigning for re-election. Riding in the motorcade but unhurt by the bullets was his successor, Vice-President, Lyndon Baynes Johnson — LBJ.

WHO WAS LBJ?

Lyndon Baynes Johnson was a vastly experienced politician from Texas who had served the electors in Washington since the 1930s. Soon after taking office, Johnson reaffirmed the US commitment to the government of South Vietnam. (Some US Presidents have been known mainly by their initials — Johnson (LBJ) and Kennedy (JFK) are two such examples.) Johnson regarded the presidency as an opportunity to give full expression to his reformist principles. He believed that America's greatest battle should be against poverty and discrimination, and his government (1963–69) poured billions of dollars of federal funds into public housing, job creation and education. He intended to create a 'great society' in America in the 1960s. But as this chapter will reveal, LBJ was also the president who plunged American combat troops into the Vietnam War. Johnson and his administration became trapped between the two conflicting policies of commitment to involvement in Vietnam and the creation of the 'great society'. In his

President Johnson meeting the troops in Vietnam in 1967.

retirement Johnson described the problem and his reasons for escalating involvement:

> I knew from the start that I was bound to be crucified either way I moved. If I left the woman I really loved — the Great Society — in order to get involved with that bitch of a war on the other side of the world, then I would lose everything at home. All my programs. All my hopes to feed the hungry and shelter the homeless. All my dreams to provide education and medical care to the browns and the blacks and the lame and the poor. But if I left that war and let the communists take over South Vietnam, then I would be seen as a coward and my nation would be seen as an appeaser, and we would both find it impossible to accomplish anything for anybody anywhere on the entire globe.[1]

'The revolving door republic'

General Duong Minh (nicknamed Big Minh because of his above-average height) led the coup against the Ngos in November 1963. The Minh government, mostly concerned about staying in power, did nothing for the peasantry and was no more successful in fighting the VC than the Diem government had been. The Minh government became equally as unpopular as Diem's and protests by workers and students quickly broke out. Within months Big Minh's government had been replaced in another military coup. Short-term governments became the norm in South Vietnamese politics for the next eighteen months.

Between November 1963 and April 1965, no less than nine governments came and went in South Vietnam — hence the name 'the revolving door republic'. By May 1965, Air Force General Nguyen Cao Ky was Prime Minister and General Nguyen Van Thieu was Chief of Staff, and between them these two ruled South Vietnam until 1975, providing stability of leadership that was needed so urgently.

As Saigon administrations came and went in 1964 and 1965, the VC took advantage of the power vacuum and built up their strength dramatically. In January 1963, VC strength stood at 23 000 guerrillas and by December 1964 this had grown to 56 000.

Attitudes to involvement

With the situation in South Vietnam deteriorating, the military and most of LBJ's cabinet advocated that the USA should take a more direct role in the war, that is, the USA should send combat soldiers to fight in Vietnam.

Johnson's top men had been inherited from Kennedy's team. Secretary of State, Dean Rusk, and Secretary of Defense, Robert McNamara, regarded South Vietnam as part of a worldwide scenario involving the USA fighting to contain the spread of communism. To these men and to LBJ, the South Vietnamese government was waging a war against a communist movement inspired and led from North Vietnam. Little thought was given to the reasons behind the unpopularity of the government they were supporting or to the leadership of the nationalist movement by the communists over the previous twenty years. Throughout 1964 the Pentagon (headquarters of the US Defense Department) drew up plans to escalate the war by bombing North

Vietnam and by introducing US combat troops. Yet Johnson, like Kennedy before him, hesitated before deepening the commitment.

GULF OF TONKIN INCIDENT

The Gulf of Tonkin lies off the coast of North Vietnam. On 2 August, 1964, the US destroyer Maddox was patrolling the Gulf. The *Maddox* was an intelligence gathering vessel, collecting information on North Vietnamese radio stations and other defence systems. The information gained by these destroyer patrols was helping commando raids by the South Vietnamese armed forces against selected targets in North Vietnam. Such a raid (code-named 34A) had taken place at the end of July. Perhaps in retaliation, at midday on 2 August the *Maddox* was attacked by torpedoes from three patrol boats of the North Vietnamese Navy. The *Maddox* returned fire and called in air support. The engagement ended with the *Maddox* untouched and one patrol boat sunk and the other two badly damaged.

Fig 5.1 The Ho Chi Minh Trail was the major supply line to the VC in South Vietnam.

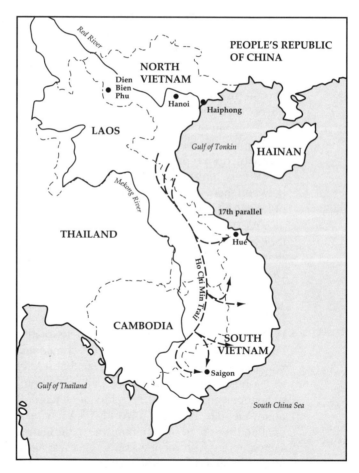

■ Were the North Vietnamese justified in attacking the *Maddox?*

On 4 August the *Maddox* and another US destroyer, the *Turner Joy,* were back in the Tonkin Gulf when a second alleged attack took place. The Johnson administration seized on these events and put before the US Congress a resolution which gave the President a virtual 'blank cheque' to

■ Should the Americans have declared war? What differences did it make that they did not?

wage war in South-East Asia as he saw fit. The Resolution passed the Houses of Congress on 7 August 1964 almost unanimously — only two senators voted against it. There was no actual declaration of war by the Americans in Vietnam, the Tonkin Resolution side-stepped the need for such an announcement.

After the second incident, LBJ ordered US airplanes to bomb patrol boat bases and supply depots in North Vietnam. In the first US bombing raid of the Second Indochina War, twenty-five vessels were reported damaged or destroyed and two American airplanes were shot down.

Source 5.1   Gulf of Tonkin Resolution

To promote the Maintenance of International Peace and Security in Southeast Asia.

Whereas naval units of the Communist regime in Vietnam, in violation of the principles of the Charter of the United Nations and of international law, have deliberately and repeatedly attacked United States naval vessels lawfully present in international waters, and have thereby created a serious threat to international peace; and

Whereas these attacks are part of a deliberate and systematic campaign of aggression that the Communist regime in North Vietnam has been waging against its neighbours and the nations joined with them in the collective defence of their freedom; and

Whereas the United States is assisting peoples of Southeast Asia to protect their freedom and has no territorial, military or political ambitions in that area, but desires only that these peoples should be left in peace to work out their own destinies in their own way: Now, therefore, be it

Resolved by the Senate and House of Representatives of the United States of America in Congress assembled.

That the Congress approves and supports the determination of the President, as Commander in Chief, to take all necessary measures to repel any armed attack against the forces of the United States and to prevent further aggression.

The United States regards as vital to its national interest and to world peace the maintenance of international peace and security in Southeast Asia. Consonant with the Constitution of the United States and the Charter of the United Nations and in accordance with its obligations under the Southeast Asia Collective Defence Treaty, the United States is, therefore, prepared, as the President determines, to take all necessary steps, including the use of armed force, to assist any member or protocol state of the Southeast Asia Collective Defence Treaty requesting assistance in defence of its freedom.

This resolution shall expire when the President shall determine that the peace and security of the area is reasonably assured by international conditions created by action of the United Nations or otherwise, except that it may be terminated earlier by concurrent resolution of the Congress.

D.J. Sagar, *Major Political Events in Indochina, 1945-90, Facts on File*, p.194

Questions

1 What is the reason for the resolution? From your knowledge, is this accurate?

2 This resolution has been described as a blank cheque. Do you agree? Quote evidence from the source to support your view.

1964: An election year

In the 1964 election, LBJ was confronted by a tough talking, conservative Republican, Barry Goldwater. In a skilled political move, Johnson painted himself as the peace candidate and Goldwater as a warmonger (one who seeks to bring about war). In the campaign Johnson promised that American boys would not be sent overseas to fight wars for Asian boys.

In November, Johnson was elected as President in his own right, with the biggest margin of votes in US political history. Both Houses of Congress were dominated by the President's political party, the Democrats. LBJ could now start building his 'great society', confident that his reforms would be sympathetically received by the Congress.

■ Why would these moves win Johnson votes?

ROLLING THUNDER

In South Vietnam the situation was becoming worse. The government was still in disarray, the VC was growing in numbers, and the ARVN was losing men and areas under its control. During 1964, the VC started receiving reinforcements from the north. These were soldiers of the North Vietnamese Army, not ex-southerners who had been returning south since the start of the insurrection. In December 1964 and the early months of 1965, the VC launched a series of damaging raids against American installations in the south. At Pleiku on 7 February, nine Americans were killed and seventy-six wounded. In response, Johnson ordered more bombing of North Vietnam on 2 March. The bombing was to continue intermittently for eight years and was designed to break North Vietnam's will to fight, bringing them to the negotiating table. Operation Rolling Thunder was the codename given to the bombing in 1965, and as it persisted it attracted increasing condemnation from around the world.

US bombers attacking North Vietnam in Operation Rolling Thunder.

Was the bombing successful?

The 'surgical' bombing of the north (targets were carefully selected by the President and his advisers at regular Tuesday breakfasts in the White House) was never successful in breaking the will of the North Vietnamese leadership nor did it ever succeed in hindering their ability to wage war. It failed to do this for a number of reasons, including the fact that North Vietnam, being chiefly an agricultural nation, did not have a large number of military or industrial targets to be bombed. Furthermore, China and the Soviet Union, North Vietnam's allies, were able to replace many of the materials destroyed by the bombing. This became increasingly clear to military advisers and their advice to involve American ground troops became louder.

ARRIVAL OF COMBAT TROOPS

The first US soldiers (apart from advisers) to land on Vietnamese soil were two battalions of marines who landed at Da Nang on 8 March 1965. Their orders were strictly limited to the defence of the Da Nang airbase and its perimeter.

However, once the President had made the decision to land US combat troops in South Vietnam, it became easier for others to argue that it was necessary to go further. Increasingly, the military and the majority of LBJ's cabinet argued for large scale troop involvement. They argued that Rolling Thunder was not deterring the north and that the South Vietnamese government was showing all the signs of imminent collapse. If the US did not send troops and in large numbers, South Vietnam would be lost.

In May 1965, the US Commander in Vietnam, General William Westmoreland, asked his President for 180 000 men to prevent South Vietnam from falling to the communists. Secretary of Defense McNamara believed that the US should go even further: he argued for more men and even greater bombing of the north. But there were voices of dissent. General Maxwell Taylor, who had been Kennedy's chief military adviser and US Ambassador to South Vietnam since July 1964, counselled, 'The white-faced soldier cannot be assimilated by the population; he cannot distinguish between friendly and unfriendly Vietnamese . . .'[2]

The final decision had to be made by the President, however, and he chose to send more American troops. Within nine weeks of the marines landing at Da Nang, 99 000 US and allied troops were in Vietnam. Having taken the initial step, Johnson was ready to go all the way. He made it clear that this was only the first of the troop commitments, that there would be more to come, as many as would be needed. On 28 July 1965 he announced:

> I have asked the commanding general, General Westmoreland, what more he needs to meet this mounting aggression. He has told me. And we will meet his needs. We cannot be defeated by force of arms. We will stand in Vietnam.[3]

The US marines in action in the jungles of South Vietnam.

Table 5.1 US troops in Vietnam

Year	Number
1955	300
1962	10 000
1965	161 000
1966	400 000
1968	536 000

Table 5.2 US casualties in Vietnam (1961–24 August 1968)

Casualties	Number
Killed in action	27 101
Air accident deaths	1753
Wounded	169 296
Total	198 150

Escalation

During the next three years, the level of US troops in South Vietnam rose steadily. America took over the war, allocating the lesser role of protecting civilians and military installations to the South Vietnamese army while the Americans searched for and fought the enemy. Table 5.1 shows the number of American soldiers in the south up to 1968, while Table 5.2 shows the corresponding casualties for the period (from 1961 to 24 August 1968).

The introduction of American troops stopped the imminent collapse of the South Vietnamese regime. Casualties amongst the VC guerrillas and their northern allies increased markedly according to US reports. Yet despite the death tolls and the massive US firepower on land and in the air, the resistance did not let up. The VC continued to fight and there seemed to be no end in sight. American fears of being trapped in an Asian quagmire seemed to have become frighteningly true.

As the war dragged on, voices in America and overseas grew in their condemnation of American involvement. As the casualties rose and the end came no closer, an anti-war movement began and grew in strength. Sections of LBJ's own administration began to have grave doubts about the war. But Johnson and his senior advisers and the military leaders preached that the war was being won. By the end of 1967, Westmoreland was publicly stating that he thought victory was in view.

HOW WAS AUSTRALIA INVOLVED?

For over a century Australians have been fearful of being attacked from the north. Our experience in World War II when Japanese forces reached New Guinea, midget submarines were in Sydney Harbour and Japanese planes were attacking Darwin confirmed these fears. With our traditional protector Britain fighting for its survival in Europe, Australia turned to the US for assistance. After World War II, and particularly because of the development of communist strength in Asia and elsewhere, Australian leaders were keen to enter into further alliances with the US.

In 1951, Australia entered into the ANZUS agreement along with the US and New Zealand. The parties agreed to work together for defence purposes and to consult if any member was attacked. SEATO (South-East Asia Treaty Organisation) was formed in 1954 at US prompting (primarily that of John Foster Dulles, Secretary of State under President Eisenhower) for the purpose of containing the spread of communism in South-East Asia. Australia, the US, France, New Zealand, Pakistan, the Philippines, Thailand and the United Kingdom were all members of SEATO and South Vietnam, Laos and Cambodia were the specific nations to be protected by the terms of the treaty.

At the time of the Vietnam War the US called on its allies and especially the members of SEATO to actively support its role in South Vietnam. Seven nations bolstered America's commitment: Australia, New Zealand, South Korea, the Philippines, Thailand, Spain and Taiwan (the last two sent only tiny forces of thirty or so men).

■ Why did the US seek help from other nations?

Prime Minister Robert Menzies.

Sir Robert Menzies, Prime Minister of Australia since 1949, had long been fearful of communism. In the early 1950s he believed that a war between the West and the communist countries was looming and he was highly supportive of the US and its foreign policy. When the Korean War broke out in 1950 Australia provided soldiers.

In the 1960s, fear of communism still gripped the government and defence was a major issue. In 1962 Australia sent thirty advisers to South Vietnam. Two years later, the government introduced National Service or conscription (compulsory enlistment in the armed forces) for all twenty-year-olds. Australian defence policy was dominated by the idea of Forward Defence which meant avoiding a war being fought in Australia by sending troops against potential enemies overseas. Conservative politicians encouraged US involvement in the Asian region, believing that this would add to Australia's own security.

On 29 April 1965, Menzies announced that Australia would be sending combat troops to South Vietnam. He explained:

> The Australian Government is now in receipt of a request from the Government of South Vietnam for further military assistance.
>
> We have decided — and this has been after close consultation with the Government of the United States — to provide an infantry battalion for service in South Vietnam . . .
>
> The takeover of South Vietnam would be a direct military threat to Australia and to all the countries of South and South East Asia. It must be seen as part of a thrust by Communist China between the Indian and Pacific Oceans . . .[4]

The opposition Labor Party and small segments of the population disagreed with the government's decision. Arthur Calwell, the leader of the Labor Party, said in parliament:

> We do not think it is a wise decision. We do not think it is a timely decision. We do not think it is a right decision. We do not think it will help the fight against Communism. On the contrary, we believe it will harm that fight in the long term. We do not believe it will promote the welfare of the people of Vietnam. On the contrary, we believe it will prolong and deepen the suffering of that unhappy people so that Australia's very name may become a term of reproach among them . . .
>
> Australia's aim should have been to help end the war, not extend it . . . How long will it be before we are drawing upon our conscript youth to service these growing and endless requirements.[5]

What was the extent of Australia's commitment?

Australia's commitment was miniscule compared with the massive American effort. At the height of their strength, Australian forces in Vietnam numbered 8300 men. Nevertheless, this was considerably more than the number Australia had sent to the Korean conflict. More than 46 000 Australian military personnel served in Vietnam altogether with 17 424 being National Servicemen. Five hundred and one Australians were killed in Vietnam with 3131 wounded in action or injured in some way. Over 804 000 twenty-year-olds registered for National Service between 1964 and 1972 and of these 63 000 were called up into the military.

Members of 5th Platoon, B Company 7th Battalion, Royal Australian Regiment, with an Iroquois helicopter, Phuoc Tuy Province, South Vietnam, 1967.

The major Australian commitment was the Australian Task Force, which was located in Phuoc Tuy Province, south-east of Saigon, between May 1966 and November 1971. Australia's role was to gain control of the province and to deny the VC access to its villagers. The Task Force base was at Nui Dat which was supplied from Vung Tau, 25 kilometres away on the coast. Phuoc Tuy had been controlled by the Vietminh during the French war and the Vietcong were strongly established there. The Australians cleared all Vietnamese from their local area and extended their control using cordon-and-search tactics. (A village would be surrounded early in the morning and troops would search the village looking for Vietcong soldiers and supplies.)

The largest land battle that Australian troops were involved in during their Vietnam service was the Battle of Long Tan (5 kilometres from Nui Dat). On 18 August 1966, D Company of the 5th Battalion were ambushed in a rubber plantation by a Vietcong regiment. When relieved three hours later they had inflicted severe casualties on their enemy despite being heavily outnumbered. The Vietcong regiment suffered 245 dead, the Australians lost 17 killed and 21 wounded.

Australians were involved in a number of search-and-destroy assignments in Phuoc Tuy Province. Australian troops would try to find VC bases in the jungles and mountains, destroy them and hopefully capture soldiers and supplies. The problem was in finding the bases with the Vietcong present. The VC would often melt away, returning well after the Australians had gone.

The Australian armed forces were involved in many other ways in the Vietnam War. Soldiers were active in civil actions such as helping Vietnamese villagers with education, hygiene and agriculture etc. The navy was part of the continuing blockade of North Vietnam and Australian pilots flying Australian planes and helicopters were active in moving and supplying infantry and attacking enemy positions.

As in the US, the war became increasingly unpopular at home, and a strong anti-war movement grew and began to voice its discontent. The 1st Battalion of the Royal Australian Regiment, who were the first to fight in South Vietnam, returned home in June 1966 to be greeted by cheering crowds. Sadly, later battalions did not receive such a welcome home.

Source 5.2   Brian Kay, an Australian veteran

Q. Looking back 20 odd years ago, what was your reaction to being called up?

A. It didn't seem to be such a big thing at the time. I was in the 3rd call-up and at that time there was only a relatively small number of troops in Vietnam, so the chance of going over there seemed only a remote possibility.

Q. When did you learn that you were going to Vietnam?

A. It was about the same time that D Coy of 6 RAR was involved in the battle of Long Tan. I had a friend in D Coy who wrote and told me all about that battle, and the fact that I would soon be in that situation was really brought home to me.

Q. Did you have a choice of whether to go or not?

A. Indirectly yes. We were told that the battalion was going but there were some men who made it quite clear that they didn't want to go, so they were transferred out of the battalion. The controversial aspect of the war was starting to gain momentum at that time and I don't think the Government wanted any adverse publicity about National Servicemen being dragged off to a war against their will.

Q. You wanted to go then?

A. I didn't think it was really a matter of wanting to go — it was more a matter of not wanting to stay behind. I believed that

Australia needed somebody to go and fight and I had been one of those chosen, and trained to do just that. I felt that I would have been shirking my responsibilities by not going, but by the same token, I may have acted differently had I have had strong feelings against Australia's involvement in Vietnam.

Q. Was there much discussion about Australia's involvement in the war?

A. Not really. We had the 'Domino theory' impressed upon us, and how important it was to keep South Vietnam free 'to keep them out of Australia's backyard.' As a result, we all felt we were doing the right thing.

Q. The adverse press seemed to gain momentum while you were in the Army. How did you react to this?

A. I was appalled at some of the things going on, such as the wharf labourers, who refused to load our supply ship to Vietnam, and the numerous demonstrations against our involvement. It really got our ire up to think that we were putting our lives on the line to protect these people back in Australia, and that's the way they repay us.

Q. In retrospect, do you think they were right?

A. Things always look different with the power of hindsight. The fact of the matter was that at the time, we were convinced we were fighting to maintain the freedom of Australia, while at the same time, these Australians were knocking our efforts, saying we were invading the country and killing the inhabitants.

Q. Do you feel that you achieved anything in Vietnam?

A. History has already answered that question.

Q. But what about while you were there?

A. No. Nothing at all. That was the most frustrating fact of the whole situation. There was never any 'hill to conquer and hold', like during the great wars. It seemed to always be a matter of going on patrol or operation to clear an area, coming back to Nui Dat and going out next day to do the same thing. It seemed so pointless, because the Viet Cong would simply re-enter the area when we left. We lost 5 men ambushed in a 'safe' village only a few miles from Nui Dat, and we later learned that the villagers had been harbouring the Viet Cong in secret tunnels. It just seemed a great waste.

Q. What was the reaction when you came home?

A. Utter relief and a strange unbelievability about the whole thing.

Q. I mean what reaction did you get from other people?

A. A very mixed reaction. Many wanted to pat you on the back and buy you a beer, while others were very volatile in their condemnation of the war, and wanted to argue the point why Australia shouldn't be involved. What really surprised me was the number of ex WWII digs. who wanted to play down our role, saying how Vietnam wasn't a 'real' war. I can still remember the arguments that went on about whether we would be admitted to the RSL or not, although I found that there were quite a few who welcomed us into Kingsgrove Sub-Branch. There was that minority, though, that made us feel anything but welcome.

Brian Kay, Kingsgrove RSL, *The Burst*, p.44-5

Questions

1 Outline Brian Kay's attitude to the Vietnam War at the time he was called up.
2 How did the soldiers feel about the anti-war protesters? Is this reasonable?
3 How did people react when Brian Kay returned home from Vietnam?
4 What was so frustrating about the fighting in Vietnam? Would this have an effect on the veterans?

An Australian patrol passes peaceful Vietnamese villagers as they drive their bullock to a nearby village in the Bien Hoa district.

THE TET OFFENSIVE

The crucial year in America's involvement in the Vietnam War was 1968. By the beginning of 1968, there were almost 500 000 US troops in South Vietnam. More than 15 000 Americans had died fighting in Vietnam by 1968. The south had been saved from collapse by the involvement of American power, and prominent military leaders were suggesting that the worst was behind them. But in America there was growing disenchantment with the government's conduct of the war. A small group of senators from LBJ's own political party had expressed their opposition and were attracting a growing band of supporters.

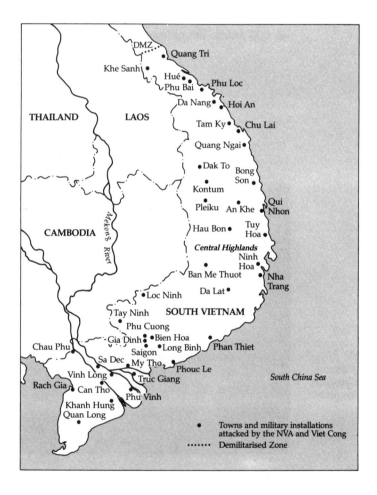

Fig. 5.2 The Tet Offensive, 1968.

Table 5.3   Losses during the Tet Offensive

■ What do the statistics reveal about the offensive?

Army	Killed	Wounded	Missing	Captured	Homeless
US/Allies	1536	7764	11	—	—
ARVN	2788	8299	587	—	—
VC/NVA	45 000	—	—	6911	—
Civilians	14 000	24 000	—	—	630 000

Source 5.3   An account of the Viet Cong's attempt to take control of South Vietnam, February 1968

Viet Cong could do it again, say US leaders in Saigon

Saigon Saturday

IN A SERIES of bitterly contested battles American and South Vietnamese troops today began to regain control of the country after the Viet Cong's massive offensive against 35 cities and towns in South Vietnam. In the capital of Saigon, the Viet Cong appeared to be withdrawing, though their forces still held strong points near the airbase and in the Chinese district of Cholon.

Despite this, and despite President Johnson's claim that the Viet Cong had failed to attain their objectives, a high ranking Embassy official in Saigon said that the Communist forces still had the power to launch a second wave of attacks, especially in Saigon. "They have shown they are still capable of presenting a real military challenge," he added. "They certainly gave dramatic evidence of this ability to terrorise and disrupt."

The enemy threw 36,000 troops into the offensive, and these included North Vietnamese regulars as well as Viet Cong guerrillas. About a third of these are reported to have been killed.

"I don't mean to imply that the Viet Cong are on the verge of collapse because of their losses," the official said. "But even though the challenge is considerable and the fighting will be severe and bitter, I think we will be able to handle it."

The United States Command's Director of Combat Operations, Brigadier General John Chasson, confirmed the Embassy's assessment of the continuing Viet Cong threat. "I must confess the VC surprised us with their attack," he said. "It was surprisingly well co-ordinated, surprisingly impressive and launched with a surprising amount of audacity."

Asked if the US had enough forces, General Chasson said: "From the operation side I would take all I can get. I don't have a surplus but around the major populated areas we have enough forces."

He described the enemy offensive as very successful. When asked if the US might have to abandon the countryside to protect the cities and towns, he said the Americans might have to "redisposition" their forces.

The first detailed picture of the Viet Cong's handling of the assault in Saigon was given by another US military spokesman.

He said reports from prisoners and other sources showed that the Viet Cong's command post for their Saigon task force had been set up in a Buddhist pagoda. A brigadier-general conducted the operations from the pagoda through a command structure known as the 214th Hanoi unit. When Vietnamese Marines stormed into the pagoda they seized enough military equipment to run a major command.

At the Saigon race track on the Western outskirts of the city guerrillas put up a stiff fight for the grandstand, the spokesman said "We found out why when we took it. They had set up an aid station there with medical supplies and were determined to hold it."

The Viet Cong succeeded in infiltrating 12 to 15 battalions — some 4,500 men — into Saigon for the offensive. As the attack broke, the Government rushed in 7,000 Marines, paratroopers and Rangers, and about 4,000 infantrymen from divisions in the field.

Prisoners said they had walked about 30 miles to get to Saigon, then began moving into the city on Monday night and were led to various points where they were issued with weapons, ammunition and food for one and a half days. The spokesman added "They were told to hold out for 48 hours and then they would be relieved."

Hugh Lunn, Robert Kaylor & Tom Buckley, *Sunday Times*, 4 February 1968, quoted in Hugh Lunn, *Vietnam: A Reporter's War*

Questions

1 What are the different reactions to the offensive in the article?
2 What effects did Tet have on the communist forces?
3 What evidence is there to suggest that the anti-communist forces were caught by surprise?
4 How reliable is this piece of evidence?

Source 5.4   Nguyen Tuong Lai, VC guerrilla leader, on Tet

During the Tet offensive of 1968, we attacked the Bien Hoa Airport. Tet was a great loss for the NLF forces. Our army had to be restructured afterward. There were three phases of fighting during the offensive: During the first phase in my area the NLF forces did the fighting. We lost too many men and in the second phase had to be reinforced by North Vietnamese units. And in the third phase, the fighting was done exclusively by North Vietnamese units, even in Tay Ninh and Saigon. The southern forces were decimated . . . and from that time on mostly served as intelligence, logistics, and saboteurs for the northerners.

In June 1968, I was assigned to attend the Tran Phu School of the Central Committee of the Communist Party at COSVN (North Vietnamese/NLF Headquarters) in Tay Ninh Province. During this time the American leadership changed from General Westmoreland to General Abrams. And due to our Tet losses and a change in American tactics, all of our units had to retreat into Cambodia. During this time the war was fought on the border. Our orders were to launch all of our attacks from Cambodia, to which we could retreat and remain safely.

We knew that the American commanders had strict orders from their higher echelon to respect the Cambodian border. That's why we abused Cambodia's neutrality. Whenever we were chased by the enemy, we knew we could retreat across the frontier demarcation into the safe zone and get some rest. We were protected by international law. Also, we knew there was a large anti-war movement in America who would not allow the American army to cross over the border.

We had to live in miserable conditions in the jungle. We were cold, wet, caught malaria, and did not have enough food when the supply section was delayed or disrupted. For example, in the Ma Da area of Binh Duong Province, for three months we had no rice. So we had to eat leaves and roots in the jungle — whatever we could find for survival.

We would spy on the American fire bases [temporary large artillery bases]. And when they would pull out, they left behind C-ration cans and wasted food. We would gather their leftovers. This helped us a great deal.

A. Santoli, *To Bear Any Burden*, p.146

Questions

1 Compare this account of Tet with Source 5.3.
2 Explain the importance of Cambodia for the communists.
3 What might the US consider militarily concerning Cambodia?

Into this political situation the National Liberation Front and the VC, backed by elements of the North Vietnamese Army (NVA), launched an offensive across South Vietnam of stunning strength and intensity. It became known as the Tet Offensive, because it began in Tet (the Vietnamese New Year), and it had at least two major aims. One was to take advantage of the growing disillusionment with the Vietnam War in the USA and to increase pressure on the USA to seek a political settlement to the war. The other aim was to ignite a popular revolution in South Vietnam which would overthrow the Saigon government and end the war.

The Tet period was traditionally a time for celebration and a truce had been arranged but in a series of surprise raids, 80 000 VC and NVA soldiers attacked virtually all major military targets in South Vietnam. A quick glance at the statistics (see Table 5.3, p. 76) reveals that the offensive was a staggering defeat for the communist forces. VC and NVA troops were driven out of almost all targets within three days and the South Vietnamese government remained intact. The ARVN fought bravely and was commended for its effort in defeating the enemy.

Reaction in America

Despite the military victory of the South Vietnamese and the Americans in the Tet Offensive, the US public turned even more strongly against the war. With the VC attacking across the country and even in the grounds of the US Embassy in Saigon, it seemed clear to the public that the Vietnam War was not being won (and not likely to be decisively won) and that it was time to begin the withdrawal of Americans from Vietnam.

■ Do you think this was fair criticism?

■ Were there clear goals?

As Colonel Harry Summers of the US Army General Staff commented:

> Public opinion at home turned when the average citizen perceived that we didn't know what the hell we were doing. That we had no plan to end the war. And we didn't know what constituted victory. By 1968, the public had given us four years, their money and their sons. So I don't blame the American people. I do blame the national leadership, including the military leadership, for not setting clear and definable goals and objectives.[6]

LBJ BACKS DOWN

By 1968, the nation was divided in controversy on the merits of the war. A large percentage believed that the USA should be scaling down its commitments in South Vietnam. An increasing number of leading and influential Americans, including senators and members of Johnson's administration, shared this view. Clark Clifford, the President's new Secretary of Defense (McNamara, disenchanted with the war, resigned in February 1968), now advised the President to consider withdrawing US forces.

Politically, the climate for LBJ was becoming dangerous. In early 1968, Senators Eugene McCarthy and Robert Kennedy (the brother of the previous President) began campaigning against Johnson for the presidency. LBJ was a shrewd politician and he could tell the way the wind was blowing. He decided to yield to the growing public disapproval of the war and, in a major speech on 31 March 1968, he announced that US troop levels in Vietnam would not increase, that the air war against the north would be restricted and that America was ready to negotiate a peace. In a further dramatic announcement he indicated that he would not seek re-election to the presidency so that he could concentrate all his efforts on bringing the war in Vietnam to an end. In private, LBJ said that he could not seek another term because of his heart condition — he had suffered two heart attacks in the 1950s.

The war, however, was far from finished. In the future lay a new president and five more years of fighting.

Activities

Key words

Define these important terms:

'great society'   Tonkin Resolution   Forward Defence
escalation   Rolling Thunder   Tet Offensive
Pentagon   SEATO   negotiated peace
34A raids

Research topics

1 Lyndon Johnson.
2 Australian involvement in South Vietnam.

What if you were . . .?

1 You are a presidential aide in 1965. Write a memo to Johnson outlining reasons for increasing US involvement in Vietnam.
2 You are a VC soldier shortly after the Tet Offensive. Write a letter to your wife or husband telling them about your experiences.

Review questions

1 Comment on the term 'revolving door republic' in connection with the South Vietnamese government after the fall of Diem.
2 What was the significance of the Tonkin Resolution?
3 How effective was Operation Rolling Thunder in fulfilling its aims?
4 Why did the USA escalate the war?
5 Why did Australia go to war in Vietnam?
6 What part did Australia play in the war?
7 What were the results of the Tet Offensive?

What would you say?

1 Lyndon Johnson, in his retirement, speaking to a journalist about his role in the Vietnam War.
2 Prime Minister Menzies announcing to cabinet the decision to send Australian troops to South Vietnam.

6 AMERICA PULLS BACK

The Tet Offensive of 1968 was the turning point of the war. For the communists the Offensive was a battlefield defeat, but yet, more importantly, it was a political victory. The dimensions and intensity of the offensive showed the US public that the war was not being won as US military leaders were insisting. Anti-war sentiment, already high due to the growing cost of the war in terms of American lives and money and the unpopularity of the draft, began spiralling upwards.

WHAT WERE THE RESULTS OF TET?

Tet was a disaster for the VC forces. VC soldiers did the majority of the fighting and incurred most of the casualties. Thereafter, the VC were overshadowed by the North Vietnamese army, who came south in increasing strength after the early months of 1968. But the VC sacrifice was not in vain. Responding to increasing public disapproval of his conduct of the war, President Johnson started a process of negotiation and de-escalation of the conflict. When General Westmoreland asked for 200 000 more troops to win the war Johnson granted him just over 20 000.

WHO SUCCEEDED JOHNSON?

The year of the Tet Offensive, 1968, was a tragic year in American history. In April, Martin Luther King Jr, the great civil rights leader, was gunned down in Memphis, Tennessee. Two months later in Los Angeles, California, Robert Kennedy was shot and killed while campaigning for the presidency. The Democratic Convention in Chicago where Vice-President Hubert Humphrey took the nomination for President was marred by ugly street battles between anti-war demonstrators and police. It seemed as if the violence of Vietnam had crossed the water to the streets of America.

Richard Nixon secured the Republican Party nomination and loudly proclaimed that he had a plan to end the war. Humphrey pledged to continue the de-escalation policies of Johnson. This pledge to continue US involvement may have cost him the election which ended in a close victory (by less than 1% of the total vote) for Nixon.

■ What is the difference between the policy of de-escalation and a plan to end the war?

Table 6.1 US troops in South Vietnam, 1962–72

Year	Number of troops
1962	9000
1963	15 000
1964	16 000
1965	60 000
1966	268 000
1967	449 000
1968	535 000
1969	415 000
1970	239 000
1971	47 000

■ Was Vietnamisation a plan to end the war?

Prime Minister Gough Whitlam.

Nixon's plan to end the war

Like his predecessors, Nixon did not want to be the first president to lose a war, but public opinion as expressed in the streets and in Congress demanded further easing of American involvement in the war. Nixon's solution was dubbed 'Vietnamisation'. It meant that US troops would begin a gradual withdrawal from Vietnam while the South Vietnamese Army (ARVN) would be armed and trained to fight the war on their own. From the middle of 1969, the ARVN began receiving billions of dollars worth of American equipment: rifles, helicopters, tanks and ships. On 7 July 1969, the first US soldiers began returning home.

The plan for Vietnamisation was part of a larger world policy which has been labelled the 'Nixon doctrine'. This change in global strategy was meant to lessen tension around the world and to ease America's burden of commitments. It meant that in the future the US would continue to provide aid for its allies but they would be responsible for their own fighting.

Withdrawal of Australian troops

In response to the US policy of Vietnamisation and to growing public disillusionment with the war, the Australian government started withdrawing its troops. Australia's withdrawal from Vietnam began in 1970 at the direction of the Liberal/Country Party government of John Gorton. Virtually all Australian troops had left South Vietnam by the end of 1971. In 1972, the Labor Party of Gough Whitlam won the federal election, ended conscription and brought the remaining troops home.

THE PARIS PEACE TALKS

After March 1968, Johnson was committed to negotiating an end to the war and the Hanoi government agreed to talks to be held in Paris. The first meetings began on 13 May 1968, and quickly descended into empty rhetoric and point-scoring. (They even argued over the shape of the negotiating table).

When Nixon came to power he directed his National Security Adviser, Henry Kissinger, to begin secret talks in Paris with the North Vietnamese. Years later it was this dialogue that would lead to a ceasefire in Vietnam. But there were still many years of bitter fighting to come.

WAR IN THE AIR CONTINUES

Part of Nixon and Kissinger's plan to end the war was to increase pressure on the North Vietnamese by heavy aerial bombing, thereby improving the bargaining position of the USA in the secret talks. Soon after assuming office, Nixon authorised the secret bombing of communist sanctuaries in Cambodia in what was codenamed Operation Breakfast. At the same time the USA also increased markedly its bombing of South Vietnam and Laos. In 1969, 160 000 tonnes of bombs descended on the Ho Chi Minh Trail, a 60 per cent increase over the previous year. The bombing was also intended to cut off continued aid and sanctuary to the communists, thereby enhancing the effectiveness of Vietnamisation.

Source 6.1 Vietnamisation

In 1972, the South Vietnamese army did a fine job of repulsing the North Vietnamese Easter offensive. I was running around in the field with US marine advisers. And I saw that the glue for the South Vietnamese dual-command structure, say where the generals of the South Vietnamese marines and airborne wouldn't talk to each other, was the US advisers. The US marine adviser and the US airborne adviser would talk and get the job done.

Without the advisers present, it would have been chaos. They were the reinforcing rods in the cement. Partly because of the American firepower and logistics they could bring in. But just as much because they supplied the vertebrae and command structure — the teamwork notion — that the South Vietnamese, because of their fragmented society and history, had not developed.

Oppositely, the North Vietnamese in 'seventy-two had one command focus, concentration, abundant supplies. The vertebrae were much stronger with the totalitarians, who had an enforced, unified structure.

From 1971 to 1973, our logistics, airpower and advisers — those three elements — offset the long-term strategic advantage of the North Vietnamese, which was the sanctuaries in Laos and Cambodia and the Ho Chi Minh Trail. If Laos and Cambodia had been truly neutral, there's no way that the South Vietnamese, with a little advisory help, couldn't have held on indefinitely. It was the geography. Even had the South Vietnamese army been the Israeli army, supplied the same way and with the same kind of leadership, the geography would have killed them.

With that six-hundred-mile [965 km] frontier where the Communists had a free shot at South Vietnam, a safe place to retreat to, and a secure supply line on the Ho Chi Minh Trail, there was no way the South could hold. The geography was against them. And of course, Lyndon Johnson and Richard Nixon preferred to make us all think about the war as if South Vietnam was an island.

Peter Braestrup, in A. Santoli,
To Bear Any Burden, pp.217-18

Questions

1 What, according to the source, was the 'glue' or 'reinforcing rods' for the policy of Vietnamisation? How did this work?

2 Why did the North Vietnamese have such well-established teamwork when the South Vietnamese had to rely on the American advisers according to the the source?

3 Do you agree that the south could have held on indefinitely if the communists did not have sanctuaries and the Ho Chi Minh Trail?

4 How did geography kill the South Vietnamese?

5 Comment on the reliability of the source.

How was Cambodia drawn into the war?

Until 1970, when he was ousted in a right wing coup, Prince Norodom Sihanouk was the leader of Cambodia. He had struggled for the previous decade to keep Cambodia neutral but with mixed success. At the mercy of more powerful countries he had been forced to allow the communists to use parts of eastern Cambodia as training and staging areas and then had no choice but to allow the Americans to bomb the same areas in 1969.

The secret bombing of Cambodia was soon not enough for the Nixon administration. Concerned that the communist sanctuaries in Cambodia were threatening the long-term success of Vietnamisation, Nixon launched a full-scale invasion of the country in May 1970 by US and ARVN troops.

"...AND, VOILA, WE HAUL OUT A DOVE...A DOVE...I'LL HAVE TO ASK YOU TO IMAGINE THIS IS A DOVE!"

A 1969 cartoon comments on Nixon's war policy.

■ What does the cartoon say about the war policy?

The invasion was not a long-term success. Huge quantities of weapons and other supplies were captured and thousands of the enemy were killed, but when the troops left the communists simply moved back into the area and started to rebuild. Furthermore, large parts of Cambodia had been bombed heavily and many thousands of civilians had been killed. Cambodia was a broken nation with a population bitter toward the Americans. A civil war broke out which would lead to the Cambodian communists, the Khmer Rouge, coming to power in 1975.

Involvement of Laos

Vietnamisation had its first big test with the ARVN invasion into Laos on 8 February 1971. The objective was to try to close off the Ho Chi Minh Trail running through Laos. No US troops fought with the South Vietnamese, as Congress had repealed the Gulf of Tonkin Resolution in December 1970 and forbidden American troops to enter Cambodia or Laos. The invasion was a disaster — of the 30 000 ARVN troops who went into Laos, one-third were listed as killed, wounded or missing. Kissinger described the invasion as 'conceived in doubt and confusion'.[1] Vietnamisation appeared to be failing the test.

■ Can you see any essential weaknesses in the policy of Vietnamisation?

WAR ON THE AMERICAN FRONT

The war had become increasingly unpopular in America, especially after 1967. Nixon's policy of Vietnamisation was partly designed to appease the growing anti-war feeling but it seemed to have little effect. In November 1969, 250 000 people attended Vietnam Moratorium Day in Washington, protesting against the war. The nature of the protesters began to widen. In the early years they had been mostly from the university campuses or churches but they came to include business people, Congressmen, unionists and Vietnam veterans. In addition, the demonstrations had spread around the world.

The Cambodian invasion was greeted with an explosion of protest across the USA. The violence of the demonstrations shocked the world. At Kent State University in Ohio on 4 May 1970, four students were shot to death by National Guardsmen who lost control when surrounded by a jeering mob of protesters. This excerpt from *Vietnam: A Reporter's War* describes the scene:

> National Guardsmen began moving across the common . . . They began firing tear gas. The students picked it up and threw it back at them . . . At roughly a quarter to one, the Kent State students around Hayworth Hall at a slight hill at the top of the common began to throw rocks at the Guardsmen nearest to them. The Guardsmen again responded with tear gas . . . and then there were several volleys of automatic weapons fire. When the students fell back, at the sound of the rifles going off, it was seen that at least three students were dead . . .[2]

Violence bred violence — colleges around the nation closed in protest and were the scenes of more demonstrations, which were often violent. In May 1971, polls showed that 61 per cent of the US population believed that involvement in the Vietnam War was wrong (in 1965 the same proportion had thought it right to go to Vietnam, and part of this turnaround in attitude can be attributed to the invasion of Cambodia).

■ Why did the Cambodian invasion provoke such protest?

Students being dispersed by National Guardsmen after protests at Kent State University in 1970. What methods are the Guardsmen using?

AN ARMY IN RETREAT

American fighting men and women in Vietnam came to understand that their country was withdrawing from the fighting and that the war was increasingly unpopular at home. Inevitably this led to a breakdown of morale and discipline amongst US troops. In 1971, a marine colonel wrote:

> By every conceivable indicator, our army that now remains in Vietnam is in a state approaching collapse with individual units avoiding or having refused combat, murdering their officers or non-commissioned officers, drug-ridden and dispirited where not near mutinous.[3]

Michael Maclear, the author of *Vietnam: The Ten Thousand Day War*, believes that the US army lost heart for the war when Lyndon Johnson decided to seek negotiated peace instead of a military victory.

> The rot began when the army was required by President Nixon to continue an open-ended fight for political 'honour', or for a signed agreement that South Vietnam would remain as it then existed — if it could; and for this, without US military guarantees, the American soldiers found themselves soldiering on indefinitely.[4]

From 1969 onwards, more and more soldiers in Vietnam became concerned with their own survival and little else. After all, they thought, what was the point of dying in a war that could not be won? And despite the withdrawals, soldiers were still being killed and wounded. In 1969, 9414 US soldiers died in Vietnam.

An increasing number of soldiers simply deserted. Between 1969 and 1971, the number of desertions in the US armed forces doubled twice in comparison with the previous three years.

Having command of US soldiers became increasingly difficult and dangerous. In 1971, a congressional committee reported that in one US division of troops in Vietnam there had been thirty-five separate incidents of soldiers refusing to go into combat. A more ugly way of avoiding combat also became increasingly popular. The term 'fragging' came into the vocabulary. It meant the murder of officers who were too insistent on actually fighting the enemy. In 1970 there were 378 such incidents recorded; before 1969 they were virtually unheard of.

An ever-expanding number of soldiers turned to drugs to escape the nightmare of Vietnam. Drugs were cheap and widely available in Vietnam. By 1971 four times as many US soldiers were being treated for drug problems as were receiving treatment for combat wounds.

An increasing number of US servicemen turned to drugs for escape after 1969.

What were the Pentagon Papers?

■ Do you think that, for an army to keep up morale, it must have a chance of victory?

A number of scandals back home in America contributed to the rising tide of opinion against the war. Such a scandal was centred around the so-called Pentagon Papers, which were in effect the Defense Department's history of America's involvement in Vietnam from 1945 to 1968. The study had been commissioned by Secretary of Defense McNamara and gathered together all government papers relating to Vietnam. They exposed the lack of precise war aims in Vietnam, the confusion in policy making, and the failure to inform the public of what was really happening. Newspaper coverage (in the *New York Times*) of the Pentagon Papers between June and December 1971 fuelled public disapproval of the government's handling of the war.

Daniel Ellsberg, one of the senior aides to McNamara, had leaked the report to the press when he turned against the war. Although the papers did not cover the period of his administration, Nixon did not want support for the war further eroded and he was fearful of public disclosure of his secret initiatives, particularly the secret bombing of Cambodia.

Nixon attempted to have the Supreme Court suppress the documents but the judges refused, citing the principle of the freedom of the press. An infuriated President ordered his aides to wage war against further government leaks and against potential dissenters. A secret group known as the 'plumbers' was formed within the White House to 'fix the leaks'. Among other questionable activities, the 'plumbers' broke into the office of Daniel Ellsberg's psychiatrist in search of incriminating evidence.

ESCALATION OF THE AIR WAR

With American ground troops pulling out of Vietnam, Nixon's strategy required continued US bombing to keep the communists from making too many advances. The huge American bombers, the B52s (the Vietnamese called them the 'whispering death') became an important part of military and diplomatic strategy. Air raids over the south and the north increased throughout 1971 and again in 1972. In Operation Linebacker in April 1972, US jets flew 225 missions against enemy positions above and below the Demilitarised Zone (at the 17th parallel, the border between North and South Vietnam). In the same operation, B52 bombers struck the north for the first time since 1967.

■ What effect do you think the B52 raids were having on North Vietnam?

The Easter Offensive

The communists launched a major offensive throughout the south in Easter 1972. Illustrating the northern domination of the communist side since Tet, the NVA provided 150 000 troops backed up by 75 000 VC regulars. New, powerful, Soviet-supplied artillery and tanks were a feature of the offensive. The communists took the northern city of Quang Tri by late April but by May the ARVN had started a counter-offensive in conjunction with heavy American bombing. Quang Tri was recaptured in the middle of September. The Easter Offensive showed the communist leadership that there was no hope for a quick victory against a well-supplied ARVN and massive US firepower.

MORE PEACE TALKS

By the middle of 1972, the chances for a negotiated peace were looking brighter than they had for many years. Hanoi was feeling the weight of US bombing and Richard Nixon's diplomacy. In February and May of that year, Nixon had visited Peking and Moscow, successfully achieving closer relations with both of North Vietnam's closest allies and suppliers. For the USA 1972 was an election year and the President was keen to announce a breakthrough in the search for peace in Vietnam.

■ How could China and the USSR have influenced Vietnam?

In October of 1972, the talks between Kissinger and Le Duc Tho, a leading member of the North Vietnamese government, brought success. Hanoi and the USA agreed to a cease-fire-in-place in South Vietnam. This meant that soldiers of both sides would remain in their positions when the fighting stopped, a condition with which the Americans had previously disagreed. In return for this concession the communist leaders agreed to the continued existence of the South Vietnamese government, a point they had always maintained was not negotiable.

Nixon meets Mao Zedong in 1972. How was this significant for the Vietnam War?

■ Was the North giving up its aim of unifying Vietnam?

■ Did Thieu have any choice but to accept the American proposals?

The stumbling-block in the cease-fire proposal proved to be President Thieu and the Saigon regime. They saw the agreement as a sell-out by the Americans. After President Nixon won a landslide victory in the election of November 1972, however, his government persuaded Thieu into accepting the terms of the agreement by threatening to reduce US aid.

The delays and the number of amendments the Americans wished to add to the original agreement made Hanoi cautious, and in December Le Duc Tho stopped the talks to have consultations with his leaders. However, Nixon was determined to achieve an agreement in the quickest possible time. He ordered a massive escalation in the bombing of the north to try to force the communists back to the negotiating table. Nixon was also showing President Thieu that he could rely on US support even after the withdrawal. The Christmas bombing of 1972 lasted eleven days and 200 000 bombs were dropped on the cities of Hanoi and Haiphong alone.

Protests flooded Washington from around the globe. Although North Vietnam denies it, the bombing probably did force North Vietnam back to the talks, and a cease-fire was finalised quickly on 23 January 1973.

Source 6.2   The Paris Agreement

In Paris the Americans would figure out how much area and population the GVN [Government of (South) Vietnam] controlled. They would subtract that from one hundred per cent, and give the rest to the North Vietnamese. So I suggested that

was not the right way to go about this, and proposed a change. Kissinger sent a message back, saying it was the most startling revelation.

I knew we were in deep trouble when the guy who is running the negotiations doesn't know that thirty to forty per cent of the country is not populated and not controlled by anyone. And many villages were not under either side's control. And he'd been conceptually giving all this neutral territory to the North Vietnamese in the negotiations.

Then, when we read the drafts of the actual agreements they were working on — what we were prepared to give as concessions to the North Vietnamese — it was clear that there was no way the government of South Vietnam was going to be able to withstand the political subversion, infiltration, and propagandising of their population prior to an election. The agreement was that the government of South Vietnam could not proselytize or enter Communist-controlled areas. Whereas existing Communist cadre could remain in place in the government's areas.

Kissinger drew this boundary line and said, "Everything that has been occupied by the North Vietnamese Army in South Vietnam is a 'Third Vietnam'. And all Communist agents in the rest of the South may remain where they are."

Once I saw that, I knew that we were fully prepared to sell South Vietnam down the river. You can be charitable and say that we didn't care. Or you can be worse, and say that we wanted to give it to the other side. My South Vietnamese counterparts looked at these maps and said, "What are you doing to us? Is your government going to agree to this? My life is forfeit. My country is gone!"

I stayed on for two more years with these people, who knew we had sold them down the river. It was an enormous eroding of their national confidence and will. First because of the terms of the Paris agreement. And secondly, the US Congress vote of nonsupport for Vietnam in 1974 — no further military aid to supply logistics and ammunition; and never again would we fly air strikes if the North Vietnamese attacked.

Once Watergate happened, no Vietnamese of any political sophistication thought that we would pay more attention to Vietnam. There was no way to reverse what our Congress had done.

I wrote a detailed position paper in the winter of 'seventy-three–'seventy-four. I stated that there would be a major North Vietnamese military attack. And the South Vietnamese government would crumble if we didn't support them. I spelled out which military commanders would fight and which would run. I gave this to my superior at five o'clock one night. The next morning he came in and said, "How many copies of this do you have?" I said, "Five." He said, "Give them all to me. It's going to be stamped Top Secret with restricted access." I said, "Who is going to read it?" He said, "Jacobson [an ambassadorial assistant] has read it and he's given it to the ambassador."

A couple of weeks later I asked, "Where's my paper? When are they going to circulate it?" He said, "You're better off forgetting about it."

E.Brady, in A. Santoli, *To Bear Any Burden*, pp. 220-1

Questions

1 How does Brady believe the South Vietnamese government was betrayed by the Americans?

2 Why would the Vietnamese think Watergate would be the end of US interest in Vietnam?

3 Do you believe the South Vietnamese were 'sold down the river'?

Cease-fire

The 'Agreement Ending the War and Restoring Peace in Vietnam' was officially signed on 27 January 1973 by the USA, North Vietnam, South Vietnam and the VC. The agreement specified a cease-fire beginning at 8 a.m. Saigon time on 28 January, the removal of all foreign troops from Indochina, the dismantling of all foreign bases and the return of all US prisoners of war. Soldiers from the ARVN, the NVA and the VC would remain in place when the cease-fire started.

Nixon proclaimed that he had achieved 'peace with honour'. What he had achieved was the end to US fighting in Vietnam. The cease-fire was only a lull in the fighting — North Vietnam was determined to unify the country and South Vietnam, armed with massive American aid, was ready to resist.

After 56 962 US soldiers had died, it was over for the American fighting man in South Vietnam. As the sign outside one of the deserted US army bases said, 'Goodbye and Good Luck'.

Source 6.3   Agreement on ending the war and restoring peace in Vietnam

(Signed in Paris on 27 January 1973, by the foreign ministers of the US, North and South Vietnam and the South Vietnamese Provisional Revolutionary Government.)

Article 2

A cease-fire shall be observed throughout South Vietnam as of 24.00 hours GMT on Jan. 27, 1973.

Article 3

The parties undertake to maintain the ceasefire and to ensure a lasting and stable peace.

As soon as the ceasefire goes into effect:

(a) The United States forces and those of the other foreign countries allied with the United States and the Republic of Vietnam shall remain in place pending the implementation of the plan of troop withdrawal. The four-party joint military commission described in Article 16 shall determine the modalities.

(b) The armed forces of the two South Vietnamese parties shall remain in place. The two-party joint military commission described in Article 17 shall determine the areas controlled by each party and the modalities of stationing.

(c) The regular forces of all services and arms and the irregular forces of the parties in South Vietnam shall stop all offensive activities against each other and shall strictly abide by the following stipulation:

All acts of force on the ground, in the air, and on the sea shall be prohibited; all hostile acts, terrorism and reprisals by both sides will be banned.

Article 4

The United States will not continue its military involvement or intervene in the internal affairs of South Vietnam.

Article 9

The Government of the United States of America and the Government of the Democratic Republic of Vietnam undertake to respect the following principles for the exercise of the South Vietnamese people's right to self-determination:

(a) The South Vietnamese people's right to self-determination is sacred, inalienable, and shall be respected by all countries.

(b) The South Vietnamese people shall decide themselves the political future of South Vietnam through genuinely free and democratic general elections under international supervision.

(c) Foreign countries shall not impose any political tendency or personality on the South Vietnamese people.

Article 10

The two South Vietnamese parties undertake to respect the ceasefire and maintain peace in South Vietnam, settle all matters of contention through negotiations, and avoid all armed conflicts.

D.J. Sagar, *Major Political Events in Indochina, 1945-90,*
Facts on File, pp.200-203

Questions

1 What happens to the different armies on and after the cease-fire?

2 Who decides which parts of the south are controlled by which side?

3 How is peace to be ensured in South Vietnam?

4 Do you think the agreement was realistic? Was it 'peace with honour'?

WATERGATE

The 'plumbers' who 'fixed leaks' in the White House were the same men arrested on 17 June 1972 in Washington's Watergate building for breaking into the offices of the Democratic Party and planting eavesdropping devices. The Watergate scandal eventually brought down the Nixon administration. Richard Nixon was forced to resign when he admitted that he had played a part in the cover-up of White House involvement in the Watergate break-in. As the scandal dragged on through 1973 and 1974 (Nixon resigned in August 1974), it diminished the ability of the Nixon administration to make all the decisions regarding Vietnam. Increasingly, Congress came to make some of the important decisions on Vietnam. Congress eventually legislated to stop all funding for military activities in Indochina in 1974.

Activities

Key words
Define these important terms:

Vietnamisation	neutral	Pentagon Papers
Nixon doctrine	communist sanctuaries	Watergate
conscription	fragging	cease-fire-in-place

Research topics
1 Watergate.
2 The US air war against the north.
3 The 1968 Democratic Party Convention at Chicago.

What if you were . . .?
1 You are President Thieu. Write a letter of complaint to the US President on the cease-fire agreement of 1973.
2 You are the editor of a large US newspaper. Write an editorial on the Pentagon Papers' revelations and government attempts to stop publication.

Review questions
1 What were the results of the Tet Offensive?
2 Explain the Vietnamisation policy and the reasons behind it.
3 How did Nixon change US strategy in Vietnam?
4 Why did Cambodia become involved in the Second Vietnam War?
5 What were the symptoms of the US army's collapse in morale after 1969?
6 Of what significance were the Pentagon Papers?
7 What did the cease-fire of 1973 achieve? Was it a sell-out?

What would you say?
1 President Nixon at a press conference after the announcement of the 1973 cease-fire.
2 A Vietnam veteran of 1971 speaking to a close friend about deteriorating morale of US troops in Vietnam.

7 CHOPPERS AND MEN IN BLACK PYJAMAS

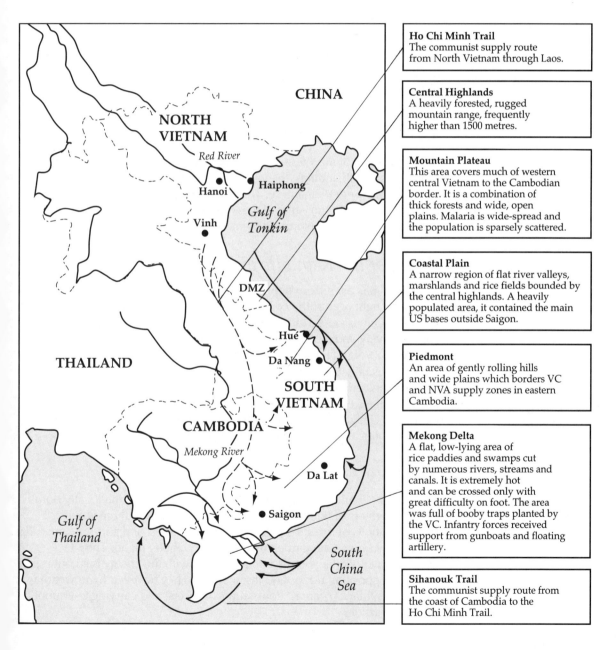

Ho Chi Minh Trail
The communist supply route from North Vietnam through Laos.

Central Highlands
A heavily forested, rugged mountain range, frequently higher than 1500 metres.

Mountain Plateau
This area covers much of western central Vietnam to the Cambodian border. It is a combination of thick forests and wide, open plains. Malaria is wide-spread and the population is sparsely scattered.

Coastal Plain
A narrow region of flat river valleys, marshlands and rice fields bounded by the central highlands. A heavily populated area, it contained the main US bases outside Saigon.

Piedmont
An area of gently rolling hills and wide plains which borders VC and NVA supply zones in eastern Cambodia.

Mekong Delta
A flat, low-lying area of rice paddies and swamps cut by numerous rivers, streams and canals. It is extremely hot and can be crossed only with great difficulty on foot. The area was full of booby traps planted by the VC. Infantry forces received support from gunboats and floating artillery.

Sihanouk Trail
The communist supply route from the coast of Cambodia to the Ho Chi Minh Trail.

Fig. 7.1 The geography of South Vietnam.

The Second Vietnam War between the South Vietnamese, USA and allied forces and the VC and northern communist armies was a different kind of war from many others. For much of its duration it was fought between lightly armed guerrillas and the high technology and firepower of the Americans and their allies. It was a war fought without front lines, without safe areas and without a clear, readily identifiable enemy.

WHERE WAS THE WAR FOUGHT?

The Second Vietnam War was fought chiefly in South Vietnam and was profoundly influenced by the topography and climate of the country. South Vietnam's climate is hot, humid and tropical. The annual rainfall is heavy and during the monsoon fighting is difficult because visibility is poor and mobility is restricted. Health hazards abound, particularly for non-Asian soldiers.

THE VIETNAMESE ARMIES

Although much of the Western coverage of the war concentrated on the Americans and their allies, the vast majority of soldiers in the Second Vietnam War were Vietnamese. Three very different Vietnamese armies fought in the south: the Army of the Republic of Vietnam (ARVN), the Vietcong (VC) and the North Vietnamese Army (NVA).

■ Why was so much media coverage given to the Americans?

Army of the Republic of Vietnam

The ARVN has often been depicted, especially by US historians, as the weak link in the fight against the communists in South Vietnam. Yet it is clear that in the Tet Offensive of 1968 and the Easter Offensive of 1972, the ARVN fought bravely and more than held their own against the communist forces.

The ARVN did have major leadership problems because the officer class had usually been trained by the defeated and unpopular French and were dominated by wealthy and upper class men. These officers knew little about the lives of the men under their command who came mainly from poor rural villages. Promotions in the ARVN were based less on competency than on political considerations and family or personal relationships.

■ What effect would the ARVN method of promotion have on an army?

Vietcong

The VC, or 'Charlie' as the Americans called them, were the locally born guerrilla fighters of South Vietnam. The VC consisted of three groups: mainforce units of regular soldiers, provincial forces, and part-time guerrillas (men and women who farmed by day and fought by night). The VC generally avoided large-scale confrontations with the enemy but continually harassed opposition troops and installations. They travelled light, wearing the famous 'black pyjamas' (loose fitting trousers) and carrying few supplies except their rifle.

VC operations in the villages of the south were more important to them than combat action against the enemy. In the villages they set up alternative governments and recruited future guerrillas. Everything possible was done to undermine the authority of the central government through persuasion, example, and, if necessary, by terror. Thousands of government officials, from policemen and tax collectors to school teachers, were kidnapped and murdered by the VC. The ordinary villager, however, was rarely touched.

■ How would VC guerillas be recruited?

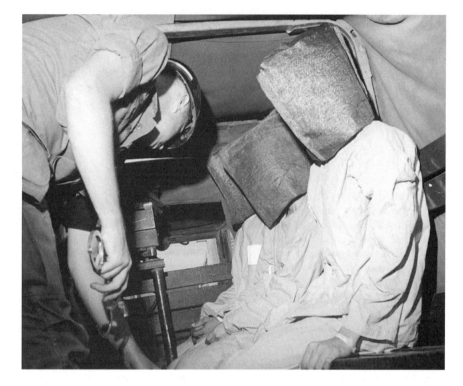

Prisoners of war being transported to an ARVN prison camp near Bien Hoa, 1969.

North Vietnamese Army

The NVA were battle-hardened professionals from the wars against the French and the Japanese. After the failure of the Tet Offensive by the communist forces in 1968, the NVA played the major role in the southern war. A massive increase in Soviet military aid helped the NVA to expand rapidly, in terms of both numbers and weaponry after 1968. In the Easter Offensive of 1972, each NVA division carried its own artillery, tank, missile and anti-aircraft units. Ultimately, the war was won chiefly by the large conventional forces of the NVA while the VC played a supporting role.

US Army

Some 3 million Americans served in Vietnam. Their experiences were as diverse as the country itself. Troops in the Mekong Delta waded through rice paddies, in the highlands US units fought NVA regiments in traditional open confrontations, others guarded the fringes of US bases or fired artillery rounds at an unseen enemy from lonely hilltop bases. Still others flew aircraft missions or were bound to desktops in Saigon. Only a minority faced combat: of 473 200 Americans in South Vietnam in December 1967, only just over 10 per cent were combat infantrymen (75 per cent were headquarters and logistics staff). According to a Veterans' Department survey, however, 76 per cent had been on the receiving end of hostile mortars or rockets. Even in the centre of Saigon they could be the victims of bomb or sniper attacks.

The US troops in Vietnam were much younger than their counterparts in World War II (nineteen compared to twenty-six). Many found it difficult to adapt to the alien environment of the war zone with its privations and frequent danger. US troops were trained for a traditional war in Europe, so they found themselves ill-equipped for war in Asia. The culture, the people and the country were foreign to their experience, and in their short tour of duty (only one year) most found it impossible to understand the Vietnamese people.

Source 7.1 US soldier in Vietnam

We landed at Vung Tau on October 21, 1965. We hit the beaches with our duffle bags and no ammunition. It was like an island resort. It was beautiful. No hint whatsoever of any kind of hostilities or war. After two days, our tanks arrived. We went by monstrous convoy across Vietnam.

Bypassing Saigon, we went straight up to the Iron Triangle, a triangular-shaped densely jungled area near Cambodia, controlled by the VC. We built a base camp [brigade-sized military base] in a rubber-tree plantation at Lai Khe. All the while we set up our base camp, we went out on operations.

The villages were pretty gross. The poverty was real bad. But I loved the kids and I loved the culture. The farmers were the best, as far as I'm concerned. No matter what country they come from, farmers only want to till the soil. They don't want a hassle from anybody.

The first night we were in the triangle, the VC tried to probe our perimeter. We killed a couple who tried to infiltrate our lines. The first time I ever saw any of our own guys get it was on our third patrol. I was walking point [lead man] and Lenny and Steve were behind me. A mine went off and wiped out the eleven guys behind them.

The guys in my unit were absolutely enraged because for the previous year we had all been very close. Every weekend our families would visit. We knew guys' wives, mothers, and fathers, their kids. And when they died it enraged us. We wanted to find the VC and kill them. But at that point it was very difficult to find them. They were ghosts. They would hit us with a mortar, plant a booby trap or mine. But you'd never see anybody . . .

Our first real battle was in the Michelin Rubber Plantation. Our whole brigade was sitting in helicopters waiting for a sister battalion to get hit, so we could immediately pull into the fight. The VC came with a human-wave attack. And we landed behind them, around the outside of the American perimeter. It was a VC regiment. They wore black pyjamas or just regular clothes. But they had all kinds of Chinese and Russian weapons — flamethrowers, rocket launchers. They were being pretty well supplied by North Vietnam through Cambodia.

We surrounded the VC, with the battalion camp in the middle. The Americans didn't even have foxholes. But fortunately, they only lost around seven guys. The VC body count was supposed to have been eight hundred, but I thought it was more. It was the first time I had ever killed anybody.

Frank McCarthy, quoted in A. Santoli, *To Bear Any Burden*, pp.106-7

Questions

1 How did the soldier react to the land and the people?
2 The Vietcong were 'ghosts'. Explain.
3 How are the communist troops described?
4 What is the fighting on the ground like?

WAR ON THE GROUND

In Vietnam there was often the sense of being surrounded. It was often impossible to know which area or village was controlled by the enemy and which belonged to the government. It was impossible, also, to tell friend from foe. As Marine captain E.J. Banks remembers:

> You never knew who was the enemy and who was the friend. They all looked alike. They all dressed alike. They were all Vietnamese. Some of them were Vietcong . . . The enemy was all around you.[1]

In combat zones the soldiers faced a constant ordeal. Plodding through rice fields or dense jungle, weakened by the all-pervading heat and rain, attacked by insects and leeches, the combat soldier's life was full of misery and boredom. And there was always the threat of a VC booby trap. Mines, grenades, artillery shells, even sharpened bamboo staves, were hidden everywhere, waiting to be stepped on or triggered. A company of soldiers might never see the enemy for months at a time but a significant number could be killed or wounded by enemy booby traps.

■ How would these fighting conditions affect soldiers?

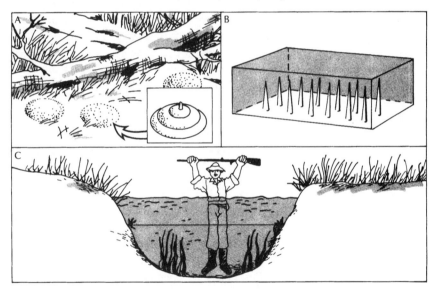

Booby Traps: (a) hidden mines, (b) punji stakes in shallow pit, (c) grenades attached to trip wires in streams.

HOW WAS THE AIR WAR FOUGHT?

America's ultimate firepower belonged to the jets and bombers that rained death on North Vietnam and communist positions in the south throughout the war. Operation Rolling Thunder, the bombing of North Vietnam which began in May 1965 and lasted intermittently for three years, dropped a daily average of 800 tonnes of bombs, rockets and missiles on military establishments, bridges, roads, rail lines and fuel storehouses. Overall, 7 million tonnes of bombs were dropped on Vietnam alone during the war, twice the number dropped on Europe and Asia in World War II.

The Haiphong Cement Factory was a major target during US bombing raids against North Vietnam.

Napalm (jellied petroleum) was often used in Rolling Thunder raids and throughout the south against suspected enemy positions or supply lines or in support of ground forces. Napalm sticks to the skin and burns through to the bone. Anti-personnel bombs, hurling tiny slivers of metal across a wide area, were also widely used in the bombing.

The Americans controlled the air space over Vietnam but not without cost. North Vietnam possessed a highly effective air defence. Its Soviet-made MIG fighter planes were modern and effective and caused considerable damage to US airplanes. Even more effective were Soviet-made SAM (surface-to-air missiles) rockets and sophisticated anti-aircraft guns.

Table 7.1 US airforce losses in South-East Asia, 1962–73

Loss	
Aircraft lost	2257
Airforce personnel killed	2118
Airforce personnel wounded	3460
Airforce personnel missing/captured	586
Cost of airforce operations	3.13 billion (US$)

What was defoliation?

South Vietnam has large areas of jungle and these provided ideal cover for the communist forces. The American solution was simple — remove the jungle. Bombing and bulldozing were not effective in clearing sufficient jungle areas, so chemical warfare was adopted. A ten year program of chemical defoliation named Operation Ranch Hand began in 1962 and released 86 million litres (19 million gallons) of herbicides over about 20 per cent of South Vietnam. The most common defoliant was Agent Orange, a compound containing the chemical dioxin, which is known to cause cancer. After the war many Vietnam veterans who had been exposed to the chemicals began to suffer from cancers and their children from birth defects.

Vietnamese agriculture will suffer the effects of the spraying for generations to come.

The campaign did not limit communist activity or the supply of materials to the south.

How were helicopters used in Vietnam?

Chinook helicopter.

The helicopter is probably the best known symbol of the Vietnam War and it revolutionised the fighting in two specific ways. It became possible to place large forces at the required position at very short notice and to evacuate or reinforce those positions equally quickly. But the helicopter was unsuited to revolutionary war because it made the troops so mobile that they rarely had to come into contact with the local population, a necessity for victory in a people's war.

The helicopter was a life-saver in Vietnam. Between 1965 and 1973, air force helicopters evacuated 406 022 patients to safe hospital areas behind the lines of defence. Thousands of soldiers and civilians who would have died without speedy medical attention were saved. The helicopter, or the chopper as it was usually called, could rescue soldiers stranded in remote areas which other forms of transport could not reach. Choppers also provided field commanders with an excellent viewpoint of the battlefield and with up-to-date and accurate reconnaissance.

Source 7.2   Inside story of the guerrilla war

We shouldered our haversacks and moved off again through lightly timbered country and, after about 30 minutes walk, came to a clearing about a half mile wide, with a patch of what seemed to be dense jungle on the other side. Despite my protests, my haversack was taken by one of the M'Nongs and Thanh said: "We must move at maximum speed." That had been part of my training — to march at very high speed, starting with 15 minutes without a break and working up to two hours at maximum speed without a break. Just for situations like this, I thought.

We set out very briskly and as we approached the centre of the clearing, I noticed the M'Nong — mighty hunters of elephants and noted for their big ears — gazing skywards behind us. Sure enough within seconds there was the heavy roar of helicopters. Then we really did put on speed. I estimated that even if we jog-trotted we still had five minutes ahead of us and although the 'copters were not yet in sight, what they could do in five minutes from the time they made such a noise was obvious. The noise grew to shattering dimensions and four ungainly, dark shapes, flying quite low appeared over the patch of jungle we had just left, bearing down towards

us like vultures on their prey as if they knew precisely where we were. We were jog-trotting by now, and while some of the guerrillas selected firing positions and made their weapons ready, I was given the signal to run as fast as I could. Four of us raced across the last couple of hundred yards at full speed. The firing had already started when we literally jumped into the forest and I was guided to a grotto in a tree-covered, rocky outcrop.

There were bursts of machine gun fire from the helicopters and a stream of automatic and carbine fire from the handful of guerrillas. From the faces of my companions, as well as by the facts of the situation, it was clear we were in the toughest spot I had been in since the start of my journey. Four 'copters could lift a company of troops — 80 to 100 — and we were ten, including myself. The roar of the helicopters, hovering now and seeking their targets, was shattering; it seemed there was no space in the ears for anything more, but still above the motors was the devastating clatter of their machine guns and the pitifully unequal reply of the guerrillas' two light machine guns. The 'copters circled and hovered, as if trying to make up their minds to land.

Suddenly the motors roared louder than ever, the squarish, whale-like noses pointed skywards and they soared up and away, flying right into the rays of the setting sun. We rushed to the edge of the forest and I was near tears of joy as one by one the guerrillas got to their feet and headed towards us. "Anyone hurt?" was the first question, and as none had been I asked why they had not landed.

"Look around you and you'll see why they didn't land," said Dinh, the stocky little chief of the unit. Then I noticed what had escaped me as we raced for cover, that there were evenly spaced, sharply pointed poles covering the latter half of the clearing, each 10 or 15 feet high. "They couldn't land here without getting spiked or fouling up their propellers," Dinh said, "these poles are planted in a very scientific pattern. That's why they hovered so long, looking for a gap."

"Why didn't they land on the other side where there were no poles?" I asked.

"Because it would have been useless. These helicopters can be effective only if they dive straight down on their prey in what the puppets call 'eagle-catches-chicken' tactics. If their troops have to advance even a few hundred yards against our fire, they will take casualties and once they have casualties they will break off any action. In any case, they knew we were near the edge of the jungle and by the time they had crossed half a mile of clearing, if we wanted to avoid action we could have faded away into the jungle where they dare not follow. Also it was near sunset and they don't stay out after dark. And we had certainly drilled some daylight into their machines. We were hitting them. I could see the tracers going in, but you have to hit a vital part to knock them down. Our experience is that once you start hitting them, they always pull out. So although the situation must have looked a bit black to you," he said with a grin, "there was really nothing to worry about."

"Their machine gun fire sounded very impressive," I said.

"Huh! It's always like that," Dinh replied contemptuously. "They make a lot of noise: fire their guns like mad but have no idea what they're blazing away at. At first it used to impress us, too. This time I watched some of their bullets going in; I could see one of them firing his gun from the 'copter doorway but by the firing angle it was clear the bullets were going nowhere near our men; I think they fire to keep up their own spirits. By the way," he concluded, "in another 15 minutes we will be in a safe area where the enemy never dares penetrate."

Wilfred Burchett, in B.J. Elliott, *World Society in the Twentieth Century*, pp. 335-7

Questions

1 Why was mobility so important to the VC?
2 How did the VC rely on the natural environment in their fighting?
3 What criticisms are made of the American soldiers?
4 Can you tell from the source that Burchett was a communist journalist? How?

WAR AT SEA

America's escalation of the war had begun with the Tonkin Gulf incident in 1964 and the navy continued to be involved. Throughout the war, the US Seventh Fleet, comprising 125 vessels and 64 000 men, controlled the waters off Vietnam. Its huge aircraft carriers set loose Phantom fighters and Skyhawk fighter-bombers against the north and south, while heavy cruisers and battleships shelled communist positions from offshore.

The Seventh Fleet conducted a naval blockade of Vietnam throughout the war. Naval ships, patrol boats and aircraft attempted to stop the traffic in military supplies going from North to South Vietnam on the thousands of junks and other small craft regularly plying their trade in the waters of the South China Sea. It was impossible to stop and search each small boat, however, so the operation did not disrupt the flow of supplies to the south.

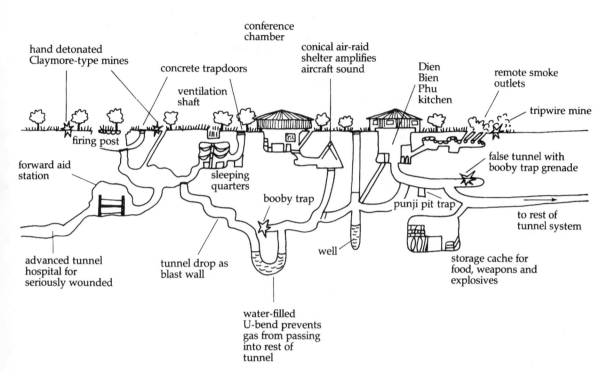

Tunnels were used extensively by the communist forces in South Vietnam. They were much more than just hiding places as the diagram shows. They were full of booby traps, including deadly snakes, and could extend for 30 km or more.

A CAMPAIGN FOR HEARTS AND MINDS

Winning the support of the villagers was important in the strategy of both sides in the Vietnam War. For the VC it was an essential part of revolutionary warfare, as well as being the focal point of their campaign against the South Vietnamese government. The USA also realised the importance of the struggle for the 'hearts and minds' of the villagers and poured an increasing amount of money into what they called 'pacification' programs. These programs were diverse in nature. Some were aimed at increasing the security of local villages by providing increased police protection or by identifying and attacking VC. Others aimed at improving the conditions in the villages by providing specialist help in education, agriculture and hygiene.

In the early years of direct US intervention, pacification did not prove very successful and the influence of the VC grew steadily. But after 1969, when the VC was in tatters after Tet and there was a more stable government in Saigon, pacification programs began to be more effective. They were so effective that US records show that, by 1972, only 1–2 per cent of South Vietnamese villages were controlled by the VC. (All such government statistics should be viewed cautiously, however.)

The government of South Vietnam never had the full support of the population in their fight against the communist-led rebellion. In the eyes of many Vietnamese, the Saigon regime remained an artificial creation of the Americans. When US troops were withdrawn and US aid was discontinued, the belief was shown to be accurate: South Vietnam fell to the NVA and the VC within two years of the cease-fire.

> ■ How does this leaflet try to persuade US soldiers to stop fighting?

US SERVICEMEN!

During the first half of 1966, the US Exp. Corps suffered over 45,000 of casualties.

In the days to come, the number of American casualties will increase manifold.

The more Johnson escalates the war, the greater the danger you are facing.

The war becomes fiercer and fiercer!

If you yourselves don't look for a way out, nobody could help you!

Oppose to your being sent to the battlefront, as the men of the 3rd Brig. 1st US Inf. Div. at Lai Khe did, on last April 66.

If forced to join the battle

— CROSS OVER TO THE FRONT'S SIDE!

— LET YOURSELVES BE CAPTURED BY THE LIBERATION ARMED FORCES!

— DON'T RESIST, THROW YOUR WEAPONS 5m FAR AWAY AND LIE STILL!

— HAND YOUR WEAPONS OVER TO THE LIBERATION COMBATANTS, QUICKLY FOLLOW THEM OUT TO SAFER AREAS!

That's how to save yourselves from a senseless and useless death!

Through the Front's lenient policy you will be treated with humanity, and the Front will arrange your repatriation, as it did with 2 US prisoners George E Smith RA 13522780 and Claude MacClure RA 14703075 on last Nov. 27th 1965.

THINK IT OVER AND ACT QUICKLY!

THIS IS FIRST OF ALL FOR YOUR OWN BENEFIT!

Leaflet distributed by the communists amongst the American troops. Part of Vietnam's psychological warfare (psywar). One way of trying to win 'hearts and minds'.

Source 7.3   An Australian veteran: Adrian Bishop

Basically speaking, the Vietnamese were already committed, at least in most areas where it counted they were. There weren't as many areas under ARVN and American control as they said there were. There were quite a lot of areas in South Vietnam which were in what they called 'liberated zones', but they were effectively under the control of the Viet Cong right throughout the war and the people knew that. A lot of the people would have two bob each way for their own survival.

We had what we called Civil Affairs and Psychological Operations We would go in and make a chicken coop and roof a few houses and build a windmill and do their dentistry (which was important because that was one of the worst things they suffered from and we had dental health), but when we'd leave the Viet Cong would come back in.

The Viet Cong made sure though that they never upset anybody, that if they took anything they would pay for it. If they got rice they'd pay, if they took chickens they'd pay. They never ripped the people off, that was one thing. They would kill somebody to make an example of him if he was overtly pro-government, but they would never rip the people off. They would never rape. That was absolutely out of the question. They were too smart for that. No raping, no burning and no pillaging. Pay for what you use or leave a promissory note, and they would honour that too, no question.

The ARVN would go in and they would knock the stuff off and, of course, that would cause absolute hatred. When they left they would pinch the rice, the chickens, the eggs — all the things which were in short supply — and that would piss the people off. They would make them natural enemies.

There was such a massive cultural difference between a Vietnamese and a white guy that even if you went in and built a windmill and did their dentistry they would just smile and bow and you could be the man from Mars. They didn't have any idea where Australia was. You were just another person stuffing up their lives as far as they were concerned.

Stuart Rintoul, *Ashes of Vietnam*, p.81

Questions

1 How reliable is this piece of evidence? How could you check its validity?
2 Why might the ARVN treat the peasants so much worse than did the VC? Could this be exaggerated?
3 How effective were Civil Affairs and Psychological Operations (psyops)? Give reasons for your answer.

Activities

Key words

Define these important terms:

frontline	booby trap	defoliation
monsoon	napalm	body counts
Sihanouk Trail	MIG	hearts and minds
infantry	SAM	pacification

Research topics

1 Pacification.
2 Helicopters in the Vietnam War.

What if you were . . .?

1 You are a North Vietnamese soldier. Relate your experiences in the Vietnam War in a journal that you keep regularly.
2 You are a US Army general. Give written advice to your successor about fighting in Vietnam.

Review questions

1 What were the differences between the Vietnamese armies?
2 Contrast the VC and US armies.
3 How did the topography and climate of South Vietnam affect the conduct of the war?
4 What problems did US soldiers have in fighting the war at ground level in Vietnam?
5 How did the helicopter revolutionise warfare in the Vietnam War?

6 Comment on the success or otherwise of pacification in South Vietnam.
7 Why didn't the Americans win the war? In discussing this consider the following points as well as your own:
  • the influence of the media coverage of the war
  • the war can be seen as a civil war, and the entrance of the US meant the loss of support of many Vietnamese
  • the influence of the anti-war movement
  • the USA did not invade the North
  • the dedication and determination of the communist forces and people
  • the aid provided by the USSR and China to the communist forces.

What would you say?

1 Westmoreland explaining his strategy in Vietnam to some journalists.
2 A soldier (US, ARUN, NUA or VC) speaking to a group of young men and women about his experiences in the Vietnam War.

8 CAMBODIA AND LAOS

Vietnam and the Vietnam Wars dominate this narrative but the smaller nations of Cambodia and Laos have important parts in the story of conflict in Indochina. Due to their geographical proximity, war in one Indochinese nation has profound effects on the others. Hence the Vietnam Wars both influenced events in Cambodia and Laos and eventually spilt over into those countries.

CAMBODIA: THE COLONY

By the 1800s the Khmer kingdom was weak and under threat from Vietnam and Thailand. As the French colonialists moved into Vietnam in the middle of the eighteenth century, Thailand posed a major threat to Cambodian sovereignty. Having secured its position in Vietnam, French power forced Thailand into renouncing all its claims on Cambodia. By 1884, real power in Cambodia lay with the French Chief Resident, the monarch having been reduced to a figurehead seen on ceremonial occasions. The King, however, still had the respect and support of his people, especially through his position as leader of the Buddhist religion.

Cambodia became one of four protectorates in the French Indochinese Federation, along with Laos, Annam and Tonkin. (Cochin-China (southern Vietnam) was ruled directly as a colony.) French rule in Cambodia was less repressive than in Vietnam and traditional society did not suffer the same violent changes. As a result, no movement for independence sprang up in Cambodia before World War II.

■ Why do you think Vietnam suffered more than Cambodia under the French?

THE FREE KHMER

Japan occupied Cambodia in World War II and declared the nation independent of French rule. King Norodom Sihanouk, who had become king in 1941 at the age of eighteen, renounced the country's relationship with the French at the orders of the Japanese. In 1942, an independence movement, the Khmer Issarak (Free Khmer), was founded and quickly gained support from students, public servants and workers in the nation's capital, Phnom Penh. The movement conducted guerrilla warfare against

■ Why do you think the Japanese would encourage independence in Cambodia?

■ Why might the King take the step of abdicating as king and entering politics?

the French throughout the war. Soldiers and advisers from the Vietminh helped the Khmer Issarak develop its organisational base.

When was full independence reached?

French military forces regained control of Cambodia after Japan was defeated in World War II, but agreed to give Sihanouk's Cambodia a wide degree of self-government. At the Geneva Conference in 1954, Cambodia's complete independence was announced and all foreign troops and bases were prohibited on Cambodian soil. In 1955, Sihanouk stepped down from his position as King and entered politics. He won the election in that year, becoming the nation's Prime Minister.

Fig. 8.1 Cambodia.

SIHANOUK AND NEUTRALITY

Sihanouk's primary goal in foreign policy was to keep Cambodia neutral and uninvolved in the Vietnam War. To that end, he fostered relationships with non-communist and communist countries alike. He realised that if Cambodia was aligned with one side or the other, then the nation would probably be pulled into the turmoil of Vietnam. He therefore declined to enter the anti-communist South-East Asia Treaty Organisation (SEATO), but did accept military and developmental aid from the USA, as well as entering into trade and economic co-operation with China and the Soviet Union.

Cambodia has always been caught between its two larger neighbours, Thailand and Vietnam, who have traditionally attempted to dominate the smaller nation. Throughout the 1950s and 1960s, Sihanouk consistently looked to China as Cambodia's protector. He explained why in 1961:

Westerners are always astonished that we Cambodians are not disturbed by our future in which China will play such a powerful role. But one should try to put himself in our place: in this jungle which is the real world, should we, simple deer, interest ourselves in a dinosaur like China when we are more directly menaced, and have been for centuries, by the wolf and the tiger, who are Vietnam and Thailand.[1]

Relations with the USA

■ How important to the communists in Vietnam was Sihanouk's disregard of their activities in eastern Cambodia?

■ Did Sihanouk have much choice?

The USA became concerned at Cambodia's developing relationship with the communist giants, especially as the USA was so heavily involved in the Vietnam conflict. In the late 1950s, it gave support to Khmer Serai guerrillas opposed to Sihanouk's rule. It became even more concerned when, in the early 1960s, the Cambodian government reached certain agreements with the North Vietnamese. Sihanouk was certain that the north would eventually be victorious in Vietnam and wanted to make sure they would respect Cambodia's borders after their success. Accordingly, his government agreed to turn a blind eye to the strategic use of eastern Cambodia by communist troops.

Relations with the Americans continued to sour. By 1966, diplomatic relations and all aid from the USA had ceased. This had serious implications for Cambodia's economy and, as the decade wore on, Sihanouk became increasingly unpopular, especially among the supporters of the Americans: the army, big businessmen and landowners. This climaxed in a successful coup against the King by these groups in 1970. Sihanouk believes that the coup had the backing of America's CIA.

THE KHMER REPUBLIC

On 18 March 1970, while Sihanouk was out of the country, a military-led coup led by Lon Nol, the Minister of Defence, toppled the government of the Kingdom of Cambodia. The nation became the Khmer Republic. Unfortunately, the new government had little support among the population and found itself under immediate attack by peasants who were loyal to the King and by Khmer Rouge guerrillas (Cambodian communists). A civil war erupted which lasted for five years and caused terrible devastation.

Sihanouk's worst fears were realised. The Vietnam War became a Cambodian war. Lon Nol was a strong anti-communist and he ordered the Vietnamese out of Cambodia. The communist forces could not afford to leave their bases in the east; instead they easily defeated the small Cambodian army. United States and ARVN troops launched their own invasion of Cambodia in April 1970 in support of Lon Nol's threatened army and to eliminate the so-called communist sanctuaries. Large-scale US bombing, which had begun secretly in 1969, increased enormously and caused terrible damage.

What did the civil war mean for Cambodia?

The civil war was a complete disaster for Cambodia. About 10 per cent of the population — 600 000 people — were killed, about one-third of the rural population became refugees and the entire social order was thrown into chaos. The ground fighting and the American bombing devastated the economy. By August 1974, 539 000 tonnes of bombs had been dropped on Cambodia. Most of the nation's rice crop was destroyed and starvation threatened thousands.

Table 8.1 Agricultural production 1968–74 (thousands of tonnes)[2]

Product	1968/69	1969/70	1970/71	1971/72	1972/73	1973/74
Rice	2503	3814	2732	2138	953	762
Rubber	51	52	13	1	15	12
Maize	117	137	121	80	73	—
Palm sugar	—	34	23	—	—	—

Source 8.1 Roots of genocide

Chhit Do: Oh yes, they did. Every time after there had been bombing, they would take the people to see the craters, to see how big and deep the craters were, to see how the earth had been gouged out and scorched.

The ordinary people . . . sometimes literally shit in their pants when the big bombs and shells came . . . Their minds just froze up and they would wander around mute for three or four days. Terrified and half-crazy, the people were ready to believe what they were told . . . That was what made it so easy for the Khmer Rouge to win the people over . . . It was because of their dissatisfaction with the bombing that they kept on cooperating with the Khmer Rouge, joining up with the Khmer Rouge, sending their children off to go with them . . .

Bruce Palling: So the American bombing was a kind of help to the Khmer Rouge?

Chhit Do: Yet, that's right . . ., sometimes the bombs fell and hit little children, and their fathers would be all for the Khmer Rouge . . .

B. Kiernan, in *Teaching History*, January 1990, p.18

Questions

1 According to the source, why was US bombing an aid to the Khmer Rouge?
2 'Terrified and half-crazy the people were ready to believe what they were told'. Is this a realistic assessment of the effects of bombing?
3 How effective was US bombing throughout the rest of Indochina?

Industry was also damaged heavily and the country's level of debt increased rapidly as export production was severely cut. The destruction of 40 per cent of the nation's roads and one-third of its bridges, mostly by US bombing, further damaged any hope of a quick recovery.

Table 8.2 Foreign trade (millions of special drawing rights)[3]

	1969	1970	1971	1972	1973	1974
Exports	65.9	41.2	13.1	6.4	4.9	1.2
Imports	99.2	68.6	55.1	65.5	42.0	22.8
Services (net)	–1.2	–2.6	–11.6	–24.0	–8.2	—
Goods and services (net)	–34.5	–30.0	–53.6	–83.1	45.3	–21.6 (estimated)

■ Why would corruption develop as a result of this assistance from the USA?

Lon Nol's Republic survived on aid from the USA and, as in South Vietnam, the flood of US money into government circles signalled the development of widespread corruption throughout the officialdom and armed forces.

What was FUNK?

Sihanouk, although in exile in Peking, retained wide popular support in Cambodia and helped to found the National United Front of Kampuchea (FUNK). This resistance front contained the King's supporters as well as the local communists who had previously been opposed to the King. (Although the communists had, in fact, been persecuted by Sihanouk's security forces since the 1950s, they were now in need of his popularity and prestige.) It was the communists, the Khmer Rouge, who grew in strength as the war continued. In 1973, Sihanouk entered Khmer Rouge territory and embraced their leader, Pol Pot, who proclaimed the ex-King Commander-in-Chief of the communist forces. Khmer Rouge numbers had grown from about 3000 in 1971 to more than 60 000 in 1973 and they had outgrown the need for help from the Vietnamese communists. The brutal American bombing in particular had caused thousands to join their cause.

Cambodian guerrilla fighters line up to welcome Sihanouk to his mountainous headquarters.

DEMOCRATIC KAMPUCHEA

By 1975, the Khmer Rouge army and forces loyal to Sihanouk were in control of most of the nation. On 17 April 1975, the nation's capital, Phnom Penh, was taken by Khmer Rouge guerrillas. Francis Ponchaud, a French priest, describes their arrival in the city:

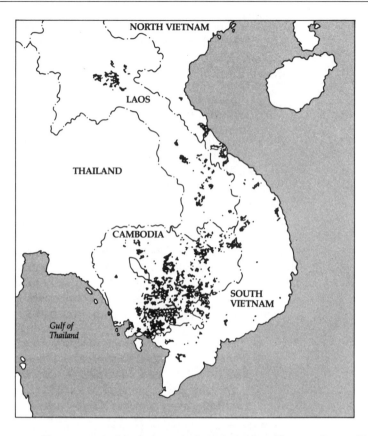

Fig. 8.2 US B52 targets in Indochina, January – August 1973.

These men in black moved along in Indian file, treading softly, one exactly behind the other, their faces worn and expressionless, speaking not a word and surrounded by a deathly silence.[4]

Five years of civil war had destroyed most of Cambodia's productive capacity and threatened the population with famine and epidemic. The Khmer Rouge solution to these terrible conditions was to evacuate the entire population of Phnom Penh immediately and brutally. Two million people found themselves on the road for weeks on end, walking into the countryside. Cripples were forced to drag themselves along, hospital patients were taken in their beds; no-one was allowed to stay behind.

Effect of the Khmer Rouge on Cambodia

Cambodia became one huge labour camp under the Khmer Rouge. They wished to change Cambodian society completely by taking it back to a pre-industrial, rural economy. All aspects of twentieth century Western society, which the Khmer Rouge believed had poisoned the Cambodian people, were eliminated. So the cities were emptied and books, films, telephones, highways and all other aspects of the twentieth century were eradicated. Agriculture was of supreme importance, therefore everyone had to work together on collective farms. These farms were really work gangs run by the Khmer Rouge with military discipline. Families were separated and Cambodians were told that they should emulate the water buffalo and be docile and do the will of Angkor (the party). A ex-French teacher gives an account of life under the Khmer Rouge in Source 8.2.

The infamous Pol Pot, leader of the Khmer Rouge government.

Estimates vary, but 1–3 million Cambodians died under the Khmer Rouge government. Those who were killed were mostly the old, the educated, city dwellers and those who were Westernised or had supported the Americans. These groups were either considered a threat to the regime or as worthless in the new Cambodia (renamed Democratic Kampuchea).

Source 8.2   Life under the Khmer Rouge

On the 17th of April 1975, the day of the 'liberation' of Phnom Penh, we were forced suddenly to leave the city. Pol Pot's soldiers told us this was temporary and that we could return in a few days. More than two million people found themselves on the road for weeks. And those who refused to go were massacred.

Many died en route, especially the sick and the old. When we arrived where they had decided to settle us, we had to start immediately to build barricades and to work the land.

Soon afterwards, the village chiefs who were chosen from among the poor and illiterate peasants, received the order to eliminate all those who had worked in any way with the administration, and all those who were classified as 'bourgeoise' (teachers, intellectuals, lawyers, doctors, engineers, artists, etc.). So I lost twelve members of my family.

These people were sometimes shot, but often killed with a knife or beaten to death. Pol Pot's men were always chosen from among the most ignorant who could be the most easily controlled.

As adults, we were forced to carry three cubic metres of rock or three cubic metres of soil. Children over six gathered human excreta for fertilising the rice fields, and had to work or carry one cubic metre of soil a day.

Every meal was a bowl of watery soup with salt and a few grains of rice. On average, they gave us the equivalent of a concentrated milk tin full of rice for five people each day.

Couples were separated. We could not get together for more than two hours every ten days. Children were taken from us and we could only see them rarely. We had to use terms like Comrade Mother, Comrade Father, Comrade Son. We were not allowed to leave the village and we had no contact with the outside world. All culture was eliminated and our only 'intellectual' activity was to listen to their conferences. These took place after work and sometimes they even woke us to repeat the same speeches. 'Hard work is needed, obey Angkor'.

Buddhism, Islam and Christianity were banned. The pagodas and temples were damaged or destroyed. The Bonzes (Buddhist priests) were killed by the thousands. Several Catholic priests and the Bishop of Phnom Penh were assassinated. Many believers were massacred. The project of Pol Pot seems to have been to revert to some sort of ancestral society, hard and pure, in which many of us had no place. According to him a million Khmers was sufficient to build such a hell, a mixture of Stone Age and slavery.

'A Chance for the Khmer people to survive' (trans. M. Osaba), in *Development News Digest*, December 1989, pp.14-15.

Questions

1 Why is liberation written in inverted commas in the first line?

2 The Khmer Rouge even changed the Cambodian calendar. The first year of their regime became Year Zero. Why would they do that?

3 What reasons might the Khmer Rouge have had to eliminate the 'bourgeoisie' and the administrators and to keep the people weak with poor food supplies?

4 'The project of Pol Pot seems to have been to revert to some sort of ancestral society, hard and pure, in which many of us had no place'. Explain.

A pile of human skulls and bones lies just outside Siem Reap, Cambodia, one of the many killing grounds during Pol Pot's rule.

When did Vietnam invade?

The Khmer Rouge were paranoid nationalists and especially antagonistic towards both the Americans and the Vietnamese. They hated the Vietnamese, partly on historical grounds and partly from the betrayal, as they saw it, of the 1973 Vietnamese cease-fire, after which the USA dramatically increased its bombing of Cambodia and Vietnamese communist aid to the Khmer Rouge ceased. This led to the armies of Democratic Kampuchea attacking Vietnam border areas in 1977 and inflicting serious damage. In retaliation, the Vietnamese army (the combined NVA and ARVN) invaded Kampuchea in December 1978 and quickly ousted the Khmer Rouge government. The Khmer Rouge fled to the Thai border where they still remain. One of the most brutal regimes in world history was finished.

Norodom Sihanouk, the most important figure in Cambodian politics and society in the twentieth century.

Norodom Sihanouk

The present king of Cambodia, Sihanouk, was born into the Cambodian royal family in 1922. He was placed on the throne for the first time by the French colonial authorities in 1941. The French mistakenly thought that the young ruler would be easy to manipulate but Sihanouk instead led a campaign which secured Cambodia's independence in 1953. Two years later, he abdicated as monarch, formed his own political movement, Sangkum, and was elected as the nation's prime minister. In 1960 he declared himself head of state. In the 1950s and 1960s, Sihanouk was able to keep Cambodia from becoming involved in the Vietnam War but at home there was rising opposition from the communists and right-wing military leaders. Eventually Sihanouk was toppled from power in 1970 by his minister of defence, General Lon Nol.

Following his removal from power he sided with the Khmer Rouge and other opponents of Lon Nol's regime. When the Khmer Rouge were victorious in 1975, Sihanouk returned home and he was placed under house arrest. After the Khmer Rouge in turn were defeated, the prince (as he is commonly known) became head of a coalition of factions opposed to the new Hun Sen government.

When the Cambodian peace plan was carried out in 1993 Sihanouk returned to again become king of his country. In 1995, he is struggling with cancer whilst desperately trying to broker a peace between the government elected in 1993 (with his son Prince Ranariddh as first prime minister) and the Khmer Rouge. At the time of writing he has been unsuccessful.

LAOS: THE COLONY

In 1899 Laos became part of French Indochina. The French colonialists made little impact on the traditional society of Laos. They did not attempt to find or exploit the country's natural resources. In Laos, as in Cambodia,

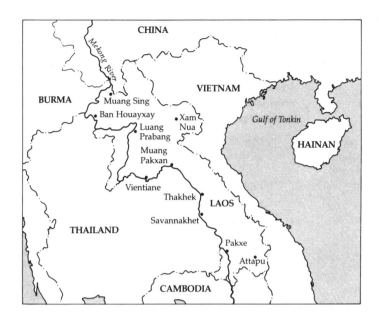

Fig 8.3 Laos.

there was no real nationalist agitation until during World War II. The French did establish a Consultative Assembly for the whole of Laos in 1923 which contributed to an increasing sense of unity in Laos.

What occurred after World War II?

When France was overrun by Hitler's blitzkrieg, Japan moved into French Indochina. As they did in Vietnam, the Japanese left the day-to-day administration to the French officials, but when imperial Japan was in headlong retreat in 1945, they compelled the King to announce the nation's independence from France. On 1 September 1945, the Free Lao (Lao Issara) movement seized power under their leader, Prince Petsarath, who declared French rule to be at an end. But in the early part of the following year, the French forces returned and expelled the Free Lao forces who subsequently escaped to Thailand.

By 1949, the French had given the Laotians a degree of independence (the French were keen to concentrate their entire attention on the war in Vietnam), and the majority of Free Lao leaders including Prince Petsarath's half-brother, Prince Souvanna Phouma, returned home satisfied and gave up resistance.

THE PATHET LAO

Laotian solders receiving instructions.

The nationalist leader who did not return home satisfied was the Prince's other half-brother Prince Souphanouvong, who had been Foreign Minister in the exiled Free Lao government in Bangkok during 1947–48. He preferred to retreat into north-eastern Laos and, in 1950, with the help of the Vietminh, he organised the Pathet Lao (State of Lao), a revolutionary movement aimed at overthrowing the French. Like the Vietminh, the Pathet Lao was a nationalist organisation with a leadership dominated by communists.

The Pathet Lao were not simply the Laotian version of the Vietminh. Laos did not have the history of resistance to colonial rule or the racial homogeneity of Vietnam so the Pathet Lao's task was even more formidable. (The largest racial group in Laos comprises only 56% of the population, whereas the largest racial group in Vietnam comprises 84%.) Their program emphasised racial equality between groups in Laos and advocated the elimination of French courses in school to be replaced by subjects emphasising Lao culture. Like the Vietminh, the main aim was to win over the villagers and to establish alternative administrations to rival the government in liberated areas. This is an early statement of part of the Pathet Lao program:

■ What are the central themes of this program?
■ Why are points (4) and (6) included?

Internal policy: (1) Widen the circle of unity throughout the country to include those of all races and religions, of both sexes and all ages, to defeat the French imperialists and their puppet governments and make the country independent, free and strong. (2) Open the opportunity for people of all tribal groups to the right of liberty and democracy for all. (3) Eliminate illiteracy which makes men deaf and blind. (4) Develop handicraft and commerce. (5) Sweep out the backward colonial rule. (6) Get rid of gambling and drunkenness. (7) Develop guerrilla forces into regional forces, and further develop into a national army.[5]

Source 8.3   The Pathet Lao

Question: Did they introduce any changes then?

Answer: Yes, they changed many things. The Pathet Lao soldiers helped the villagers farm rice and build houses. They gave rice to people who didn't have enough. Then they changed the status of women. Women became equal to men. Women became nurses and soldiers. They told the wives not to be afraid of the husbands any more.

Question: Didn't the husbands become angry?

Answer: Sometimes they did. But they were taught that there is not to be any more oppression. People agreed. The Pathet Lao would say: "Look, she's human, you don't have special rights." Most husbands agreed that it was a good idea. They would think, it's good for me too.

They changed everything, so many things. I can't finish telling you how many things. For example, take money. Before, in the town, everything was for hire. If you were sick and wanted to go to hospital, you had to have money and spend your money. Now it was free. No money was necessary.

Now people began to cooperate. The Pathet Lao trained doctors and sent them to the villages. Up until 1967-1968 the doctors were soldiers. There were civilian medics after 1967-1968.

Old men and women and all children went to school. The Pathet Lao gave them books. The teachers were villagers, not Pathet Lao cadres. Mainly, the instruction was literacy and some political instruction at first.

Question: How did the cooperation come about?

Answer: Well, cooperation began among the peasants. This was the job of the Pathet Lao cadre in the village. He was supposed to work with the peasants. No force was used.

Say, for example, that there were three families and two of them agreed to cooperate. Then the cadre would go to talk to the third family. He would get the other two families to come and help the third one who was uncooperative. Then they would talk about it. The two families would say: "We helped you so why don't you help us too?" They tried to shame him into helping.

The Pathet Lao cadres formed Phouak Khana Louk (awakening groups). There was generally one cadre in each village. During harvest, two or three others would come to help. They were sent from outside to the village. The cadres are rotated. The government supports them. They bring their own rice, just like the soldiers.

N. Adams & A. McCoy, *Laos: War and Revolution*, pp. 456-7

Questions

1 What does the source say about Pathet Lao methods of revolutionary war?

2 According to the source, what things have changed since the Pathet Lao took charge?

3 How do you think the peasantry would react to the methods of the Pathet Lao?

4 Do you think the interviewee may be biased? Why or why not?

After Geneva

The Geneva Agreement of 1954 granted Laos full independence and allowed the Pathet Lao to consolidate its forces in the northern provinces of Phong Saly and Sam Neua, adjoining North Vietnam. In 1957, a coalition government was formed under the leadership of the neutralist Souvanna Phouma. Members of the Royal Lao Government were also in the coalition. They represented the rich aristocracy, having supported French rule and Western influence. The Pathet Lao, also part of the government, agreed that the northern provinces should come under the government's control. Prince Souphanouvong became a part of the ministry. At the elections of 1958, the Pathet Lao showed its popularity and strength by winning thirteen of the twenty-one seats contested. The USA subsequently withdrew its funding to the new communist-dominated government. Without aid from the USA, the coalition government fell quickly.

CIVIL WAR

For the next eighteen years Laos was locked in a battle between the conservatives backed increasingly by the USA and the Pathet Lao supported by the North Vietnamese (the NVA maintained up to 100 000 soldiers in Laos during 1963–71). As expected, the neutralists favoured non-alignment with either side as Sihanouk had attempted in Cambodia. In 1962, a second coalition government was tried (after another Geneva Conference) with Phouma as Prime Minister and Phoumi Nosavan (one of the leading rightists, a military officer supported by the upper classes and the Americans) and Souphanouvong as his deputies.

American intervention

As they did in Vietnam, the Americans stepped into the breach when the French withdrew. Laos became another 'hot' battlefield in the Cold War, with the US providing money and weaponry to stop the spread of communism. After 1962, American aid to Laos totalled $200 million every year (this was many times the yearly budget of Laos). The Laotian economy, like the South Vietnamese and Cambodian, became completely dependent on the continued provision of American capital.

In 1964, US planes began bombing areas under the control of the Pathet Lao and the sections of the Ho Chi Minh Trail located in Laos. The raids lasted for eight years and Laos became the most bombed nation in the world. Under President Nixon, US planes were flying more than 1000 flights per day over Pathet Lao territory. By 1970, more bombs had been dropped on Laos than on both Vietnams. French journalist Jacques Decornoy reported:

> Another peasant remarked: Before, I understood nothing about what was said against American aid, against the United States. After the raids on my village, I know what they mean. Everything American, far and wide, is hated by the people.[6]

The raids only served to increase support for the communists. It has been estimated that the air war produced 500 000 refugees, about one in six of the Laotian population.

■ Do you know of any other countries where the CIA has been so heavily involved behind the scenes?

The role played by the USA in the war in Laos was well hidden. The Central Intelligence Agency (CIA) formed two fake airline companies which supplied food and equipment to the Royal Laotian army, as well as running their own secret army numbering 30 000, chiefly consisting of Hmong tribesmen.

Communist triumph

All of America's efforts and money were in vain. The communists continued to grow in strength. By 1973, the Pathet Lao (in 1965 they took the name Neo Lao Hak Sat or Lao Patriotic Front) were in charge of three-quarters of the country. Another coalition government was formed in 1973, again headed by Souvanna Phouma. But as in Vietnam and Cambodia, the communists could not be denied and the Laotian civil war ended in 1975 with the communists victorious. The country was renamed the People's Democratic Republic of Laos with Prince Souphanouvong as President.

Activities

Key words
Define these important terms:

Khmer Issarak	Democratic Kampuchea	Pathet Lao
neutrality	FUNK	racial equality
sanctuaries	Angkor	coalition
Khmer Republic	Lao Issara	Neo Lao Hak Sat

Research topics
1 The philosophy of the Khmer Rouge.
2 The Princes — Sihanouk and Souphanouvong.

What if you were . . .?
1 You are Sihanouk after the Khmer Rouge has taken power and you are under house arrest. Write a letter to your friends in China regarding your position.
2 You are a Pathet Lao revolutionary. Write a propaganda leaflet designed to win over the peasants.

Review questions

1 Compare French rule in Cambodia and Laos with French rule in Vietnam.
2 Trace Cambodia's moves towards full independence. Account for Sihanouk's foreign policy in the 1950s and 1960s.
3 Discuss this statement: 'Cambodia under the Khmer Rouge suffered an Asian holocaust'.
4 Account for the rise in popularity by the Khmer Rouge and the Pathet Lao in Cambodia and Laos.
5 What effects did the civil war of 1970–75 have on Cambodia?
6 What part did the USA play in Cambodia and Laos before 1975?
7 Why do you think the communists were successful in winning power in Laos?

What would you say?

1 A Pathet Lao guerrilla explaining the movement's program to a group of Laotian peasants.
2 A Cambodian villager tells how he survived the last twenty years of Cambodian history.

9 REBELLION AT HOME

Throughout the long years of the Vietnam War, an anti-war movement grew in the USA and in the countries of its allies in South Vietnam. From the very beginning of US and Australian troop involvement in Vietnam, there were protests against the war. By the end of 1967, the movement had begun to have an influence on the political debate over Vietnam in the USA. At no stage during the war did a majority of the US people support the total withdrawal of American forces from Vietnam, but an increasing number voiced their disapproval of the conduct of the war through demonstrations and civil disobedience.

ARGUMENTS FOR AND AGAINST THE WAR

Why send troops to Vietnam?

Successive American administrations sent troops to Vietnam for basically the same reason. They believed that it was necessary, indeed vital, to their own interests to stop the government of South Vietnam from falling into communist hands. Communism was an evil that was an abomination to freedom and democracy, principles which the USA stood for and held dear. Therefore communism had to be contained. President Harry Truman set out the containment doctrine in March 1947.

> The second way of life [communism] is based upon the will of a minority forcibly imposed upon the majority. It relies upon terror and oppression, a controlled press and radio, fixed elections, and the suppression of personal freedoms. I believe that it must be the policy of the United States to support free people who are resisting attempted subjugation by armed minorities or by outside pressures.[1]

From the containment policy grew the 'domino theory' which stated that it was necessary to stop one nation from falling under communist control so that other nations would not in turn fall. Even nations like the USA or Australia were under eventual threat if the falling dominoes were not stopped. Australia's Minister for External Affairs, H.R. Casey, explained the domino theory in October 1954:

If the whole of Indochina fell to the communists, Thailand would be gravely exposed. If Thailand were to fall, the road would be open to Malaya and Singapore. From the Malay Peninsula the Communists could dominate the northern approaches to Australia, and even cut our lifelines with Europe.[2]

Thus Indochina became trapped in the cold war between the USA and the USSR. But there were other subsidiary reasons for sending troops. As the war dragged on with no victory in sight, the US government's prestige and reputation worldwide came into consideration. No US President and his administration was willing to be the first to lose a war or to withdraw and suffer a humiliating peace.

■ Were there other reasons for Johnson's continuing commitment to the Vietnam war?

Why oppose the war?

Support for the Vietnam War was high during the early years of American involvement. Few questioned President Johnson's decision to escalate the war. The Tonkin Resolution passed both Houses of Congress with only two votes against it. As the number of casualties increased and as the dead or crippled returned home to American towns and cities, however, opponents began to make themselves heard. In addition, the violence of the war was being shown on the nightly news.

By late October 1967, opinion polls showed that the number of voters who wanted to pull out of Vietnam had doubled from 15 per cent to 30 per cent and leading public figures began to raise objections. The loudest voices came from the US Senate, including Senators Fulbright, Kennedy, McCarthy, McGovern, Mansfield and Morse.

But not only senators were opposed to the war. Many young Americans disputed America's right to be there. Many refused to serve in the army or to register for the draft (the US version of conscription).

The anti-war movement argued passionately against involvement in the Vietnam War for many reasons, including:

- what is happening in Vietnam and the rest of Indochina is a civil war and should be left to the Vietnamese to solve
- the USA and its allies are supporting an unpopular, corrupt, military dictatorship yet they say they are fighting for freedom
- it is impossible for foreign troops to win a revolutionary war in Asia because of unfamiliar culture, terrain and conditions; more and more soldiers and weapons will be sent to their destruction for no good reason
- the USA, the most powerful nation on earth, is bullying a small, peasant-based nation; supposedly in order to save Vietnam, it is laying it waste
- millions of innocent civilians are being killed or injured, particularly by the bombing
- napalm, defoliants, anti-personnel bombs and other such devices are brutal and immoral methods of waging war
- the USA stands for the freedom and self-determination of all nations, therefore what is happening in Vietnam is against America's fundamental beliefs
- government money flooding into the Vietnam conflict should be spent on poverty and inequality back home in America.

THE ANTI-WAR MOVEMENT IN THE USA

Early days

Involvement by America in any war always produced anti-war sentiment, but the Vietnam War split the nation as no other conflict had. Protests against US involvement began after the Gulf of Tonkin Resolution was passed but these were only isolated and confined chiefly to a few university campuses. By the middle of 1965, after the introduction of combat troops, however, a Harris poll showed that only 57 per cent of Americans supported the President's actions, a much smaller proportion than Johnson would have hoped for.

Throughout the early years, protest centred around the youth of the nation, especially those who were better educated. The universities had been at the centre of the civil rights campaign which had been at its most intense in the first years of the decade. Protests for civil rights seemed to flow easily into participation in the anti-war campaign on the nation's campuses.

As the number of US troops in Vietnam grew rapidly in 1965, the protests in America and in other nations around the world grew in size. On 27 November 1965, 35 000 demonstrators gathered outside the White House in Washington DC to listen to speeches against the war by Benjamin Spock, the world authority on children, and Coretta King, wife of the black civil rights leader, Martin Luther King Jr. The demonstration was organised by SANE, the National Committee for a Sane Nuclear Policy (the anti-nuclear movement of the late 1950s and early 1960s also contributed to the membership of the anti-war movement).

■ Were there similar ideas behind the civil rights and anti-nuclear movements and the anti-war campaign?

Earlier in the same month, the attention of the entire nation was focused on Vietnam and the depth of feeling on the subject was revealed when two young men, emulating the Buddhists in South Vietnam, had publicly burned themselves to death in protest at the war. A Quaker named Norman Morrison burned himself to death outside the Pentagon on 2 November and seven days later, Roger Allen Laporte, a member of the Catholic Worker Movement, died in the same fashion outside the United Nations building.

Students protest

America's youth of the early 1960s was the best educated generation that the USA had ever produced. Yet they were a discontented generation. Many regarded their parents' generation as materialistic and competitive, these qualities having created an unjust and unequal society on the brink of nuclear war. Many opted out of the so-called 'rat-race' and joined communities dedicated to peace and love. They urged people to make love not war. In the words of the Beatle, John Lennon, they sang 'All we are saying is give peace a chance'.

Only a minority of college students actually protested in the streets against the Vietnam War and against the draft which had doubled as a result of the increasing troop commitments.

How did the students oppose the war?

A mass demonstration in the USA against the Vietnam War. What do the posters say?

■ Do you think you would have gone to Vietnam or avoided the draft?

The students of America found innovative methods to protest against US involvement in Vietnam. Apart from mass demonstrations, the nation's universities were disrupted by students and staff holding 'teach-ins' at which normal lessons were cancelled and replaced by discussions on the rights and wrongs of the US commitment in South-East Asia. 'Sit-ins' were organised to disrupt the organisation of the war in the USA: students sat on railway lines to stop trains carrying troops or supplies and in the middle of recruitment offices to upset further induction.

Resistance to the draft became a major feature of the anti-war movement: at marches across America people burned their draft cards in symbolic protest. The Draft Resistance Movement was formed which arranged protests against the draft and gave advice on how to avoid or defer the call-up. Several methods were found (some of which could lead to a gaol term): failing the interview — guides on how to fail were made available; deferment by marriage or enrolling in college; refusing to answer the draft notice; or leaving the country. A quarter of a million Americans avoided the draft with only one-tenth of that number being charged for breaking the draft laws.

Source 9.1   Avoiding the draft

'My name is John Lacey. I was born in 1945 and brought up in New York. I left America in 1967 just after leaving college. I did this to avoid being drafted. I went to Canada and then to Sweden where I lived till there was an amnesty for draft-dodgers which let me return to the USA.

Was I a coward? Did I let my country down? In one way I was a coward for I left rather than go to jail for my refusal to join the army. But I wasn't afraid to fight. I refused to serve in Vietnam because we had no right to be there. We only brought untold suffering and destruction to that country. We acted like the bully of the world and used all our vast military might against a small nation of peasants.

Some people might say that I was not in a position to judge what was happening in Vietnam. However, there were many war veterans who hated the war just as much as I did. They saw the injustices at first hand and they condemned the war too.

I'm very bitter about our government's actions. They lied to justify their actions and while they spent millions on bombing North Vietnam the problems in the ghettoes of our big cities grew worse and worse. The Vietnam War has left a deep scar on my country.'

J. Cannon *et al.*, *The Contemporary World, Conflict or Co-operation?*, p.26

Questions

1 What reasons did Lacey have for avoiding the draft?
2 How important to Lacey do you think was the decision to avoid the draft? Would it have been an easy decision? Why or why not?
3 What counter arguments would supporters of the war have had for US involvement?

Black opposition

Black civil rights leader, Martin Luther King Jr, spoke against the war from the middle of 1965. Like many other Black leaders, he was concerned that the war would stem the flow of much-needed funds to the fight against poverty and inequality, two problems faced by many American negroes every day. He was concerned also that the draft deferment system (being able to avoid going into the army) meant that Blacks were less able to avoid call-up than white Americans.

King's fears were realised. As the war continued, Congress refused to continue passing the funds needed for increases in domestic spending on slum clearance, education and health care. America's Black population comprised about 13 per cent of the total population, but in Vietnam 28 per cent of combat soldiers were Blacks.

■ Do the disadvantaged, for example the US Blacks, always do more than their fair share of fighting?

The veterans

In 1967, Vietnam Veterans Against the War was founded and quickly grew in numbers. These veterans marched in demonstrations and spoke against the war to prospective soldiers (the films *Coming Home* and *Born on the Fourth of July* show disabled veterans doing this). The usual tour of duty in Vietnam was only one year and rapidly thousands of Vietnam veterans, many crippled or disfigured by the war, became a commonplace sight on the streets of America. The reality of the war was brought vividly home to the US public.

1967

By the middle of 1967, the anti-war movement had diversified away from the campuses. Its members were from all walks of life: teachers, students, feminists, war veterans, intellectuals, professionals, movie stars, pacifists and civil rights activists. (It is important to remember, however, that at every stage of the war in Vietnam, a large section of the population agreed with the President's policies. Opinion polls differed as to what the exact numbers were, but it is fair to say that even at the war's end the US public was almost evenly divided on the subject of involvement in Vietnam.)

Major demonstrations against the war became commonplace. The crowds listened to speeches, burnt draft cards, displayed their banners and chanted slogans like: 'Hey, Hey, Hey, LBJ! How many kids did you kill today?' or 'Hell no. We won't go'. Often the protests ended in violence. In October 1967, 50 000 protesters marched on the Pentagon and were met by 10 000 troops; 1000 were arrested after a virtual battle developed.

Tet

As mentioned in chapters 5 and 6, the Tet Offensive was a turning point in the Vietnam War. It heralded an increase in opposition to the conflict both on the streets and in the corridors of power and influenced Lyndon Johnson to the extent that, in November, he called for immediate negotiations and an end to the bombing.

The presidential election campaign of 1968 was dominated by the issue of Vietnam. It erupted in violence in Chicago at the Democratic Convention when 10 000 demonstrators battled with police, and it led to the election of Richard Nixon who had claimed in the campaign that he had a plan to end the war.

NIXON AND THE PEACE MOVEMENT

Under Nixon, the war continued for four more years but the number of US troops dropped dramatically in accordance with the policy of Vietnamisation. In the first years of his administration, protests continued. The Vietnam Moratorium Movement organised massive rallies across the nation in October and November of 1969. (A moratorium is a nation-wide strike in protest at something.) Nixon, however, took little notice; on the day of one particular protest, he said he watched a football game on television. Again in 1970 and 1971, after the invasions of Cambodia and Laos, there were large and violent demonstrations but Nixon was in the end unmoved. The war remained unpopular but the protests on the streets eventually died down as American troops came home in larger and larger numbers. The effect of the anti-war movement will be discussed at the end of this chapter.

Pro-war demonstrators in New York (mainly construction workers) clash violently with opponents of the war. Is there an age difference? Is that significant?

Table 9.1 Popular support for two Presidents during the Vietnam War[3]

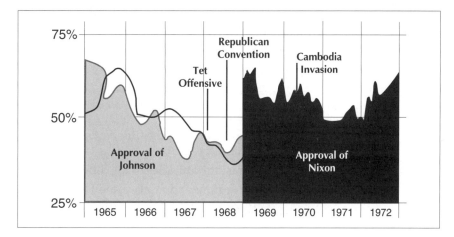

A Case Study: My Lai

A savage and disturbing incident which occurred at the small village of My Lai in central Vietnam in March 1968 played a sizeable part in increasing the disenchantment with the war. Lieutenant William Calley was the leader of a platoon of men in 'Charlie' Company in the early months of 1968. The troops took heavy casualties from booby traps, mines and snipers yet were not able to bring the VC to combat. Enormous frustration developed and culminated in a massacre of civilians in the village of My Lai.

My Lai was suspected of housing a VC battalion but when 'Charlie' Company entered the village no enemy troops were sighted. Despite this, at Calley's direction his troops shot, bayoneted or beat to death 200–500 men, women and children. The US Army attempted to cover up the story but it was eventually published across America in November 1969. The US and worldwide public were horrified. Calley was the only soldier convicted of anything concerning the massacre; he served only a few years under house arrest despite being sentenced to life imprisonment at his trial.

NOTE: All sides were guilty of atrocities in the Vietnam War: My Lai came only weeks after the needless slaughter of hundreds of civilians by the communists at Hué in the Tet Offensive.

Source 9.2   My Lai

The most disturbing thing I saw was one boy and this is what haunts me . . . A boy with his arms shot off, shot up and hanging on and he just had this bewildered look on his face like what did I do, what's wrong . . . he couldn't comprehend.

Fred Wilmer, 'Charlie' Company

I feel that they were able to carry out the assigned task, the orders that meant killing small kids, killing women because they were trained that way, they was trained that when you get into combat it's either you or the enemy . . .

Kenneth Hodges, former Sergeant 'Charlie' Company

The only crime that I have committed is in judgement of my values. Apparently I valued my troops' lives more than I did that of the enemy.

William Calley, Lieutenant 'Charlie' Company

It's why I'm old before my time. I remember it all the time. I'm all alone and life is hard. Thinking about it has made me old . . . I won't forgive as long as I live — think of the babies being killed, then ask me why I hate them.

My Lai villager

Four Hours at My Lai, Yorkshire Television

Questions

1 Comment on how the different sources have been affected by the My Lai massacre.

2 Contrast the attitudes of the different sources to the events in My Lai.

3 What argument do Calley and Hodges use to justify their actions in My Lai? Do you think this is a valid argument?

Lt. William Calley accused of mass murder in the 1968 My Lai massacre.

Questions (continued)

4 What factors could lead to a massacre of civilians as occurred at My Lai in 1968?

5 Americans were divided in their reactions to the story of My Lai and in whether or not US soldiers should be punished for their actions in wartime. Why do you think My Lai caused controversy?

6 Should anyone have been punished for My Lai? If so, who and to what extent?

THE ANTI-WAR MOVEMENT IN AUSTRALIA

Early days

As in the US, most of the population in early 1965 was either blissfully unaware that Australians had become involved in Vietnam or were supportive of government decisions to do so. The majority of Australians believed that communism posed a direct threat to Australia and that fighting the enemy in South Vietnam made good sense.

The early protests tended to be by individual clergy or by groups which were more concerned about halting conscription. Two such groups were the Youth Campaign against Conscription and the Save our Sons organisation.

By October 1966, however, stronger protests against the war were being made. President Johnson visited Australia at this time and while thousands welcomed him favourably, his visit was marred by anti-war demonstrators, some of whom threw themselves in front of his car and splashed his car with paint. In Sydney, when the President's motorcade was brought to a halt by protesters, the then NSW Premier Robert Askin told the driver to 'ride over the bastards.' Later in the same year the Liberal and Country Party government, which supported LBJ's policies and had sent Australians to Vietnam, were returned with a massive majority in the federal election. This suggests that the majority of Australians still supported the war in 1966. The government certainly saw the election in that light and increased the number of troops in South Vietnam.

Lyndon B. Johnson in his car in Melbourne, 1966. Demonstrators had hurled paint at his car.

What was the conscription issue?

Australia's anti-war movement was also strongly connected to protests against conscription. This was probably more so than in the US, as Australia had a long history of opposition to conscription for overseas service during the twentieth century. In World War I the nation had split bitterly over the issue with two national referendums refusing the government the power to send conscripts to fight in Europe.

The Labor leader in 1966, Arthur Calwell, was a resolute opponent of conscription:

> These boys, with not only their careers, but possibly their lives at stake, are to be selected by some form of lottery, or Russian roulette. Someone has called the lottery a lucky dip. Should it be called an unlucky one? One will go and twenty-nine will stay. Is this equal treatment before the law?[4]

(The Australian conscripts were selected by lottery).

Those campaigning against conscription used a variety of methods. These included demonstrations of different sorts and at different venues, including outside parliament and the homes of prominent politicians; the burning of draft cards; sit-ins; raids on government offices; and even chaining themselves to the gates of army barracks. The Draft Resistance Movement was formed in 1968.

Table 9.2   The withdrawal of Australian forces from Vietnam [5]
(Gallup Polls)

	April 1969	Aug. 1969	Oct. 1969	Oct. 1970
Continue %	48	40	39	42
Bring Back %	40	55	51	50
Undecided %	12	5	10	8

Australia's Vietnam Moratorium

As the war continued the protests grew more numerous and militant and Australian society became more divided over the issues of Vietnam and conscription. At times the violent responses of the police to the demonstrators served to heighten their passion and encourage violence in response.

The highpoints of Australia's anti-war campaign were the Moratorium marches of May and September 1970 and June 1971. They were held to protest against conscription and Australia's involvement in Vietnam. The demonstrations called for an end to conscription and support for the South Vietnamese regime and for the total withdrawal of all foreign troops in Vietnam. Up to 200 000 people across Australia from all walks of life attended marches, meetings, concerts and church services during the first Moratorium. In Sydney alone 265 000 leaflets, 8000 posters, 12 000 badges and 10 000 armbands were distributed. The Moratorium campaigns generated great support and equally great opposition within Australia. At the very least, they placed the Vietnam issue at the forefront of political issues in the early 1970s.

In Melbourne, demonstrators stage a sit-down strike on tram lines.

Source 9. 3 Moratorium posters/leaflets

**SUPPORT
AUSTRALIA'S OWN
MORATORIUM AGAINST
THE WAR IN VIETNAM**

**OUT with Apathy
OUT with our troops
OUT with the National Service Act**

For five years we have been participating in a war condemned by the world as unjust and inhuman.

**EXERCISE
YOUR DEMOCRATIC RIGHT
AND RESPONSIBILITY
SPEAK OUT WITH US
DURING MORATORIUM WEEK
3rd TO 10th MAY 1970**

CONTACT US NOW

EASTERN SUBURBS MORATORIUM COMMITTEE
37 Sturt Street, Kensington   6 Duxford Street, Paddington
Phone: 3491549 or 313176 or 309127 or 612522

(Please tick where indicated)

I would like to help with ☐   I enclose donation
Moratorium activities   towards your work $ ....

Name: ....

Address: .... Phone: ....

VIETNAM IS YOUR CONCERN

Authorised by Mrs O'Sullivan, 37 Sturt Street, Kensington
Printed by Comment Publishing Company, 27 Steam Mill Street, Sydney.

Against The War . . .

Clearly the Vietnam war is not ending. The policies of 'Vietnamization' and 'progressive withdrawal' are in fact an attempt to end opposition to the war, rather than to end the war itself, to placate outraged public opinion while the war goes on. Responding to this situation Australians from all walks of life will organise and participate in a series of protests against the war culminating in nationally co-ordinated action during the week ending May 8-9-10. This is the Vietnam Moratorium Campaign a Moratorium against business as usual to end the war now.

Its objectives are:

IMMEDIATE withdrawal of Australian and all other foreign troops from Vietnam;

IMMEDIATE repeal of the National Service Act.

All Moratorium activities in pursuance of these objectives shall be of a non-violent nature. The campaign in N.S.W. is directed by a body of sponsors which is open to all who support these objectives. It aims to provide all Australians opposed to the war with an opportunity to publicly declare their commitment to strike against the war.

VIETNAM MORATORIUM CAMPAIGN MAY 8.9.10

Questions

1 What are the arguments used in these posters?

2 Design your own anti-war poster.

3 What were the objectives of the Moratorium?

Jim Cairns

The unofficial leader of the Moratorium movement was a Labor party politician, James (Jim) Ford Cairns. He was born in Victoria in 1914, educated at state schools and for a time was a member of the Victorian police force. For ten years, 1945–55, Cairns lectured in economics at Melbourne University. In 1955 he entered the House of Representatives as the member for Yarra and became a leading light of the Labor Party's left wing during the 1960s.

An advocate of non-violence, he led the Victorian Moratorium movement against the Vietnam War and conscription. On 8 May 1970, Australia's first Moratorium march was held. The biggest march was in Melbourne where Cairns led over 70 000 participants. It was a triumph of peaceful protest, a point of special significance to Cairns. When the 70 000 sat down in the heart of Melbourne and observed a two-minute silence Cairns was jubilant. He commented: 'Nobody thought this could be done'.

In 1973 Cairns chaired a meeting to welcome delegations from North Vietnam and the Vietcong. In 1975, he told parliament that communist victories in Vietnam and Cambodia would bring an end to the suffering of those nations. His political and social philosophies made him a controversial figure in Australian public life and he was a particular target of conservative party verbal attacks. During the Vietnam War years he was tragically and brutally bashed at his home.

With the election of a Labor government for the first time in twenty-three years in 1972, Cairns went on to become treasurer and deputy prime minister. He was dismissed, however, by Whitlam in July 1975 for misleading parliament. He resigned from parliament in 1977. He has since published a number of books concerning the alternative lifestyle movement and believes that real social change is not possible through government, but that individuals must work towards their own personal liberation and fulfilment.

THE EFFECT OF THE ANTI-WAR MOVEMENT

It is difficult to decide how much political impact the anti-war movement did have. Perhaps Johnson was influenced by the protests when he began scaling down America's part in the war in 1968, perhaps Nixon was moved to speed up troop withdrawals after 1969, perhaps Congress was pushed towards limiting the President's power to wage war in Vietnam. No doubt the opposition did have some effect but it is impossible to measure it precisely. One of the leaders of the American movement in 1968, Senator Eugene McCarthy, has said:

> I'm inclined to believe the war would have ended just about when it did, even if there had been no protest, if I had not campaigned, because they didn't end it on policy finally: they just ended it because they were losing it, and . . . the soldiers wouldn't fight.[6]

It is certain the anti-war protests did highlight the issue and forced the majority of the population to think seriously about Vietnam. Furthermore, the public was educated in how to register political opposition, and numerous other social issues — including the role of women in society and the nuclear arms race — were set still more firmly on the political agenda.

Activities

Key words

Define these important terms:

military dictatorship	'sit-in'	Vietnam veteran
SANE	draft resistance	atrocity
'teach-in'	movement	

Research topics

1 Anti-war poetry and music.
2 The Moratorium movement in Australia and the US.
3 Your parents and relatives — their involvement in the anti-war movement.

What if you were . . .?

1 You are a supporter of the war in the USA. Write a letter to a newspaper explaining why America should be in Vietnam.
2 Write your thoughts and feelings on the sources and information in the My Lai case study.

Review questions

1 Why did successive US governments send troops to Vietnam?
2 Why did so many oppose the Vietnam War?
3 How did the anti-war movement change over the years of the conflict?
4 In what ways did the anti-war movement protest against the war?
5 Trace the growth of the anti-war movement in Australia.
6 What effect did My Lai have on attitudes to the war? Why?
7 In your opinion how successful was the anti-war movement in ending the war?

What would you say?

1 A draft evader explaining why he chose not to fight in Vietnam.
2 A student arguing with his parents on whether he/she should be able to go and march in the Vietnam Moratorium demonstration.

10 ENDS AND BEGINNINGS

Very few people believed that the cease-fire of 1973 was the beginning of peace in Vietnam. North Vietnam was still totally committed to unifying the nation and South Vietnam was certainly not ready to surrender to the communists. The rest of Indochina was also torn by disorder. In Laos another fragile truce had been arranged between the communist Pathet Lao and the Royal Lao government, and in Cambodia in 1973, the civil war was still raging bitterly. (See chapter 8 for the history of Cambodia up to 1979.)

HOW DID THE VIETNAM WAR END?

Up to the time of the cease-fire, an estimate 1 million communist fighters had been killed while almost 660 000 South Vietnamese soldiers had died in the Second Indochina War (the French Indochinese War was the first). In addition, hundreds of thousands of Vietnamese civilians were dead and almost one half of the population of South Vietnam had lost their homes.

Despite the terrible costs and disregarding the cease-fire, the fighting continued at low levels (in one year 50 000 Vietnamese were killed). Government troops controlled much of South Vietnam (estimates differ between three-quarters and two-thirds of the territory) and its population. Both sides used the cease-fire period to prepare for the inevitable outbreak of full-blooded hostilities. The communists infiltrated reinforcements of men and material down the Ho Chi Minh Trail while the South Vietnamese received enormous aid from the US in military supplies (the South Vietnamese Air Force became the fourth largest in the world).

The US withdraws further

In 1974, the US Congress, reflecting the will of the American people who primarily wished to forget about the Vietnam War, began to reduce its level of support to the Saigon regime. In October 1974, Congress approved only $700 million in aid to South Vietnam, about half of the sum requested by President Ford. (Ford replaced Nixon, who had been forced to resign because of the Watergate scandal.) Two months before, the Congress had legislated to cease all US bombing throughout Indochina.

President Thieu of South Vietnam claimed that by 1975 the war-making ability of the South had been cut by 60 per cent because of the diminished backing of the American government. The North's capabilities, according to Thieu, had grown largely because of continued aid from the Soviet Union and China.

The final offensive

When the communists launched their Spring Offensive in March 1975 through the central highlands, it was envisaged that another two years of fighting would be necessary before final victory. But the offensive became an overwhelming victory when ARVN units fled south from the battlefield after being defeated. More than 1 million refugees fled with them in a desperate attempt to escape the fighting.

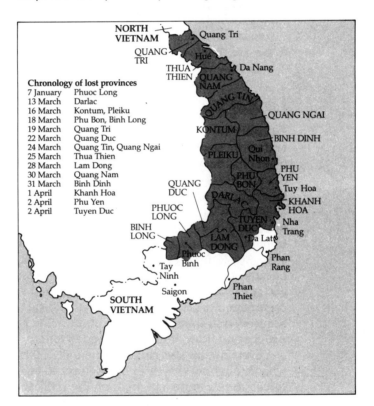

Chronology of lost provinces

7 January	Phuoc Long
13 March	Darlac
16 March	Kontum, Pleiku
18 March	Phu Bon, Binh Long
19 March	Quang Tri
22 March	Quang Duc
24 March	Quang Tin, Quang Ngai
25 March	Thua Thien
28 March	Lam Dong
30 March	Quang Nam
31 March	Binh Dinh
1 April	Khanh Hoa
2 April	Phu Yen
2 April	Tuyen Duc

Fig. 10.1 Provinces of South Vietnam lost to the communists by 2 April 1975.

By the middle of April, Saigon was for the taking. On 21 April 1975, President Thieu resigned, and on 30 April, the flag of the Provisional Revolutionary Government of Vietnam was raised above the presidential palace in Saigon. The century's longest war, the ten-thousand days war, was over.

Refugess, laden with their belongings, fleeing towards Saigon.

DID THE STRUGGLE END FOR VIETNAM?

The Vietnam War ended in 1975, but the problems facing the nation certainly did not. In 1981, Vietnam's leader Pham Van Dong commented:

> Yes we defeated the United States. But now we are plagued by problems. We do not have enough to eat. We are a poor, underdeveloped nation . . . waging a war is simple, but running a country is very difficult.[1]

The scars of 30 years could not be healed overnight and would stand in the road of recovery for years to come. Some of the problems caused by the war are listed below.

- The bombing had inflicted enormous damage on the nation's economic infrastructure (buildings, roads, rail, bridges etc.).
- Large areas of forests and crop land had been destroyed or were unusable. Sixty per cent of rubber plantations and 60 000 hectares of mangrove forests were destroyed, for example.
- Tens of thousands of agricultural animals had been destroyed.
- The cities of the South were enormously overcrowded as a result of the refugee flood in the last days of the war. Unemployment and inflation were rife in the South, and the withdrawal of US aid had ruined the economy.
- The war had used virtually all stocks of oil and petrol, products necessary to power machines on farms and in factories.
- In the ensuing years hundreds of thousands of Vietnamese would flee to other nations to seek a better life and to escape the communist dictatorship.

Exhausted Vietnamese refugees arriving on a foreign shore.

Lack of aid

Probably the greatest problem faced by the Vietnamese nation since the end of the war has been the lack of international aid. No country on the planet has been so ravaged by war as Vietnam (except the other nations of Indochina), and for recovery to begin the generous assistance of the international community was required. (After World War II the nations of Western Europe would not have been able to rebuild without the financial aid of the Marshall Plan.) But tragically for Vietnam, the United States cut off all financial aid and trade with Vietnam after 1975, thereby creating an enormous obstacle to Vietnamese recovery. The US did this partly because of the humiliation it suffered due to its defeat in Vietnam and partly in response to Vietnam's alignment with the US's Cold War opponent, the USSR. Using its great political influence, the US succeeded in shutting Vietnam off from other advanced capitalist nations and from desperately needed funds.

Vietnam also earned the enmity of its traditional enemy, China, who throughout the 1970s drew closer to the US. Vietnam was forced to rely more and more on the USSR for aid and assistance. All this has changed, of course, with the collapse of communism in Eastern Europe in the late 1980s, the subsequent end of the Cold War and the more recent cessation of the US trade embargo on Vietnam in February 1994.

■ Do you think Vietnamese recovery hinges entirely on overseas aid?

NEW WARS

When a nation is struggling to recover from the damage caused by decades of fighting, the last thing it needs is a new war, but Vietnam had to endure just that. As mentioned in chapter 8, Vietnam invaded Cambodia (then called Democratic Kampuchea) in 1978. Throughout the 1980s, Vietnam kept large numbers of troops in Cambodia to bolster the government they had put in power after the overthrow of the Khmer Rouge. The Vietnamese occupation put further financial strain on an economy already in grave difficulties and, by September 1989, Vietnam was forced to withdraw its soldiers from Cambodia.

War with China

The war with Kampuchea also strained relations with Vietnam's largest and most powerful neighbour, the People's Republic of China. The Khmer Rouge had been supported by China since the early 1970s. China saw the Vietnamese invasion as an example of Vietnamese and Soviet expansionism and reacted accordingly.

This antagonism culminated in the Sino-Vietnamese War of 1979. In late February 1979, approximately 30 000 troops of the Chinese People's Liberation Army struck across the northern border of Vietnam. Within three days, the Vietnamese counter-attacked. By the first week in March, the war reached a stalemate. The Chinese withdrew in that week and peace was restored. Both sides claimed victory. Hanoi claimed that 'badly defeated Chinese troops had been forced into a humiliating retreat . . .'[2] while Peking claimed 'a telling blow to the Soviet Union's scheme of expansion in South East Asia'.[3]

■ Was the invasion of Cambodia an example of Vietnamese expansionism? (Look back at chapter 8.)

THE ECONOMY

Vietnam is struggling still to rebuild its economy. Up until 1989 Vietnam relied very heavily on aid and assistance from the USSR. Its economy was a Soviet-style communist economy with agriculture and industry owned and run centrally by the government. With the collapse of the USSR, the subsequent ending of Soviet aid and the continuing poor performance of the Vietnamese economy, the Vietnamese leaders decided to make major reforms to the economic system. The US policy of isolating Vietnam financially and the cost of the Vietnamese troops in Cambodia added to the economic crisis.

In 1986, the Communist Party announced widespread reforms which echoed changes in communist-run economies across the globe. This policy, called Doi Moi or 'Renovation', moved away from the traditional reliance on central planning, fixed quotas and collectivised agriculture towards a free market approach encouraging profit-making and production incentives. It has moved towards what the Chinese have called 'free market socialism'. In the political sphere, the Communist Party remains firmly in control.

Small signs of improvement in the Vietnamese economy emerged in the late 1980s. In 1988, many foreign companies were expressing an interest in doing business in Vietnam. Samsung television sets were already being made in Ho Chi Minh City and a British company was assembling aluminium windows in Vung Tau.

The end of the embargo

Changes to the economy in 1986 did lead to small gains for the Vietnamese but big improvements were hamstrung by a lack of business investment and the urgent need to rebuild much of Vietnam's infrastructure. By the early 1990s, the first of these problems was starting to be solved: money for investment purposes began flowing in from countries like Japan, Australia, Taiwan and Hong Kong. With the US trade embargo officially lifted on 4 February 1994, billions of dollars of international investment and aid will be available. As Louise Williams comments, 'the lifting of the embargo marks the re-entry of Vietnam into the international community . . . the private US investment and aid which is expected to flow into Vietnam . . . will make the long-overdue reconstruction of the nation possible' (see p.8).

Source 10.1 Vietnam's economic expansion

Vietnam's Big Bang

Paul Keating will be the first Australian Prime Minister to visit Vietnam since Harold Holt in 1966. But, as Lindsay Murdoch reports, the reality of the country is different to the media hype that came with the lifting of America's trade embargo.

Since Lac Long was released from jail in 1980, five years after the last helicopter left the roof of the American Embassy in Saigon, he has grudgingly given bribes to local officials who came to his shoe shop every Lunar New Year.

But this year the former South Vietnam Army lieutenant decided it was time to test Vietnam's new freedoms. "This year there was no whisky for them . . . nothing. I told them all to go away," he says. "But I still worry. The communists have not collapsed 100 per cent. Sure, things are freer now. You can see the smiles on people's faces.

But I worry sometimes that it is a trap."

Just along a bustling street from Lac Long's shop in the now Ho Chi Minh City, Thanh Hoang Nguyen sits in his 47-room boutique hotel, remembering a different Vietnam back in 1981 when he got on a creaking, 11-metre boat with 35 people, mostly children, and set sail across the South China Sea hoping for a new life.

"At the time I saw no future

here . . . but things are different now," he says.

Since the day he wept on his first day of work at a rubber factory in the Sydney suburb of Brookvale, Mr Nguyen, 41, says he knew he would return to his mother and friends in Vietnam. "I was homesick for the country I risked my life to leave," he says.

Nguyen, now an Australian citizen, is one of scores of budding entrepreneurs in Vietnam who are trickling back to their homeland to set up businesses and take up long-term residence. It is a country on the make, flavour of the month among businessmen since the US lifted the trade embargo that had ensured its former enemy remained isolated and poor.

But Vietnam's old communist leaders — essentially the same men who orchestrated the defeat of the Americans 20 years ago — are not quite sure what they want the country to become or where it is heading.

On a corner across the road from the old presidential palace in Saigon, where communist tanks crashed through the gates in April 1975, a huge red and white poster reads: "Long live the glorious Communist Party of Vietnam."

Communist Party?

Ho Chi Minh, the hero of communist Vietnam's wars against the French and Americans and their so-called "imperialist puppets", would probably turn in his grave if he could see the country he led for almost 25 years until his death in 1969.

If they force us into war, we will fight. The struggle will be atrocious, but the Vietnamese people will suffer anything rather than renounce their freedom.

— Ho Chi Minh in the early 1960s

The communists in Hanoi are now presiding over an economy that sometimes seems so *laissez faire* the World Bank has called it "hyper-capitalism".

Just about everyone in Vietnam seems to want to sell, make or accomplish something. No matter whether it is cutting up beer cans into toy copies of American helicopters or selling a multi-million-dollar block of land in the heart of Hanoi, the Vietnamese are in a hurry to make a buck.

Vietnam's economy is growing at an average 8 per cent a year. Inflation has dropped from 800 per cent to 17 per cent. Rice production is at a record high. Exports are surging. The Government has introduced an ambitious reform program. But the country is at a turning point.

Perhaps predictably, the people who are finding it most difficult to adjust to change are the aging communists.

The Communist Party's determination to maintain a monopoly on political power contradicts a pragmatic decision in 1986 to open the country to a market economy.

Its decision-making processes are racked by wrangling over the pace and content of reforms. Some cadres worry that the inevitable reforms will curb their intimidating power.

Improved prosperity for many Vietnamese has temporarily placated the hidden hard men of the party and bought time for the cadres to grapple with policies. But the party knows that when people achieve economic freedom they will demand political freedoms. It is repelled by the thought of a multi-party system. Ironically, though, it is looking to its former fiercest critics for role models, notably Singapore.

Vietnam has been largely misread. The reality is different to the hype created by the media in the lead-up to the February lifting of the US embargo. Investment has tended to happen much more slowly than the headlines suggest and to be much less than foreigners are in principle willing to commit.

Vietnam's almost 70 million people are among the world's poorest, with a per capita GNP of less than $US200. The country is primarily an agricultural economy with an extremely high population density on its agricultural land: 900 people per square kilometre. After decades of war and mismanagement, Vietnam has a collapsed infrastructure. More than 1 million workers and soldiers have lost their jobs in the public sector in recent years, swelling the ranks of the unemployed. Rapid population growth and lack of money have put severe strain on the delivery of social services such as health and education, once the country's sacred cows.

The bloated, incompetent bureaucracy ensures applications are difficult to get approved.

Ray Eaton, a Bangkok-based Australian who has developed close links with the Vietnamese leadership over the past five years, says forecasts that Vietnam will soon become a newly industrialised country are far too optimistic.

"It is certainly not the desire of the Vietnamese Government to have a boom-type economy with all the risks of hyper-inflation and economic instability," Eaton says. "On the contrary they prefer to have steady, well-implemented growth."

Hanoi's social set is being served cocktails on the balcony of the city's majestic but severely worn opera house. "The recent decision of the Clinton Administration in lifting the US embargo signals the beginning of a dramatically exciting period for Vietnam," says the man from Baker and McKenzie, the big US-based law firm. A giant string of firecrackers is lit to mark the opening of the company's new office. Vietnamese like things opening with a big bang.

Vietnam will take at least 10 years just to build the roads, ports, telecommunications and other infrastructure needed to meet the basic demands of an emerging economy.

The Government is looking for direct foreign investment of $US12 billion to $15 billion by 2000 to sustain the upgrading of infrastructure and industrialisation. Observers doubt it will attract anywhere near that amount.

At the same time the country will have to develop an effective legal structure. Companies are busily signing joint venture deals with little guarantee of legal protection if things do not work out with their Vietnamese partners, which is often the case.

Lindsay Murdoch,
Sydney Morning Herald, 26 March1994

Questions

1 Contrast the experiences of Lac Long and Thanh Hoang Nguyen.
2 Outline the improvements in the Vietnamese economy.
3 'The country is at a turning point.' How? What is it?
4 What are the main problems that Vietnam has to overcome to develop its economy?
5 Which social problems have developed with economic growth? Is this inevitable?

Dangers and problems

As Vietnam opens itself up to the international market it will have to deal with the social changes. Problems endemic in western culture like crime, corruption, rampant materialism, drug abuse, etc. will increasingly become issues for this one party dictatorship. How the Communist Party deals with these developments will decide its fate.

Other problems already besetting Vietnam include:

- an education system lacking facilities and with a narrow curriculum
- a major population shift from country areas to cities, which are already struggling to provide services
- a growing drug problem and AIDS epidemic
- growing inequalities between the country and the city and between the North and the South
- an overly complex and outdated legal system which hinders growth and investment
- widespread corruption and smuggling in all layers of the economy, especially the bureaucracy.

Source 10.2   A new enemy for Vietnam

Vietnam starts fight against lethal new foe

Beside the putrid Saigon River, a man in his 20s wearing wrap-around sunglasses draws brownish opium into a needle from a biscuit tin at his feet before methodically injecting a succession of customers.

Up to 100 people a day come to see the Needleman at his shooting gallery a few streets from the downtown building boom of Vietnam's southern city: a woman in her 20s wearing a baseball cap squats so the needle can be manoeuvred into a well-used sore at the base of her neck; a wrinkled old man shuffles forward and gets his fix in each of his pocky arms; a boy aged about 15 proffers the back of his hand.

Twenty years after winning the war, Vietnam's aging communist leaders face a grave new danger as the country emerges from economic isolation.

Vietnam is Asia's new frontier for AIDS, with the multiple use of needles by drug pushers identified as one of the main causes of a surge in infections.

Health officials and other experts in Vietnam fear that the disease will soon spread rapidly through the population, as it did in the late 1980s in neighbouring Thailand.

Vietnam's National AIDS Committee has warned in a report that if current trends continue, as many as 500,000 adult Vietnamese could be infected with HIV in five years.

In this prudish country, where prostitution and drug-use are considered serious crimes, the Government has approved a revolutionary campaign to promote safe sex and awareness of the danger of spreading AIDS, particularly through repeated use of needles.

The committee's report said: "The Government of Vietnam has decided that it is now the time to act because there is still a possibility to curb the rapid spread of HIV, thereby preventing many thousands of young women, men and children from becoming infected."

The Interior Ministry estimates there are about 300,000 prostitutes and 120,000 drug users who use needles. The number of prostitutes is equal to estimates for Thailand, long regarded as Asia's most decadent country.

Mr Robert Bennoun, an Australian social worker who is a project manager for the Save the Children Fund, said: "The problem is daunting. But I feel cautiously optimistic about the Government's response so far . . . the Vietnamese are not trying to hide the problem as other countries have done. They are doers, not just talkers."

Vietnam's isolation since the end of the war in 1975 and the lack of rigorous testing for HIV led to assumptions the country had a low rate of infection.

But startling evidence emerged last year that the recent opening of the country to outsiders has brought social change which is fuelling its spread, including a dramatic increase in sexual activity and drug use associated with higher wages for some but worsening poverty for others who now have to fend for themselves.

"We have seen the increasing exploitation of vulnerable groups of people, including street and disadvantaged young children," Mr Bennoun said.

Ms Barbara Franklin, an American who last year studied AIDS in Vietnam for Care International, says Vietnam now is in much the same situation as Thailand was in 1988, before HIV spread from drug users and prostitutes to the population over three years.

"Vietnam has vanquished many powerful enemies in the past," she said. "But AIDS is a new kind of enemy."

Lindsay Murdoch,
Sydney Morning Herald, 7 March 1994

Questions

1 How large are the problems of drugs and prostitution in Vietnam?
2 Why have these problems surfaced only recently?
3 What is the Vietnamese government's response and why is Robert Bennoun 'cautiously optimistic' about it?
5 What other social changes and problems will Vietnam face because of the opening up of the country?

CAMBODIA AFTER 1979

Despite Vietnam's continuing economic woes, Cambodia has been the most troubled nation in Indochina in the 1980s and 1990s. It has remained at war since the Vietnamese invasion in 1978. Up to 1991, when a peace accord was signed, Cambodian government troops fought against a resistance comprised of three groups: the Khmer Rouge (the ex-governing party of Democratic Kampuchea led officially by Khieu Samphan), the Khmer People's National Liberation Front (led by former Prime Minister Son Sann) and a group centred around Prince Sihanouk and his son, Prince Ranariddh. At the time of publication, fighting continues between a new Cambodia government and the Khmer Rouge, which refuses to join the peace process or to lay down its weapons.

Fear of Khmer Rouge

Most Cambodians are terrified by the prospect of a Khmer Rouge return to power. Before the Vietnamese withdrew, this frightening rhyme was often seen on village walls:

> When you eat from a small pot;
> Remember the big pot.
> When you wear a flowery silk sampot
> Don't forget the thick black material you once wore.
> When the Vietnamese are gone,
> Each pit will hold one hundred corpses.

Cambodians understand the big pot and the thick black material as referring to the time of the Khmer Rouge, when everyone ate the same food and wore the same plain clothing. The message is that if the Khmer Rouge return, so will the genocide of the past, when mass graves were needed to bury all the dead.

Cambodia has never recovered from the damage done by the Khmer Rouge. In their mad regime they destroyed almost all of the infrastructure of a modern industrial state; or all that remained after the terrible destruction of the civil war and the US's bombing raids. Cambodia experienced terrible famine in the years immediately after 1979 and has continued to struggle economically. Tragically for Cambodia, when the Vietnamese invaded and installed the pro-Vietnamese Hun Sen government, Cambodia was also isolated from the world community and desperately needed aid. Heng Samrin and Hun Sen's government did make some progress in improving education and health and in rebuilding some of the infrastructure destroyed.

Cambodia's leaders, like the other Indochinese governments, were forced to move towards a more open economy. In the late 1980s, Vice Prime Minister Kong Sam-ol said, 'We are making progress but it's so painfully slow . . . We worry that Pol Pot could return and send us back to the countryside.'[4]

Heavily armed Khmer Rouge guerrillas in the 1980s. Who were they fighting then?

The withdrawal of the Vietnamese

In September 1989 the last Vietnamese occupation forces withdrew from Cambodia. The occupation had become far too expensive in a number of ways for a nation undergoing its own traumas. As the Cold War was coming to an end, Vietnam needed to look to better relations with China and the US. And Vietnam simply could no longer afford the financial cost, or the cost in blood of staying in Cambodia. Vietnam suffered over 115 000 killed or wounded during the occupation of Cambodia.

A new Cambodia?

In 1989 a peace proposal developed by Australia's Foreign Affairs Minister Gareth Evans was put forward. The plan was to have national elections supervised by a United Nations force. Cambodia in the meantime would be governed by a neutral coalition, a Supreme National Council where all four factions were represented. Despite many difficulties, the plan was eventually approved by all factions in 1991.

In October 1993, elections were held, a new constitution was adopted and the monarchy (King Sihanouk) was restored to Cambodia. The election result was a victory for the royalist party, FUNCINPEC (the National United Front for an Independent, Neutral, Peaceful and Cooperative Cambodia) led by Sihanouk's son Prince Ranariddh, who became First Prime Minister. Hun Sen became Second Prime Minister.

The future

The dreaded Khmer Rouge stand in the road of peace in Cambodia today. In 1992 they refused to abide by the terms of the peace agreement that the four factions had signed. They boycotted the national elections and have continued to wage a guerrilla war against the new government. The election of the new national government in 1993 and the ending of the trade embargo against Vietnam should enhance prospects for the Cambodian economy. But a complete cessation of hostilities is necessary for Cambodia to reconstruct its broken society.

Source 10.3   The problem of the Khmer Rouge

Khmer ambush hits Evans's noble peace plan

There was a time when Gareth Evans could have been a contender for the Nobel Peace Prize. Stranger people have received one — Henry Kissinger for starters — but Evans's chances are fading fast with the unravelling of the peace plan he helped broker in Cambodia.

As Australian Foreign Minister, Evans took a leading role in a United Nations-sponsored peace plan that was supposed to disarm the butcherly Khmer Rouge guerrilla forces and turn them into a normal part of the Cambodian political process.

Evans was widely tipped to be rewarded with a Nobel Prize for his efforts in Cambodia following the 1989 withdrawal of the Vietnamese forces which had ousted the Khmer Rouge leader, Pol Pot, from power in 1978.

Although the Vietnamese had forced Pol Pot to retreat from the capital Phnom Penh, he still managed to control about a third of Cambodia.

The peace plan promoted by Evans led to UN-supervised elections in May last year, but the bloodshed within Cambodia shows no signs of stopping.

The UN idea was that the Khmer Rouge were supposed to surrender their arms and participate in the election. They did neither and, despite defections and an alleged loss of morale, now seem in a position to expand the amount of territory they hold.

Their resilience was shown earlier this month when they re-took Pailin, the town at the centre of a lucrative gem and timber trade, after it had been briefly captured by the Cambodian Army.

As a result, Evans is now saying that Australia may have to give weapons and training to the Cambodian Army to bolster its chances of keeping the Khmer Rouge at bay.

It is all a long way from the diplomatic triumph he was supposed to have achieved with the culmination of the elections only 12 months ago.

Part of Evans's problem is that Australian foreign policy is now entirely dominated by trade issues — his department has even been merged with the old Trade Department.

Nothing is supposed to be said or done which might upset our trading partners, especially Asian "tigers" such as Thailand.

Yet most observers believe the Khmer Rouge forces can only survive with the active cross-border support of the Thai military and business. The Thais continue to supply arms and sanctuary to Pol Pot's forces in return for access to the gems and timber centred on the Khmer Rouge-controlled town of Pailin.

The Thai Government has even let a leading Pol Pot supporter, Khieu Samphan, cross the border on a Khmer Rouge diplomatic passport.

Admittedly, the Thai Government could have trouble getting its corrupt generals to stop dealing with Pol Pot, but so far Australia and other governments can hardly be said to have made a concerted effort to ensure a crackdown.

One of the reasons stems from a reluctance to suggest that an Asian "tiger" should do anything that gets in the way of trade, even trade with such a murderous bunch as the Khmer Rouge.

There is the additional problem of the previous refusal of the US and China to distance themselves from Pol Pot, despite his responsibility for slaughtering more than a million people in the Cambodian "Killing Fields".

For many years, US leaders were happy to see Pol Pot survive as a thorn in the side of the Vietnamese who'd humiliated them during the Indo-China war.

Under strong pressure from US business interests anxious to resume trade with Vietnam, the Clinton Administration is now restoring relations with Hanoi.

However, any attempt to start arming the Cambodian Government, or pressuring the Thais to cut off support for Pol Pot, is likely to run into stiff opposition in Washington.

Clinton is already under heavy criticism for letting human rights concerns interfere with trade with Asia and is likely to tread softly on this particular issue.

The Chinese, who had launched an unsuccessful military attack on Vietnam in 1979, continued to supply arms to Pol Pot until at least 1990 in an effort to keep Hanoi off balance.

The Chinese leadership, which has won many plaudits in the West for introducing a free market while attempting to maintain dictatorial rule, has no interest in persuading the Thais to abandon Pol Pot.

Back when Evans was basking in praise for helping implement the UN peace plan, he angrily sneered at anyone who suggested that it was wrong to place any trust in Pol Pot.

But for the peace plan to have any hope of success it required Pol Pot to surrender his arms. His refusal to do so doomed the whole project to the failure which is now unfolding with yet more suffering for the Cambodian people.

The withdrawal of the 22,000 UN personnel who had supervised the process leading up to last May's election has left a deeply corrupt Cambodian Government headed by the gravely ill King Norodom Sihanouk.

Sihanouk had originally been overthrown by a US-backed coup in 1980 as part of the extension of the Vietnam War into Cambodia. The US-supported "strong man", Lon Nol, was supplanted in 1975 by Pol Pot who then subjected Cambodia to a four-year reign of terror before he was evicted from Phnom Penh by Vietnamese troops in December 1978.

The Vietnamese withdrawal in 1989 left an unstable situation in which Pol Pot and three other warring factions jostled for power amid continuing bloodshed.

Throughout the entire period, Sihanouk proved to be a weak and vacillating leader, constantly switching sides and hiding out in China and North Korea.

He is a thin reed on which to base claims to a Nobel Peace Prize.

Brian Toohey, *Sun-Herald*, 22 May 1994

Questions

1 Why was Evans a possible candidate for a Nobel Peace prize?
2 How and why is the peace plan failing?
3 What are the attitudes of Australian and US governments to Cambodia, Thailand and the Khmer Rouge?
4 What is the possible future for Cambodia, according to Toohey?

LAOS AFTER 1975

Unlike the two other nations of Indochina, the communist takeover of Laos was achieved without great bloodshed. The country's third coalition government in 20 years was set up in 1974 and peace between the Pathet Lao and the opposition was interrupted only by occasional clashes. The Pathet Lao had out-manoeuvred the chiefly right-wing opposition, who suffered from internal bickering and were unpopular because of their inefficient administration and corruption. In the end, the communists took over peacefully when most of the opposition fled the country, as communist armies moved towards the capitals of Vietnam and Cambodia.

Since 1975 Laos has experienced peace, apart from infrequent attacks by embittered refugees located on the border with Thailand. Yet approximately one tenth of the population, or about 300 000 Laotians, have fled to Thailand and then to Western nations. They have fled for various reasons — some to escape political repression (estimates vary but between 10 000 and 40 000 Laotians were sent to re-education camps after 1975), others to escape the grinding poverty or the strict controls of a communist society.

As in the rest of Indochina, Laos's communist government has introduced sweeping reforms designed to raise production levels and the standard of living. In 1985 local enterprises and managers were given the authority to make products of their own choice, to select staff and set salary levels. The way was made clear for foreign investment to enter the country. This latter change followed the collapse of the Soviet Union and the loss of Soviet aid. The reforms have led to modest economic improvements, especially in the big towns.

Laos has moved to closer relations with Thailand, Vietnam and China; the three nations that surround it. The Australian-built Friendship Bridge across the Mekong River from Laos to Thailand will help the developing relationship between those nations. In the 1990s, foreign businesses and money have begun to flow into Laos to take advantage of Laos's natural resources and her strategic position between two of the world's fastest growing economies, China and Thailand.

Laos will continue to have major problems for some time. The late Prime Minister, Kaysone Phomvihane, listed some of his country's problems in 1991. He said they included, 'a poor communications network, deteriorating education and health systems, . . . uncontrolled destruction of the country's forests, a cumbersome bureaucracy, a growing trade imbalance and rising budget deficit.'[5]

Laos is one of the poorest nations on the planet but there are encouraging possibilities for growth. Laos now exports hydroelectric power to Thailand (both of its dams are partly funded by Australia) and has valuable deposits of raw materials including gold, coal and iron ore and timber (Australian companies have already signed exploration agreements concerning these minerals). Tourism is also on the increase and Laos is perfectly placed to be the link between the booming economies of the South-East Asian region.

The Australian-built Friendship Bridge, the first road link between Laos and Thailand.

Source 10.4   A promising future for Laos?

Laos on the road to Gundagai

Thirty years ago, when the Kingdom of Laos boasted only 10 kilometres of paved road — a narrow strip of bitumen that went as far as the Foreign Minister's tennis court and then stopped — no-one spoke with much optimism about the future.

The nation was bogged down in an interminable civil war, largely fought out in the mountains, with rightists and leftists backed by their respective cold-war patrons. An air of somnolence and lassitude — not to mention a powdery white dust — hung over the Mekong River towns, of which Vientiane was the largest with 200,000 people.

Laos reeled from one crisis to another; President Kennedy spent more time worrying about the future of Laos than he ever did about Vietnam.

Too often, foreigners made light of it all. "The situation in Laos," a diplomat observed after yet another setback for the endearingly inept Forces Armée

Royale, "is critical but not serious". *Time* magazine told its readers that Laos was a land "where underdeveloped is an unwarranted compliment". Someone said there was less to Vientiane than meets the eye.

Today, Laos, which has just hosted a whistle-stop visit by the Australian Prime Minister, remains as underdeveloped as ever. Some of the problems stem from colonial neglect and some from 30 years of war. But there is more to it than that.

The leaders of the Communist Pathet Lao came to power in 1975, abolishing the monarchy and frightening away about a quarter of the population — including almost everyone with any skills or higher education.

After two decades of socialism, Laos remains one of the poorest nations in the world, with per capita income of about $A300. Senior officials earn $60 a month. About 85 per cent of the population is engaged in

agriculture — mostly at subsistence level. Three people in 10 are illiterate. There is no railway — the French built a station at Thakhek but never got around to laying any track — and the road system is atrocious.

Why, then, are people speaking of light at the end of the tunnel?

The first part of the answer has to do with domestic change.

The hard-line policies introduced by the Communists — including the closure of private business, the nationalisation of industry and the collectivisation of agriculture — which were known to have failed disastrously in the Soviet Union, China and Vietnam, brought the economy to near-collapse.

Chastened, the Government decided in 1985 to move away from a Soviet-style command economy and encourage foreign investment. That has led to modest but encouraging growth, most notably in the major towns.

Laos now boasts a modest textile industry — in 1992, garment exports overtook electricity and timber as the top export earner — and the country is increasingly open to foreign tourists.

Then there is the international dimension.

For 16 years, Communist Laos was as dependent on Soviet handouts as non-Communist Laos had been on Western handouts. The implosion of the Soviet Union in 1991 dealt a double blow: it not only shook the ideological certitude of local communist leaders (who raged impotently that the "imperialists" had brought the great Soviet Union down and warned that tiny Laos must be on its guard) but it triggered an abrupt loss of aid from Moscow, Laos's most important benefactor.

Countries like Australia, Sweden, France and Japan stepped up their aid transfers, as did international financial institutions. But the aid, while welcome, was never going to cover the shortfall.

As a result, Laos has moved to improve relations with its three most important neighbours — Thailand, China and Vietnam.

The people of Thailand and Laos are bound by ties of blood, language, culture, history and geography, but relations have often been strained. Many Thais look down on the Lao, whom they portray as "country cousins". There are, in fact, more ethnic Lao in north-east Thailand than there are in all Laos, where the Lao live along the river valleys, leaving equally numerous ethnic minorities in the mountains.

At the same time, Laos has sought better relations with the United States, which had turned it into the most heavily bombed nation in history.

Laos will never become an industrial dynamo. For one thing, it has only 4.4 million people. For another, transport costs are high, largely because Thailand has a habit of exploiting its position as Laos's major outlet to the sea.

But Laos does have other things going for it.

One is minerals and energy. Laos has two hydro-electric dams that generate power for export to Thailand — both are partly funded by Australia. More are on the way. An Australian company, Transfield, is developing the Nam Theum No 2 hydro-electric project, the largest single enterprise investment in Laos. The Tasmanian Hydro-Electric Commission has an agreement to develop three more hydro projects and transmission network.

Laos also has coal, gold, gemstones and iron ore. Once again, Australians are active: CRA Exploration and Normandy Poseidon have signed contracts to explore for minerals, including gold.

Another area targeted for development is agriculture and forestry. Thai timber companies have ripped the heart out of the old royal teak forests in Sayaboury Province, just as they have plundered the forests of Burma and Cambodia. But experts say that deforested areas can be planted with commercial timber.

Australia was one of the first countries to help Laos in this area: in the early 1970s, Canberra provided Laos with 500 000 river red gum saplings. While the eucalypts are no match for teak, they fill an urgent need for hardwood. What is more, the trees can be harvested in 30 years instead of 90 for teak.

Tourism is a third growth area, with arrivals reaching 80,000 in 1992, up from 2,000 only three years earlier. But some of the most ambitious proposals stem from Laos's unique position. Like the last piece in a brightly coloured regional jigsaw puzzle, Laos locks into place between the booming economies of southern China and Thailand. That may prove highly beneficial.

In 1866, the French dreamt of using the Mekong Rover as a "back door" to the supposed riches of Yunnan, a dream that foundered after a two-year expedition.

Today, the French colonial road system, especially sections of Route Nationale 13, which once linked Luang Prabang and Saigon (now Ho Chi Minh City), is being upgraded with assistance from the Asian Development Bank. China is completing roadworks in northern Laos.

By 1995 it will be possible to drive from Beijing to Singapore. The $42 million bridge over the Mekong, designed and built by Australians, will form a crucial link in the chain.

Most of this is promising. The people of Laos can expect a higher standard of living, with better education and health care.

But it is hard not to feel some concern about the future and a measure of regret at what may be lost if Laos throws itself open to the sort of "development-at-all-costs" philosophy that has taken hold in some other parts of Asia.

There is concern over damage to the environment, already suffering as a result of slash-and-burn agriculture, wartime bombing and the rapacious practices of Thai logging companies. There are also concerns over the spread of prostitution and AIDS.

Then there's the potential impact on Lao culture.

If it becomes possible to drive from Beijing to Singapore, then Laos, a charming Asian backwater, may be turned into a turnpike country, complete with service stations and McDonald's fast-food outlets.

Luang Prabang, the old royal city on the banks of the Mekong, with its saddle-roofed wats and graceful pirogues, may end up as a South-East Asian Gundagai.

David Jenkins,
Sydney Morning Herald, 9 April 1994

Questions

1 What problems does Laos have today?
2 How has the Lao communist government moved to solve the problems?
3 What advantages does Laos have?
4 What concerns are there for the future?
5 Can you explain the title?

CONSEQUENCES OF THE CONFLICTS

It is not possible to list all the consequences of the terrible and long-lasting wars that have bedevilled Indochina over the last 45 years. It is possible only to give a summary of some of the consequences:

For Indochina

- Millions of Indochinese were killed, wounded or made homeless.
- Over 2 million Indochinese have become refugees.
- Vietnam, Cambodia and Laos became communist nations.
- Vietnam became a unified nation.
- Vietnam was admitted to the United Nations in 1976.
- Enormous economic damage throughout Indochina was caused by ground fighting and bombing.
- Hostility developed between Vietnam and China as a result of the Indochinese conflicts.
- Vietnamese dominance in Indochina increased (this has changed with the Vietnamese withdrawal from Cambodia and the end of the Cold War).
- Continuing hostility from the US (up until 1994), which refused to offer financial aid or to recognise Vietnam diplomatically.
- Vietnam became closely allied with the USSR, which became the nation's biggest supplier of aid. This changed in the late 1980s.

For the United States

- The US's humiliation in Indochina made US governments less likely to send troops overseas to fight aggression. After the Gulf War in 1991, US President Bush spoke of beating 'the Vietnam syndrome once and for all'.
- A decline in American prestige (in the short term) as the US was viewed as being less able and less likely to defend its allies overseas.
- A total of 56 962 US soldiers were killed and over 270 000 were wounded.
- Many Americans were disillusioned by their government's handling of the war.
- Thousands of embittered and troubled Vietnam veterans had problems re-establishing their lives and received no public recognition nor honour for their service.
- The US spent $30 000 million approximately towards the war each year after 1965. As a result domestic programs were short of funds, especially those for the relief of poverty.

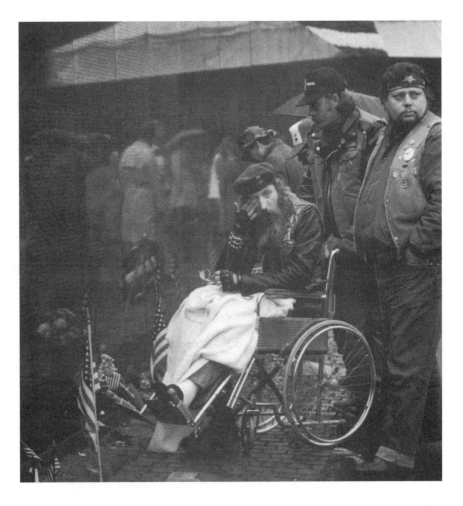

Vietnam veterans next to the Vietnam War Memorial in Washington DC. The memorial consists of two granite walls with the names of all the US soldiers killed or missing in the Vietnam War. The walls form the shape of a 'V'.

THE FUTURE?

The future is unclear for the countries of Indochina. If the region can be completely returned to peace and international aid flows generously, and trade with other nations continues to develop, then Indochina should take its place amongst the rapidly developing economies of Asia. Considering the suffering of the last 50 years, Indochina deserves that much.

Activities

Key words

Define these important terms:

international financial aid	occupation	Soviet expansionism
dissent	genocide	Cold War
embargo	Doi Moi	free market socialism
infrastructure	FUNCINPEC	

Research topics

1 The economies of Indochina today.
2 Prince Ranariddh and FUNCINPEC.
3 Doi Moi.
4 Australian involvement in Indochina today.

What if you were . . .?

1 You are President Thieu of South Vietnam. Write an excerpt from your memoirs about the last days of South Vietnam.
2 You are a leader of an Indochinese nation. Describe your hopes and fears for the future.

Review questions

1 Describe the end of the Vietnam War.
2 What have been the consequences of the conflicts for the nations of Indochina?
3 Why were the Indochinese countries isolated after the war?
4 Why did the Vietnamese initiate the policy of Doi Moi? What has it meant?
5 Examine the history of Cambodia and Laos since 1979.
6 What are the consequences of the conflicts in Indochina for the US and Australia?
7 What do you think lies ahead for Indochina?

What would you say?

1 A Vietnamese government minister defending his government's record since 1975.
2 A Cambodian leader appealing to the Khmer Rouge for an end to the civil war.

NOTES

Chapter 1
1 Adapted from P. Bennoun *et al., the Peoples from Indo-China*, p. 33.
2 Adapted from Bennoun, p. 64.
3 Adapted from Bennoun, p. 79.
4 C. Leinster, 'Vietnam Revisited: Turn to the Right?', in *Fortune*, 1 August 1988, p.22.
5 M. Hiebert, 'The toughest battle', in *Far Eastern Economic Review*, 27 April 1989, p. 68.
6 James Pringle, 'Pressures for peace', in *Far Eastern Economic Review*, 25 February 1988, p. 31.
7 Louise Williams, 'Indochina on brink of huge growth', *Sydney Morning Herald*, 18 December 1993, p. 14.
8 Tony Wright, 'Veterans to get Viet memorial, says PM', *Sydney Morning Herald*, 14 April 1994, p.5.

Chapter 2
1 J.A. Hobson, *Imperialism*, 1902.
2 S. Karnow, *Vietnam: A History*, p. 118.
3 Karnow, p. 112.
4 Karnow, p. 107.

Chapter 3
1 A. Cole (ed.), *Conflict in Indochina and International Repercussions*, p. 17.
2 D.J. Sagar, *Major Political Events in Indochina, 1945–90, Facts on File*, p. 187.
3 Source unknown.
4 E. O'Ballance, *The Indo-China War 1945–54, A Study in Guerrilla Warfare*, p. 19.
5 M. Maclear, Vietnam: *The Ten Thousand Day War*, pp. 5–6.

Chapter 4
1 Sagar, pp. 186–7.
2 P.A. Poole, *Eight Presidents and Indochina*, p. 44.
3 Karnow, p. 226.
4 N. Sheehan, *A Bright Shining Lie*, p. 191.
5 Sagar, p. 191.
6 A. Santoli, *To Bear Any Burden*, (ix)
7 Poole.

Chapter 5
1 Karnow, p. 320.
2 Maclear, p. 127.
3 Karnow, p. 426.
4 G. Spenceley, *A World in Shadow*, p. 73.

5 Spenceley, p. 73.
6 Santoli, p. 175.

Chapter 6
1 Maclear, p. 299.
2 Quoted in J. Crew and D. Wright, *Revolution in the Modern World*, p. 199.
3 Maclear, p. 279.
4 Maclear, p. 279.

Chapter 7
1 Karnow, p. 467.

Chapter 8
1 The Committee of Concerned Asian Scholars, *The Indochina Story*, p. 56.
2 Economist Intelligence Unit, *Quarterly Economic Report*, Annual Supplement, 1975.
3 Economist Intelligence Unit, *Quarterly Economic Report*, Annual Supplement, 1975.
4 Peter Stalker, '*The road to Kampuchea*' in *New Internationalist*, No. 84, p.9.
5 S. Warshaw, *South East Asia Emerges*, p. 153.
6 The Committee of Concerned Asian Scholars, p. 44.

Chapter 9
1 Spenceley, p. 13.
2 Spenceley, p. 72.
3 US Gallup Polls
4 D. Stewart (ed.), *Case Studies in Australian History*, p. 222.
5 Australian Gallup Polls
6 Maclear, p. 238.

Chapter 10
1 Karnow, pp. 27–8
2 T. R. Caldwell, 'Propaganda and contemporary Asian military thinking: The Sino and Vietnamese War of 1979', in *Asian Teachers Association Bulletin*, September 1982, p. 29.
3 Caldwell, *Asian Teachers Association Bulletin*, September 1982, p. 29.
4 In 'Goodbye to Cambodia', by Ron Morean, *Newsweek*, 19 July 1988, p. 109.
5 David Jenkins, 'Laos on the Road to Gundagai', *Sydney Morning Herald*, 9 April 1994.

CAST OF CHARACTERS

Bao Dai (1913 –) The last Emperor of Vietnam, 1925–45, Head of State in South Vietnam until deposed in a referendum by Diem in 1955. Left Vietnam for France.

Duong Van Minh (1916 –) Called 'Big Minh', one of the coup leaders against Diem, 1963. Head of State of South Vietnam, January to October 1964. As President he surrendered to communist forces in April 1975. Allowed to emigrate to France in 1983.

Ho Chi Minh (1890–69) Founder of Indochinese Communist Party (1930) and Vietminh (1941). Led North Vietnam until his death.

Holt, Harold (1908–67) Australian Prime Minister, 1966–67. Leader of the Liberal Party after the retirement of Menzies. Increased Australian involvement in Vietnam. Famous for saying 'All the way with LBJ'.

Johnson, Lyndon Baines (1908–73) Became US President after assassination of Kennedy, 22 November 1963, re-elected in November 1964. Escalated Vietnam War, refused to seek re-election and retired from political life, 1969.

Kennedy, John Fitzgerald (1917–63) Became President in January 1961 after defeating Republican, Richard Nixon. Increased military aid and the number of US advisers in South Vietnam, assassinated 22 November 1963.

Kissinger, Henry (1923–) Member of National Security Council from 1968 and US Secretary of State 1973–77, architect of detente with USSR and China. Negotiated 1973 cease-fire in Vietnam War.

Lon Nol, General (1913–85) Commander-in-Chief of Armed Forces under Sihanouk, leader of the coup which ousted Sihanouk in 1970, President of Khmer Republic from 1972 until overthrow in April 1975. Left Cambodia for exile in the US.

McNamara, Robert (1916–) US Secretary of Defence, 1961 to February 1968 under Kennedy and Johnson. Became disillusioned with the war and resigned February 1968. Commissioned the Pentagon Papers. Head of the World Bank 1968–81.

Menzies, Sir Robert (1894–1978) Prime Minister of Australia for record term, 1949–66. Committed Australian troops to South Vietnam, 1965. Retired from politics in 1966.

Ngo Dinh Diem (1901–63) Minister of the Interior under Bao Dai in the 1930s, went into exile 1945. President of US-backed South Vietnam from 1954 until his overthrow and murder in the November 1963 coup.

Ngo Dinh Nhu (1910–63) Brother of Ngo Dinh Diem. Head of South Vietnamese security forces. Also assassinated, November 1963.

Nguyen Cao Ky (1930–) Air Vice Marshal, anti-communist commander of South Vietnamese Air Force from 1963, Premier of South Vietnam (1965–67), Vice President (1967–71). Fled to US in April 1975.

Nguyen Van Thieu (1923–) A leader in the coup against Diem 1963. President of US-backed South Vietnam 1967–1973. Opposed the signing of the Paris Peace Agreement. Left Vietnam April 1975. Settled in Britain.

Nixon, Richard Milhous (1913–94) US Vice President, 1953–61. Lost 1960 presidential elections to Kennedy. Elected President 1968, ordered 'secret bombing' of Cambodia 1969, introduced Vietnamisation after 1969. Resigned 1974 because of the Watergate scandal.

Pol Pot also called Saloth Sar (1928–) Joined the anti-French resistance in the 1940s and the Cambodian Communist Party in 1946. Studied in Paris 1949–53 then returned to Cambodia and taught in a private school. From 1963 concentrated on building up the Communist Party and became its secretary. In 1976 became Prime Minister of the Khmer Rouge government which was ousted in 1979.

Ranariddh, Prince (1944–) The second oldest son of King Sihanouk. One of Cambodia's two Prime Ministers and leader of FUNCINPEC, half of the country's ruling coalition.

Rusk, Dean (1909–) US Secretary of State under Kennedy and Johnson, 1961–69, a strong 'hawk' (supporter of the Vietnam War). Became Professor of International Law at the University of Georgia.

Sen, Hun (1951–) In 1994, the second of Cambodia's Prime Ministers and leader of the Cambodian People's Party. Was elected Premier of Cambodia in 1985 and a leading member of the government up to the elections in 1993. In the mid-1970s was a commander in the Khmer Rouge army but fled to Vietnam and fought with the Vietnamese to oust Pol Pot in 1979.

Sihanouk, Norodom (1922–) King of Cambodia, 1941–55, political head of Cambodia, 1955–70, ousted by Lon Nol's coup. Campaigned with the Khmer Rouge against Lon Nol but arrested by Pol Pot when communists took power. From 1979 a leading member of the Cambodian resistance to the government of Heng Samrin and Hun Sen. Restored to the throne in October 1993 after serving as Head of State from 1990 as part of the UN peace plan.

Souvanna Phouma, Prince (1901–84) Neutralist leader of Laos and Prime Minister for most of the period between independence in 1953 and communist victory in 1975. As leader of the neutralist faction involved in the struggle against the Pathet Lao and the Rightists under Phoumi Nosavan.

Souvanouvong, Prince (1909–) Half-brother of Souvanna Phouma. After World War II he opposed French rule and was foreign minister in a Free Lao exile government in Thailand, 1947–48. Helped to form the Pathet Lao in 1950. A member of coalition governments during the civil war, he became President of Laos when the communists were victorious.

Vo Nguyen Giap, General (1912–) Co-founder of Vietminh in 1941, Commander-in-Chief of Vietminh armed forces, conqueror at Dien Bien Phu, 1954, made Defence Minister of Vietnam in 1976.

Westmoreland, William (1914–) US General, Military Commander in South Vietnam 1964–68, oversaw the buildup of US forces after 1965. Said in late 1967 that victory was in sight ('the end begins to come into view').

Whitlam, Edward Gough (1916–) Australian Prime Minister, 1972–75. Leader of the Labor Party which ended conscription and Australian involvement in Vietnam on coming to office.

GLOSSARY

Agent Orange The most common defoliant used in Vietnam. Vietnam Veteran organisations maintain that its use has caused disease and birth defects amongst veterans and their children.

ARVN Army of the Republic of Vietnam (South)

CIA The Central Intelligence Agency is responsible for protecting the interests of the US abroad.

Coup d'etat An armed rebellion or revolt against the existing government.

Communism A political system characterised by a one-party government and a command economy where the government owns the means of production.

Capitalism A political system usually characterised by free elections. Economically, private individuals own the bulk of the means of production.

Containment The foreign policy of the US as enunciated by President Truman after World War II which indicated the need to stop the spread of communism.

CPP Cambodian People's Party, political wing of the 1980s communist government. Has now renounced communist theory.

Defoliation Chemical warfare aimed at destroying or reducing plant cover and food availability for the enemy.

DMZ Demilitarised zone, the piece of land between North and South Vietnam where no military hardware was allowed.

Domino theory Part of Cold War philosophy which stated that if one country fell to the communists then surrounding countries would also fall.

Doves American opponents of the Vietnam War.

DRV Democratic Republic of Vietnam (North).

Embargo A restriction of something, trade in the case of Vietnam.

Forward Defence Australian defence policy which stated that it was necessary to fight an enemy overseas before Australia itself became threatened.

Fragging The wounding or murder of officers by their men because the officers were intent on combat. The term comes from the weapon that was often used, the fragmentation grenade.

FUNK National United Front of Kampuchea. A resistance group opposed to the Khmer republic after 1970.

FUNCINPEC Cambodian royalist political party which received the most votes in 1993 elections. Headed by King Sihanouk's son and First Prime Minister, Prince Ranariddh.

Hawks American supporters of the Vietnam War.

Indochina Literally the region between India and China. Consists of the countries of Vietnam, Cambodia and Laos (although some definitions also include Burma, Thailand and Malaya).

Khmer Rouge The Cambodian Communist Party which took power in 1975 and renamed the country Democratic Kampuchea.

National Service Conscription into the armed services.

NLF National Liberation Front.

NVA North Vietnamese Army.

Pacification Attempts to eliminate Vietcong influence in the villages of South Vietnam and to win over the peasantry to the South Vietnamese Government.

Pathet Lao   Communist-led guerrilla army and independence movement of Laos.

Pentagon Papers   US Defense Department study into American involvement in Vietnam 1945–68.

Refugees   People forced to leave their countries because of persecution, often political or religious. Many refugees are seeking better economic conditions.

Re-education camps   After the communist victories, authorities in Vietnam and Laos sent thousands of their countrymen to these camps to be instructed in communist theory and obedience to the government.

RVN   Republic of Vietnam (South).

Tet   Vietnamese New Year. In 1968 the communists launched an offensive at this time to achieve a surprise attack.

Tonkin Resolution   1964 resolution of the US Congress which gave the President wide powers to conduct the war in Vietnam.

Vietcong   Communist-led guerrilla army and political movement whose aim was to topple the South Vietnamese government.

Vietminh   Communist-led movement for independence in Vietnam founded by Ho Chi Minh in 1940.

Watergate   Political scandal which forced President Nixon to resign in 1974. Named after the building housing the offices of the Democratic Party, which was broken into by Nixon's supporters in 1972.

UNTAC   The United Nation's Transitional Authority in Cambodia which was to oversee the peace process.

DOCUMENTARIES AND FILMS

Four Hours at My Lai, Yorkshire Television, 1988

Frontline, Neil Davis

The Prince and the Prophecy, James Gerrand, 1989

Vietnam: A Television History

Vietnam: The 10 000 Day War

Long Tan — The True Story

Apocalypse Now

Coming Home

Full Metal Jacket

Platoon

The Deerhunter

Dear America

The Odd Angry Shot

Good Morning Vietnam

The Killing Fields

Born on the Fourth of July

BIBLIOGRAPHY

Adams, N. S., and McCoy, A. W., *Laos: War and Revolution*, Harper & Row, New York, 1970.

Barnes, J., *The Pictorial History of the Vietnam War*, Bison Books, London, 1988.

Bennoun, P., Bennoun, R., and Kelly, P., *The Peoples From Indo-China*, Hodja Educational, Richmond (Vic.), 1984.

Bonds, Ray (ed.), *The Vietnam War: The illustrated history of the conflict in Southeast Asia*, Lansdowne Press, London, 1983.

Brodie, S., *Tilting at Dominoes: Australia and the Vietnam War*, Child and Associates, Sydney, 1987.

Browne, Malcolm W., *The New Face of War*, Cassell, London, 1965.

Buchan, A., *The USA*, Oxford University Press, London, 1963.

Buss, C.A., *Southeast Asia and the World Today*, D. Van Nostrand, New Jersey, 1958.

Caldwell, T.R., 'Propaganda and contemporary Asian military thinking: The Sino and Vietnamese War of 1979' in *Asian Teachers Association Bulletin*, September, 1982.

Cannon J., Clarke, B., and Smuga, G., *The Contemporary World: Conflict or Co-operation?*, Oliver & Boyd, Edinburgh, 1979.

Cole, Allan B., (ed.), *Conflict in Indo-China and International Repercussions*, Cornell University Press, New York, 1956.

Crew, J., and Wright, D., *Revolution in the Modern World*, University of New England, Armidale, 1980.

Economist Intelligence Unit, *Quarterly Economic Report*, Annual Supplement 1975.

Edwards, Richard, *The Vietnam War*, Wayland, England, 1986.

Elliott, B. J., *World Society in the Twentieth Century*, Hulton Education, London, 1973.

Esper, George & The Associated Press, *The Eyewitness History of the Vietnam War*, 1961–75, Villard, New York, 1983.

Fincher, E. B., *The Vietnam War*, Franklin Watts, New York, 1980.

Graff, E., and Hammond H. E., *Southeast Asia: History, Culture, People*, Globe Books, New York, 1981.

Hiebert, M., 'Less corruption in store', in *Far Eastern Economic Review*, 28 April 1988.

Hiebert, M., 'The toughest battle', in *Far Eastern Economic Review*, 27 April 1989.

Hobson, J. A., *Imperialism*, 1902

Honey, P. J., *Genesis of a Tragedy*, Ernest Benn Ltd, London, 1968.

Houghton, G., and Wakefield, J., *Laos & Kampuchea*, Macmillan, Australia, 1988.

Isaacs, A., Hardy, G., and Brown, M., *Pawns of War: Cambodia and Laos*, Boston Publishing Co., Boston, 1987.

Karnow, Stanley, *Vietnam: A History*, Penguin, Harmondsworth, England, 1984.

Kennedy, B., and Kennedy, B., *Vietnam: A Reunited Country*, Longman Cheshire, Melbourne, 1980.

Kiernan, Ben, *How Pol Pot Came to Power*, Verso, London, 1985.

Kiernan, Ben, 'Roots of genocide', in *Teaching History*, January 1990.

Lawson, Don, *The War in Vietnam*, Franklin Watts, New York, 1981.

Leinster, C., 'Vietnam Revisited: Turn to the Right?' in *Fortune*, 1 August 1988.

Lunn, Hugh, *Vietnam: A Reporter's War*, University of Queensland Press, St Lucia, 1985.

Maclear, Michael, *Vietnam: The Ten Thousand Day War*, Thames Methuen, London, 1981.

McGarvey, Patrick J. (Intro.), *Visions of Victory: Selected Vietnamese Communist Military Writings, 1964–1968*, Stanford University, California, 1969.

Morean, Ron, 'Goodbye to Cambodia' in *Newsweek*, 19 July 1988.

Newman, Bernard, *Let's Visit Vietnam*, Burke Publishing, London, 1983.

O'Ballance, E., *The Indo-China War 1945–54, A Study in Guerrilla Warfare*, Faber & Faber, London, 1964.

O'Callaghan, D. B., *The United States since 1945*, Longman, Essex, England, 1983.

Osaba, M. (Transl.), 'A chance for the Khmer people to survive', in *Development News Digest*, December 1989.

Pringle, James, 'Pressures for peace', in *Far Eastern Economic Review*, 25 February 1988.

Rintoul, Stuart, *Ashes of Vietnam: Australian Voices*, Mandarin/Octopus Publishing Group, Port Melbourne, 1989.

Sagar, D. J., *Major Political Events in Indochina, 1945–90, Facts on File*, 1991, Oxford, UK, 1991.

Santoli, A., *To Bear Any Burden*, E. P. Dutton, New York, 1985.

Sheehan, Neil, *A Bright Shining Lie*, Jonathan Cape, London, 1989.

Spenceley, Geoff, *A World in Shadow*, Oxford University Press, Melbourne 1989.

Stalker, Peter, 'The road to Kampuchea', in *New Internationalist*, No. 84.

Stewart, David (Ed.), *Case Studies in Australian History*, Heinemann Educational, Richmond (Vic.), 1986.

Summerfield, G. (Ed.), *Voices: The third book*, Penguin, Hardmondsworth, England, 1968.

The Committee of Concerned Asian Scholars, *The Indochina Story: A Fully Documented Account*, Pantheon Books, New York, 1970.

Tuchman, Barbara W., *The March of Folly*, Michael Joseph, London, 1984.

von der Mehden, F. R., *South-East Asia, 1930–1970*, Thames and Hudson, London, 1974.

Warshaw, S., *South East Asia Emerges*, Diablo Press, California, 1975.

White, G., *America: From New World to World Power*, Longman Cheshire, Melbourne, 1986.

Further Reading

Bowden, Tim, *One Crowded Hour*, Collins, Sydney, 1987.

Braestrup, P. (Ed.), *Vietnam as History*, University Press of America, Washington, 1984.

Burstall, Terry, *The Soldiers' Story*, University of Queensland Press, St Lucia, 1986.

Buttinger, Joseph, *Vietnam: The Unforgettable Tragedy*, Horizon, New York, 1977.

Caldwell, Malcolm, and Tan, Lek, *Cambodia in the Southeast Asian War*, Monthly Review Press, New York, 1973.

Charlton, Michael, and Moncrieff, Anthony, *Many Reasons Why, The American Involvement in Vietnam*, Scolar Press, London, 1978.

Davidson, Phillip B., *Vietnam at War, The History: 1946–75*, Presidio Press, USA, 1988.

Etcheson, Craig, *The Rise and Demise of Democratic Kampuchea*, Westview Press, Colorado, 1984.

Hammer, Richard, *One Morning in the War, The Tragedy at Pinkville*, Rupert Hart-Davis, London, 1970.

Higgins, Hugh, *Vietnam*, Heinemann, London, 1982.

King, Peter (Ed.), *Australia's Vietnam*, Allen & Unwin, Sydney, 1983.

McAuley, Lex, *The Battle of Long Tan*, Arrow, London, 1987.

Osborne, Milton, *Before Kampuchea: Preludes to Tragedy*, Allen & Unwin, Sydney, 1979.

Pentagon Papers, Volumes I–IV, Beacon Press, Boston, 1971–72.

Poole, P. A., *Eight Presidents and Indochina*, Robert E. Krieger Publishing, New York, 1978.

Rowe, John, *Vietnam, the Australian Experience*, Time Life, Sydney, 1987.

Shawcross, William, *Sideshow: Kissinger, Nixon and The Destruction of Cambodia*, André Deutsch, London, 1979.

Sheldon, Walter, *Tigers in the Rice*, Crowell-Collier Press, London, 1969.

Thee, Marek, *Notes of a Witness: Laos and the Second Indochinese War*, Random House, New York, 1973.

The Herald in the Classroom, The Vietnam War, Sydney Morning Herald.

Vo Nguyen Giap, *The Military Art of People's War*, Monthly Press Review, New York, 1970.

INDEX

Agent Orange   96, 14–15
air war   68, 81, 86–7, 95–6, 106,
   113–14
Angkor, Kingdom of   27
anti-war movement   80, 116
   arguments against   117
   effects   126–7
   in Australia   123–6
   in the USA   118–21
Army of the Republic of Vietnam
   (ARVN)   60
   stengths and weaknesses   92
   Vietnamisation   81
Association of South–East Asian
   Nations (ASEAN)   21
Australia
   attitude to Vietnam today   21
   combat troops   71
   extent of commitment   71–3
   opposition at home   73, 123–6
   reason for involvement   70
   withdrawal   81
Bao Dai   33, 40, 52
Binh Xuyen   52–4
booby traps   95
Buddhist crisis   62
Cairns, Jim   126
Calley, William   122
Calwell, Arthur   71
Cambodia
   1970 coup   82, 105
   after 1979   136–8
   civil war   105–7
   early history   26–8
   French rule   31, 103
   French takeover   31, 104
   geography   3
   independence   47, 104
   Khmer Rouge takeover   107–8
   peace plan   10, 110, 137
   relations with USA   105
   today   4, 10
   WWII   38, 103–4

Cao Dai   52–3
capitalism   22
Catholicism   30
China, People's Republic of
   aid to North Vietnam   42, 68
   attitude towards Vietnam today
      20
   Chinese Revolution   33, 45
   influence in Vietnam   28
   Nationalist Chinese troops in
      Vietnam   41
Central Intelligence Agency
   (CIA)   38, 105, 114
containment policy   116
communism   22
Diem, Ngo Dinh   33, 52
   anti–communist campaign   56–7
   assassination   63
   Buddhist crisis   62
   defeats sects   53
   on elections and land reform
      54–5
   unpopularity   61
Dien Bien Phu   46
domino theory   45, 116
Drafts Resistance Movement   119
Eisenhower, Dwight   59
Evans, Gareth   21, 137–8
France
   imperialism   29–30
   beginning of Indochinese War   41
   rule in Indochina   31–4
   takeover of Vietnam   24, 30–1
   WWII   38–9
Geneva Conference   47, 51, 54, 113
Giap, Vo Nguyen   41–2
glasnost   22
Gorbachev, Mikhail   20, 22
guerilla war   32, 41–4, 97, 112
helicopters   97
Ho Chi Minh   34–5
Ho Chi Minh Trail   66, 128
Hoa Hao   52–3

Indochina
   and imperialism   29–32
   climate   5
   consequences of conflicts   142
   geography   1
   society   28
   WWII   38–9
Indochinese Communist Party   33
Japan   38–9
Johnson, Lyndon
   1964 election   68
   after Tet   78, 120
   escalation   70
   Great Society   64–5
   Tonkin Gulf incident   66–7
   visit to Australia   123
Kampuchea, see Cambodia
Kai–Shek, Jiang   45
Kennedy, John   60, 64
Khmer Republic   105–7
Khmer Rouge   83, 105
   after 1979   136–8
   beliefs   108–9
   increasing strength   107
   takeover of Cambodia   107–8
   Vietnam invasion   110
Kissinger, Henry   81, 83, 86
Korean War   46
Ky, Nguyen Cao   65
Laos
   after 1975   139–42
   civil war   113
   communist victory   114
   early history   26
   economic changes   9–10, 139
   French rule   31–2, 110–11
   geography   5
   independence   47, 113
   takeover by France   31
   today   5, 6, 9–10
   treaty with Vietnam   6
   WWII   38, 111

Long, Emperor Gia   24
Long Tan, Battle of   72, 73
Mao Zedong   44
Menzies, Robert   71
Minh, General Duong   65
mission civilisatrice   29
moratorium marches   121, 124–5, 126
My Lai   122–3
Nationalist Party of Vietnam   33, 34
National Liberation Front   58–9
National United Front of Kampuchea   107
Nixon, Richard
    1968 election   80
    ceasefire   87–9
    Christmas bombing   87
    increases bombing   86
    Nixon Doctrine   81
    peace movement   121
    Pentagon Papers   85–6
    secret bombing of Cambodia   81, 82
    Vice President   45
    Vietnamisation   81–2
    visits Moscow, Peking   86
    Watergate   90
Nol, Lon   105
North Vietnam
    land reform   56
    reconstruction   56
North Vietnamese Army (NVA)   76–8, 86, 93, 113
Office of Strategic Services (OSS)   38, 44
pacification   99–101
Pathet Lao   5, 111–14, 139–40
peace talks   81, 86–9
Pentagon Papers   85–6
perestroika   22
Pol Pot   107, 109, 136–8
Potsdam Conference   40
refugees   16–19, 130, 139, 142
revolutionary war   42–4

Roosevelt, Franklin   44
South–East Asia Treaty Organisation (SEATO)   70, 104
Sihanouk, Prince Norodom
    biography   110
    coup against   105
    FUNK   107
    neutrality   104–5
    relations with USA   105
    resistance groups   136
Souphanouvong, Prince   111–13, 114
Souvanna Phouma, Prince   111, 113, 114
strategic hamlets   61
Tet Offensive   75–8, 80, 120
Thieu, Nguyen Van   65, 129
Tonkin, Gulf of   66–7, 117, 118
Truman, Harry   45
Trung sisters   24, 25
Tunnels   99
Union of Soviet Socialist Republics (USSR)/Russia
    aid to Vietnam   42, 68
    attitude to Vietnam today   20
    Ho Chi Minh   34–5
    Revolution   33
United States of America
    aid to France   44–5, 59
    aid to South Vietnam   59, 60
    attitude to Vietnam today   21
    Cambodia   105
    casualties   70
    consequences of war   143
    end of embargo   7–8, 131, 132, 137
    escalation   70
    Laos   113–14
    reaction to Tet   78
United States Army   84–5, 93–5
United States Navy   98–9
Vietminh
    anti-communist campaign   56–7

first Indochina war   41, 46–7
founded   35, 41
land reform   55
OSS   44
Pathet Lao   111
revolutionary war   42–4
WWII   38–9
veterans
    opposition to war   120
    problems of readjustment   11–15, 143
Vietcong   57–8, 92–3
    increased support   57, 65
    increasing casualties   70
    NLF   58–9
    pacification   99–100
    reinforcements   68
    Tet   76–8, 80
Watergate   90, 128
Westmoreland, William   69, 70
World War II   38, 39, 103–4, 111
Vietnam
    attitudes of other nations   20–1
    costs of war   130
    domination of Indochina   6, 30
    economic problems   130–2
    early history   24–5
    end of second Indochina war   128–9
    first Indochina war   41–2, 46–7
    geography   2
    independence   35
    independence movements   32–5
    rule by France   31–4
    social problems   134–5
    takeover by France   30
    war with Cambodia   110, 131
    war with China   131
    WWII   38–9
Vietnam, South
    geography and climate   91–2
    politics   52–5, 65
    Tet   75–8

ACKNOWLEDGMENTS

The author and publisher wish to thank copyright holders for granting permission to reproduce copyright materials. Copyright holders are acknowledged where known, otherwise sources are indicated.

Text
Pilita Clark, Washington Correspondent, *Sydney Morning Herald* for 'US lifts trade embargo on Vietnam' by Pilita Clark;
Cornell University Press for extracts reprinted from *Conflict in Indo-China and International Repercussions: A Documentary History, 1945–1955* edited by Allan B. Cole, copyright © 1956 by Fletcher School of Law and Diplomacy, used by permission of the publisher, Cornell University Press;
B.J. Elliott for extract by W. Burchett reprinted from *World Society in the Twentieth Century*, published by Stanley Thornes (Publishers) Ltd;
Facts on File, Inc., for extracts reprinted from *Major Political Events in Indochina* by D.J. Sagar, copyright © 1991 D.J. Sagar, reprinted with permission of Facts on File, Inc., New York;
Harper Collins Publishers, New York for extracts reprinted from *Laos: War and Revolution* by Nina S. Adams, copyright © 1970 by Nina S. Adams and Alfred W. McCoy, Harper Collins Publishers Inc.,
David Jenkins for 'Laos on the road to Gundagai';
David Lague for 'Govt finally faces medical facts';
Kim Leang for 'I feel like an animal in a cage';
Longman Group UK for extracts reprinted from *The Contemporary World* by Cannon et al;
Lindsay Murdoch and *Sydney Morning Herald* for 'Vietnam's Big Bang' and 'Vietnam starts fight against lethal new foe';
Random House UK Limited for extracts reprinted from *A Bright Shining Lie* by Neil Sheehan;
Reed Books Australia for extracts reprinted from *Ashes of Vietnam* by Stuart Rintoul, Octopus Books;
Reuters for 'Sihanouk losing hope for peace' by Mark Dodd;
University of Queensland Press for extracts reprinted from *Vietnam: A Reporters War* by Hugh Lunn;
Van Nostrand Reinhold for extract from *Southeast Asia and the World Today*, by C.A. Buss;
Louise Williams for 'Hanoi looks to growth as it finally wins the peace'.

Photographs
Australian Associated Press, pp. 110 top, 123 top; Australia Picture Library, pp. 21, 60, 64, 110 bottom; Australia War Memorial, pp. 72 (COL/67/781/VN), 74 (CUN/66/161/VN); Brendan Esposito/Fairfax Photo Library, p. 20; Camera Press Ltd, pp. 5, 119; Camera Press/Austral International, pp. 47, 96, 130 top; Embassy of the Lao People's Democratic Republic, pp. 111; Herald and Weekly Times Ltd, pp. 71, 81;
National Archives and Records Administration (USA), pp. 69, 93; National Library of Australia, p. 125; Naval Historical Centre, Washington, p. 68; Popperfoto, pp. 62, 84, 87, 107; Reuters News Agency, p. 22; Rex Features/Austral International, p. 140; Sipa Press/Austral International, p. 108; Stock Photos Pty Ltd, pp. 10, 19; Suddeutscher Verlag, p. 34; Sygma/Austral International, p. 30; United Nations High Commissioner for Refugees, p. 130 bottom; United Press International, p. 136; Universal Press Syndicate, copyright © 1969, reprinted by permission of Editors Press Service, Inc., p. 83; Wide World Photos, Inc., pp. 42, 85.

Disclaimer
Every effort has been made to trace the original source of copyright material contained in this book. The publisher would be pleased to hear from copyright holders in order to rectify any omissions or errors.

British–Australian thriller author L. A. Larkin has been likened to Michael Crichton and John Grisham. To write *The Genesis Flaw*, Larkin drew on experiences in Zimbabwe, consulted with geneticists and worked closely with a hacker, even attending a secretive hackers' conference. *The Genesis Flaw* has been nominated for four crime fiction awards.

L. A. Larkin lives in Sydney and London, and teaches mystery and thriller writing.

www.lalarkin.com
www.facebook.com/LALarkinAuthor
@lalarkinauthor

By L. A. Larkin

The Genesis Flaw

Thirst

Devour

The
Genesis Flaw

L. A. Larkin

CONSTABLE · LONDON

CONSTABLE

First published in Australia in 2010 by Pier 9, an imprint of
Murdoch Books Pty Limited

First published in Great Britain in 2016 by Constable

1 3 5 7 9 10 8 6 4 2

A CIP catalogue record for this book
is available from the British Library.

ISBN: 978-1-47212-590-3

Printed and bound by CPI Group (UK) Ltd, Croydon, CR0 4YY

Papers used by Constable are from well-managed forests and
other responsible sources.

MIX
Paper from
responsible sources
FSC® C104740

Constable
An imprint of
Little, Brown Book Group
Carmelite House
50 Victoria Embankment
London EC4Y 0DZ

An Hachette UK Company
www.hachette.co.uk

www.littlebrown.co.uk

To Michael, who believed in me

Chapter 1

He kicked the leather chair away and instantly the rope snapped tight. He hadn't thought of the pain to come, when he'd threaded the rope through the light fitting and tested it could bear his 110 kilos. His throat crushed, he couldn't call out even if he'd wanted to. His lungs burned and the veins in his face felt close to bursting. His brown eyes bulged as if in surprise. But he knew he had to die. It was his only option.

In the last throes of death, as his heart beat so loudly it was all he could hear, his legs thrashed madly and his body, naturally, tried to save itself. But the chair, where he had sat and made all those terrible decisions, was too far away. He registered a warm wetness in his pants and a moment's shame swept over him. He couldn't even die with dignity.

In that second, he saw his personal assistant finding him the following morning, the pungent smell of stale urine and God knows what else forcing her to turn away repulsed. He saw Jane and Thomas in his mind's eye, and silently told them he loved them.

Mouth agape, eyes bloodshot, the last image he saw was the night sky, clear and filled with stars, through his office window. His foot gave one final twitch and then went limp.

The office was silent except for the almost inaudible hum of the air conditioning and the creak of the rope straining as his body swung. The thick glass windows kept out any city noise. The moonlight shone on his bald head, highlighting the dark regrowth that he shaved so carefully every morning – even that morning. His wife, Jane, and three-month-old son, Thomas, watched him, smiling, from the digital photo frame. Seconds ticked by and the digital image changed to one of Tony and Jane on their wedding day two years ago, taken outside the sandstone church. He'd been slimmer then and looked very handsome in his dark suit. In the photograph, he was looking at his wife adoringly.

Next to the silver photo frame lay a white envelope, addressed in blue ink, 'To my beautiful wife and son'. Its whiteness contrasted with the golden honey colour of the Huon Pine desk. Tony stared vacantly, no longer able to hear the whooshing sound of the door opening. A man's large-boned hand hovered over the sealed envelope, and in the moonlight his shadow made him appear twice as big as he was. He picked up the envelope and, without opening it, placed it in his jacket pocket.

The body had stopped swinging, and the intruder stepped towards it. He stood for a long moment in front of the dead man. One corner of his mouth turned up: a hint of a smile. He raised his second finger to his temple and saluted the man he'd been sent to kill. Then, turning, he quickly walked towards the glass door. It slid open and he stepped through it, careful to avoid the security spy-eye camera in the executive suite of offices. As the door closed, the words 'Tony Mancini, CEO and Senior Vice President' glinted, etched in the frosted glass.

Tony had made his last executive decision.

Chapter 2

Turning off the ignition, she knew she was too late. In the dwindling light, the whitewashed weatherboard farmhouse resembled a sepia photograph. Through a haze of dust, she watched as her brother, Keith, pushed himself up from the soft cushions of the three-seater swing chair. For a fit farmer in his thirties his movements were unsteady and deliberate, like an old man's. He left the long evening shadows of the verandah and stood on the top step, one hand clinging to the railing. He didn't wave.

With the air conditioning off, the heat of the summer's day rose from the scorched earth, permeating the car's interior. Serena kept both hands on the sticky steering wheel. If only she'd left Sydney earlier. If only she'd said no to the interview. Her bloodshot eyes squinted as the last of the sun's tendrils released their grip on Swift Farm, her family home. The people on the verandah disappeared into darkness. The century-old pear trees, heavy with ripening fruit, resembled blackened, gnarled fingers scratching at the corrugated-iron roof. For as long as she could remember, colourful parrots had heralded the end of each day with their raucous squawking. But even their cries were muted. Her brother waited patiently.

Serena opened the car door and stepped out. The shallow trench-lines of the driveway – formed by generations of car tyres – felt familiar. Her long hair, normally clipped up, fell loosely around her face. In another place, on another occasion, her figure would

3

have drawn admiring glances. A neighbour had once said the then-teenage Serena should become a model. That had been before her striking curves developed. She had replied that she didn't want to do something as boring as ponce up and down a catwalk. She wanted to use her brains.

Someone hit the exterior light switch and, for a moment, she was blinded by the brightness. The light revealed Serena's head of thick, strawberry blonde hair, and her white T-shirt, khaki shorts and long runner's legs. She stepped through the patchy grass of the front yard to the verandah. She could now see Keith's heavily pregnant wife sitting on the cushion next to the one her husband had vacated. Serena's unusual eyes, hazel with a star of amber around her irises, searched her brother's face for a sign.

'Am I too late?'

She hoped he would say, 'No, come quickly. He's asking for you.' But Keith shook his head and the pity in his eyes destroyed the last vestige of Serena's composure. Part of her didn't believe him, didn't believe it possible her dad was dead. 'I must see him. Where is he?'

Keith walked down the steps and took her arm. He led her into the house. Everything looked exactly as it always had and reinforced her hope that Keith was wrong. If her father were dead somehow the house would have changed with his passing. But a newspaper was open and the dining chair sat away from the table at an angle. Someone had been reading about a footy star disgracing himself. Why would any of that matter if her dad were no longer there?

Keith looked at her but Serena just stared at the polished floorboards, at the black stain left many years ago by a science experiment she had accidentally spilt. She moved slowly even though her head was pounding and her mind was screaming out the question 'Is he?'. Her feet were heavy, as if she had lost the feeling in them.

She couldn't see the bed at first. She took another step. The bedroom door opened inwards, blocking her view. She caught sight of the wrought-iron bedpost and saw the sheet raised in a small pyramid where her father's feet rested. Serena looked further up the sheet, hardly daring to look at his face. She counted off a few seconds to see if his chest rose and fell, but it did not. Her heart seemed to spasm. No chest movement meant no breath, she told herself and then shoved the thought away. She forced herself to look at his face and took in a sharp breath. Serena felt as though she had sucked in boiling water. Her lungs burned.

His eyes were closed. His face was waxy grey. But his expression was peaceful. It showed none of the pain he must have suffered at the end. His lips were slightly parted. She had to be sure, so she leaned over her dad and listened for his breath. She brushed her ear against his lips and they felt warm and soft. Shocked, she straightened.

'You're wrong. He's alive.'

Keith just looked at her, unable to speak.

She was sure her dad's body would have been cold by now if he were dead. He had to be sleeping. Serena touched her father's cheek. It felt as it always did. She moved her hand over his fine grey hair and stroked the thinning strands.

'It's all right, Dad, I'm here now. It'll be all right.'

She held her breath to stop her tears flowing but it didn't work.

'Dad, talk to me,' she said.

Keith placed a hand on her shoulder.

'Serena, he's gone.'

She shook her head.

'He can't have. He can't go.'

Silently, Keith turned and left her. She barely noticed.

'Hey, Dad,' Serena said, and sat on the edge of the mattress next to his pillow. 'Sorry I'm late. I wanted to say how much I …'

She couldn't finish. Tears blinded her. She lay down on her mother's side of the bed, and placed one arm gently over his chest and one above his head. It reminded her of when she was a kid and would dive into her parents' bed in the mornings. Except, then her dad had cuddled her. Now she cuddled him.

Time passed but Serena was unaware of it. Her body kept his warm. She imagined he was still alive.

'Serena,' she heard.

Her brother was at her side. She didn't move.

'Serena, Dad needs some time to himself. You can see him again a bit later.'

She sat up. Her face was red and wet. Her nose ran like a toddler's. She swung her legs around so they touched the floor and stood shakily.

Her brother caught her arm and led her away from the bed. She looked back at her dad and saw that next to him was an indent left by the weight of her body.

'Did he suffer?' she asked.

The momentary pause told her everything she didn't want to know.

She shook herself free from Keith's grip and touched the cold metal of the bedpost. It dawned on Serena that his death should never have happened and she awoke from her stupor. She faced her father.

'Dad, I'm so sorry. I let you down again. But I'll make them pay. I promise.'

Chapter 3

The lobby of the Rooney Agency and Big Noise PR did double-duty as a café and art gallery. Sculptures on plinths were like obstacles in a pinball machine, as people wove in and out trying to avoid knocking them over. One bronze piece looked like a giant artichoke. Another was made of balls of light, which changed colour as busy office workers walked by, the colours supposedly reflecting their moods. It turned coffee-bean brown as Serena passed. She smiled and thought it must mean 'needs caffeine'.

As she strode to the lobby café in her designer dress, she hoped that nobody could guess her state of mind on this, the first day of her new job. Perhaps if they'd looked closely, beneath the row of red beads covering her chest, they might have noticed an agitated flush. Or if they'd known her well, they would have noticed her shoulders were slouched instead of her normally upright posture. Despite applying her make-up carefully that morning, she'd been unable to hide the blue-grey semicircles under her eyes. She remembered Tracey telling her always to apply her 'war paint', that it would mask the tell-tale signs of even the worst hangover. But she doubted its magic today. Perhaps they'd been right: she wasn't ready. The truth was, she felt sick to the stomach.

She had time for a coffee, so she joined a short queue, and contemplated having some raisin toast to calm her nervous stomach. She was unaware of the glances she was getting from male passers-by. A woman in front of her ordered a flat white and stepped aside.

'First day?' the café owner asked Serena.

'Yes, is it that obvious?'

'No, I just never seen you around before.'

'A long black, please,' Serena said.

'I make it extra special for you,' he replied with a wink and grinned, revealing a wide gap in his front teeth. She paid for her coffee and stepped aside to wait for it. She found a copy of the *Australian Financial Review* and flicked through the paper.

'Long black for the beautiful lady!' called the barista. Serena smiled, walked away and then realised she'd forgotten to ask for sugar, so went back to the counter to pick up some sachets. She tore open three and poured in their contents. Like her dad, she had a sweet tooth. She smiled as she remembered his fifty-ninth birthday party: only four weeks ago. His pale face, wracked with pain, had lit up at the sight of the chocolate mud cake she'd baked. Two weeks later, her dad was dead.

'You bastard!' a man shouted behind her.

The voice was high-pitched and shrill. Despite the noise in the lobby, it reverberated off the marble floors and glass walls. Everyone, including Serena, turned towards the source of the sound. A small crowd of people waiting for their coffees partially blocked her view. A dishevelled man in his sixties with glasses and an ungroomed beard raised his skinny arms in the air and propelled himself at a man in a dark suit. The target of the attack had his back to her. As the older man grabbed the younger man's lapels, the victim tried to pull away.

'You killed her!' the man yelled with such vehemence the businessman recoiled and dropped his briefcase. He shoved the screaming man away from him. The aggressor bent like a bow and staggered back a few steps, his scrawny frame unbalanced by the force of the well-built younger man's thrust.

'Can I get some help here?' the businessman called out. He was American, his accent Texan. Serena still couldn't see his face.

'Listen, I don't know you. Please leave me alone,' he said, slowly and calmly, his arms held out for protection.

'Liar!' the older man yelled, charging again. 'How can you forget me? I'm Fergus McPherson, remember?'

The businessman grabbed McPherson's swinging arms and held them tightly.

'Yes, of course, Professor, I recognise you now.' His tone softened immediately. 'I'm so sorry for your loss.' The younger man shoved McPherson away with a force that belied his sympathetic tone.

'Like hell you are!' McPherson screamed as a security guard threw him to the floor.

Simultaneously, a bull-necked man in a chauffeur's uniform ran to the businessman, picked up his briefcase and steered him rapidly towards the elevators. Pinned to the floor by the beefy guard, McPherson whimpered.

'Al, stop this,' he called after the businessman, stretching out his only free arm. His voice sounded like the last hiss from a deflated football.

The businessman didn't look back.

McPherson tried again. 'Please, for the love of God, stop. New Dawn will only make things worse. Al, it's not too late.'

Al disappeared through closing elevator doors.

The assailant lay on the floor sobbing, oblivious to the bystanders staring at him as if he were a two-headed creature in a research laboratory. The guard yanked him to his feet and shoved him through a door behind the reception desk.

Serena was rooted to the spot. The force of the old man's anger had shocked her. She glanced at the door he'd been dragged through and wondered what would happen to him. He'd sounded crazy with grief and she could understand that. But she had to pack away those feelings somewhere they could be ignored. She couldn't allow them to dent the confident, competent image she needed to present today. Serena took a few sips of her coffee as she rolled the torn sugar sachets between her fingers. She wondered who the American was and how he'd provoked such fury. She hadn't managed to get a good look at him, but from the cut of his suit and his chauffeur-come-bodyguard, she guessed he was someone important. Rooneys was the building's major tenant. Could he be a client? An uncomfortable thought crossed her mind. No, it couldn't be.

Serena pushed her half-drunk coffee across the counter. She didn't feel like it anymore. Despite her determination to stay focused on her new job, the word 'killed' reverberated in her head. He had said 'killed', hadn't he?

Chapter 4

She knocked at her new boss's half-open door and, without waiting for an answer, took a deep breath and strode in. Martin Delaney beckoned her to sit down. The floor-to-ceiling windows on the nineteenth floor offered panoramic views across Sydney. The silvery waters of the Harbour rippled between North Sydney and the CBD, and from this height the green and gold ferries looked like toy boats in a bath. Delaney, tanned and in his forties, lounged back in his steel-grey leather chair as he unashamedly looked Serena up and down.

'Consider it done,' he said, charm dripping off him like fat off roast pork. He tapped his earpiece and ended the phone call.

'Welcome, Serena. It's good to have you on board.'

'Thank you, Martin, it's good to be here,' she replied, giving him her friendliest smile.

He leaned forward, his elbows on the desk, revealing sterling silver golf club cufflinks.

'You're good. Very good. We both know that. But no matter how good you are, you wouldn't be worth a cracker without Lenny White.'

Lenny was her old queen of a boss who ran the London agency. Four years ago, she'd started in one of his pitch teams and rapidly advanced to pitch director, or 'pitch doctor'. It was Lenny who had given Serena her big break: the chance to head the pitch for the Sony worldwide account. She'd won it, and many others since, helping to make London the most profitable Rooneys office in the world, and Lenny extremely wealthy along the way. But when he'd heard that Serena blamed the firm's biggest client for her father's illness, he had confronted her. 'Don't be so bloody stupid,' he'd said. 'You're my shining star. I need you. Now promise me it's over; otherwise, my dear,' he'd said, ostentatiously clicking his fingers, 'your career will be nothing more than a memory.' Serena had raced back to Australia when she'd heard her father's condition had worsened. Lenny had reluctantly pulled the necessary strings for her.

Martin's nasal drone intruded on her thoughts. 'He saved your career. If you even consider doing anything like it again, not even God himself will be able to save your arse. You will be out this door so quickly, your feet won't touch the ground. Do I make myself clear?'

'Perfectly.'

'So, remember what's in your contract,' said Martin. 'Stay away from Gene-Asis. Don't go near them, don't speak to them, don't even fucking think about them. Do that and we'll get on just beautifully,' he continued, smiling broadly.

She tried to return his smile. *And I was here wasting my time with you when I could have been with Dad when he died,* she thought. Two weeks ago, she'd been sitting in this very chair, selling herself into the Sydney pitch director's role. Lenny had called in a favour and arranged the interview.

Martin stood up, ran his hands through his curly hair and came round to her side of the desk.

'Good. Now we all know where we stand.' He threw a USB flash drive in her lap. 'Everything you need is on that. The pitch is in eight weeks. It's a billion-dollar account. The previous pitch doctor, Matt Stevens, was a dick. Got himself arrested. I mean, who does coke in public? Anyway, he's out of the picture now and, six months in, we need you to take over. You have to win it.'

'Martin, it all depends on how good Matt was. We don't have time to go back to the drawing board. I normally have six to nine months to prepare.'

'Tough. You've got eight weeks, so deal with it. I expect you to earn that salary package you negotiated.'

She ignored the comment. 'What's the team like?'

'Pretty good. But you have whoever you want. If you need any of your London team out here, just say the word. That Sony win was something else.' He fidgeted with a cufflink. 'So, can you handle it?'

'Of course,' she replied. She'd win the Mitsubishi Asia-Pacific account, whatever it took.

He paused, staring over her shoulder at the door, distracted for a moment.

'I think you'll find we work pretty much the same as London. Clients come first. Always.'

'Knock, knock.'

Serena recognised the woman's voice instantly – Gloria Philladitis. She swallowed hard and turned to face the door.

'Sorry to interrupt, Martin, but I wanted to greet our new arrival and let you know Al Bukowski from Gene-Asis is in the boardroom.'

Gloria mouthed the company name in an exaggeratedly slow way, like a porn star reciting the name of the first book of the Bible: 'Genesis'. Both Martin and Gloria looked at Serena, searching for a reaction. Serena's grip on the tiny flash drive tightened and her pupils dilated, but neither of them picked up on her agitation.

'Gloria. What a lovely surprise!' she said, unconvincingly. 'I didn't know you were coming to Sydney.'

'Why would you?' Gloria sneered.

'I thought you'd returned to New York.'

'I will for the launch, but that's none of your business.'

Gloria's New Yorker abrasiveness had got under Serena's skin when they'd met in London. But Serena kept her cool.

'Before you say anything, let me assure you I have no interest whatsoever in Gene-Asis,' said Serena. 'I have my own account to focus on.'

'Well, just keep it that way,' Gloria replied.

One side of Martin's mouth briefly curled into a smirk, in amusement at the women's rivalry. His brow then knitted into a frown.

'Did he say why he's here? Jesus, why fly all the way from New York? They must be pissed off.'

Gloria nodded in Serena's direction but Martin missed the hint. 'Perhaps we should discuss this later.'

'What? Oh, of course,' he replied, finally getting the message. 'I don't like it,' he went on, chewing his fingernail.

Gloria began to walk away and then stopped at the door.

'Serena, I never got to say ... you know ... how sorry I am about your dad.'

Gloria's sneer was gone. Serena even thought she saw a flicker of compassion.

'Thank you.'

Gloria's overpowering Chanel No. 5 lingered behind her after she left. 'Serena, we'll talk later.' Martin nodded towards the door. 'Jodi's your PA. She'll show you around.'

Martin hustled Serena out and turned towards reception. Serena stopped in the corridor to watch him. A purple wall, which turned out to be a door, rolled back at the flick of a switch to reveal an enormous boardroom. Martin stepped inside. Gloria was talking to a man in a black suit, the same businessman who'd been in the lobby earlier. There was nothing about his behaviour to suggest he'd been violently attacked: his smile was broad and warm, and his movements relaxed. Gloria was hopping from one stiletto to the other, flicking back her dark hair and grinning toothily. Serena had never seen her behave like a smitten schoolgirl before.

Serena could only see Bukowski's profile but now she recognised him from all the research she'd done. The man who'd haunted her dreams was standing a few metres away. Her stomach churned as the purple soundproofed door shut tightly.

Chapter 5

It had been four years since Serena had seen the Flynn brothers and all day she'd been looking forward to their company. The Flynns had been Serena's next-door neighbours and the brothers were her constant companions when she was growing up. John leaned against the doorframe with his head nonchalantly tilted to one side. His mischievous smile hadn't changed, but Serena noticed a touch more grey hair around his temples and that he wore it longer, curling just above the neckline of his crumpled T-shirt. Droplets of water from his hair temporarily darkened the blue cotton. He squeezed her into a tight hug and placed his chin on her head, which not many men could do: Serena was 173 centimetres tall. She closed her eyes for a second, enjoying the familiarity.

'I can't tell you how good it is to see you, Johno,' she said, breathing in his scent. His skin smelled of sun and shower gel.

'You've been to the beach,' she said, still leaning into his shoulder.

He pulled away and gazed at her. 'Yes,' he replied. An awkward silence ensued.

The evening sun streamed into the hallway behind John. Ahead, Serena could see into the lounge room: stylish faux suede sofas, what looked like a Noguchi coffee table, a number of healthy-looking indoor plants and a fish tank. This was not the bachelor pad she'd been expecting.

'Great to have you back at last.' John paused. 'Seri, I'm sorry I didn't make the funeral. I feel really bad. I was overseas at a wanky conference. I couldn't get out of it.'

She hadn't been called Seri for a while.

'Don't worry. I … it's fine.' She didn't want to talk about it. Every time she did, tears welled up. 'So, how are you?'

Before he could answer, she heard a voice from inside. 'Seri!' shouted Barry, who'd appeared from the kitchen with a tea towel thrown over his shoulder. His arms were open wide and he wore a huge grin. 'Give us a hug.'

Serena and Barry swayed from side to side in an embrace that was more like a wrestling match. They both laughed. Younger and shorter than John, Barry – or Baz as they called him – had dark, closely cropped hair. He released her.

'Perfect timing, dinner's ready. Tonight, for your dining pleasure, my speciality: seafood linguine.'

Serena grimaced. 'Is it safe?'

'It's okay, he won't poison you, I promise,' John said.

'But, just in case, have some wine. That way you won't feel a thing,' said Baz. He led them into the kitchen, where the smell of chilli, ginger and lemongrass greeted her. 'I started cooking a little early, so do you mind if I dish up?'

'God, no, I'm starving,' she replied.

Once they were seated, John raised his glass. 'To Seri; it's great to have you back,' he said.

'Now, I want to hear all about London. And I mean all,' said Baz, winking.

Serena laughed. 'If you're expecting a load of goss, I'm afraid I'm going to disappoint,' she said, before launching into a potted version of the past four years: her work; the pitches she'd won; her skiing trips to Austria and Switzerland; her best mate, Tracey.

'So, you still haven't got yourself a fella?' asked Baz.

John flicked him a furtive glance, which he duly ignored.

'No, no boyfriend. Hasn't been for a while. But that's okay. Work takes up most of my time.'

John looked down at the table for a moment. He shifted uncomfortably on the wooden stool.

'You always were a workaholic,' said Baz. 'I remember you studying like crazy for your HSC, and your birthday was the weekend before the first exam and you wouldn't leave your books to celebrate. We organised a party at our place, remember? And had to lure you over there by pretending we wanted to study.'

She smiled. 'Yes, I do. And after all that, John got top marks without even trying.'

'I'll let you into a secret,' said John. 'I hacked the exam papers. I knew the questions.'

'What! You never told me that. Why didn't you tell me what the questions were?' said Serena, playfully smacking John on the arm.

'Because you'd have got all righteous on me.'

Serena blanched. 'Was I that bad?'

'Nah,' said Baz, 'because you had us getting you into trouble. So, anyway, back to London. You must have met someone over there?'

Serena looked down and twirled the wine glass stem between her fingers. 'Not really, it was all work. When a pitch was on, we'd work night and day for weeks. And when that pitch was over, we'd be onto the next one.' She looked up at Baz, deliberately avoiding John's gaze. 'But enough of me,' she continued, 'what about you two?'

'Ah, you know me,' Baz winked. 'Love 'em and leave 'em. Nothing's changed. Still doing recruitment. But this one.' He nodded at his brother. 'Full of surprises.'

'Ooh, do tell,' Serena said.

'He's gone full-on corporate,' Baz said.

'What?'

'And get this,' he continued. 'Chief information security officer. For a bank.'

'No way!' Serena laughed raucously.

'Are you finished yet?' John said.

'What I can't believe is, he's now paid a fortune to stop people doing exactly what he used to,' Baz went on. 'He even employs hackers.'

'Officially, we don't do that,' John said, smiling at last.

'Of all the places I thought you'd end up – and prison was one of them – I never ever would've picked a bank!'

'Thank you very much,' said John, in mock indignation.

Baz reached for another bottle of wine. 'Let's make things a little more cosy.' He tossed Serena some matches. 'Be a love and light the candles, will you?'

The image on the matchbox caught Serena's eye: a 1950s bombshell posing seductively in a pink corset.

'Great matchbox,' she said.

'Have them. I picked them up in a bar.'

'Thanks, I love fifties stuff.' She popped the matchbox in her bag. 'I picked up a whole load of it at Portobello markets; you know, the big antique market. I've got one of those square black Bakelite phones with a rotary dial, and the most gorgeous French-polished wooden valve radio. I'm having it all shipped back.'

'Sounds awesome. Is it coming to Sydney or the farm?' Baz said.

'Here. I'm looking for a place to rent. I'm in a serviced apartment for now, courtesy of Rooneys.'

'What about here? We've got a spare room,' said John.

'You sure?'

'Yeah, 'course,' he replied.

Baz looked serious for a moment.

'Um, Seri, you need to know something, before you decide.'

'That you have smelly feet? I know,' she replied, laughing.

'Uh, no. I'm a recruiter in biotech now – you know – life sciences and pharmaceuticals. That includes Gene-Asis.'

'Oh.'

She put down her fork and wiped her mouth with a paper napkin.

'I thought you should know.'

'It doesn't matter. I decided not to do anything.'

'You what?' John clearly hadn't meant to let his surprise show. 'I mean, why?'

She could feel her face reddening. Voices of revellers on a nearby balcony floated through the window. It sounded to Serena as if they were laughing at her.

'I need the bathroom,' she said as she left the kitchen. The brothers looked at each other in silence.

Serena felt a familiar weight on her chest. She'd hoped leaving the farm would give her some respite from guilt's nagging appetite. She felt as if a rat were gnawing through her ribcage, trying to get to her heart. It was unbearable. She sat on the bath's edge, waiting for the moment to pass. After a few minutes, there was a soft knock on the door. She unlocked it to find John standing in the hallway. He opened his mouth to speak, stopped, then tried again.

'I'm sorry, Seri, I was surprised. That's all. Mum and Dad said you were talking to a lawyer. You were going after Gene-Asis. I didn't mean anything by it.'

'I couldn't do it. I mean …' Her voice trailed off. He put his arm around her and led her to the lounge room. 'Let's sit and you can tell me what happened.'

She smiled up at him. 'I could always talk to you. God, I've missed you,' she said, leaning into his chest. John had been her childhood protector and confidant. In fact, she'd always been closer to John than to her own brother, which Keith had always resented.

'The lawyer said he'd take it on but it'd take a lot of time and money. Expert witnesses. Geneticists. It could go on for years. And did I really want to do this.'

She stopped and gazed out of the window at the tops of the trees. The party next door was in full swing. The music was louder.

'So you spoke to a lawyer *before* he died?'

'Yes, this was when I was still in London. I never met the guy; we talked on the phone. Some hotshot city lawyer who worked on the James Hardie case. At the time I didn't realise Dad only had a few weeks to live.'

'So you decided to drop it. There's nothing wrong with that.'

'Not then. Dad'd heard what I was doing. He phoned and told me to leave it. It was nobody's fault, he said. Dad was really insistent. You know how stubborn he can … could be. And he wanted to spend time with me while he could. So I flew home.'

'That's what I'd have done,' John said.

She could feel the tears coming.

'You did the right thing: you followed his wishes.'

Serena composed herself before she continued. 'But, John, I knew. I did my research. I knew in my heart the pollen from that T-Speed canola caused the cancer, but I gave up.'

'Come on, Seri, your lawyer was right. It would've dragged on for years and the chances of winning were next to zero.'

'Yes, but …' She dropped her head and tucked her hair behind each ear as it fell forward. 'John, my reasons weren't that noble. It was Lenny who changed my mind.'

'Who's Lenny?'

'My boss in London. How he'd heard, I have no idea. I hadn't breathed a word to anyone at work, for obvious reasons. Anyway, he said that I couldn't continue at Rooneys if I took their biggest client to court. I knew that. But I was full of myself and thought I could get a job somewhere else. Lenny put that into perspective in his own inimitable style. He said I had two choices: I could continue my "meteoric" rise as a pitch director and could even be running the show in London when he retired. Or I could go after Gene-Asis and become a pariah. I'd be "toxic," he said. I'd never get another job in advertising.'

'What a prick.'

She shook her head.

'No, he was just telling me how it really was. And he did get me the job here.' Serena scanned John's face for signs of disapproval. 'Anyway, that's why I didn't do anything. I've worked like a slave to get where I am today and I just couldn't throw it away. The truth is I'm too selfish.'

She paused and looked into his pale blue eyes. He raised his chin in acknowledgement but directed his gaze over her shoulder, avoiding eye contact. She could tell he was hiding his thoughts from her. All her life he had been the only person she could tell everything to because he'd never judged her. Well, until he'd made a comment shortly before she'd left for the UK. She'd been boasting about winning a cigarette company's account and her subsequent big bonus. He'd frowned and said, 'What happened to you, Seri? You're not the girl I grew up with.' She'd been floored. 'At least I'm making something of my life,' she'd replied, pissed off.

'You think I've done the wrong thing, don't you?'

John looked at her. 'What I think doesn't matter. What matters is you got to spend precious time with your dad before he died.'

'But I was at a bloody interview,' her voice cracked, 'when he …'

Baz appeared in the doorway. John shook his head so Baz quietly withdrew.

'You did your best. You've got to stop beating yourself up,' he said.

Serena stood up and paced the room. 'Dad always went on about standing up for what you believe in, but where did it get him? Nowhere. And when I wanted to go after Gene-Asis, he really got angry. He said I was biting off more than I could chew and I'd just destroy my life for a case I had no chance of winning.'

She was red-faced with sudden anger. But she wasn't angry with John. She was angry with herself. And with her father.

John said carefully, 'Look, forget about it. You need time to grieve. And who knows? If T-Speed causes cancer, there'll be other victims out there. You can have another go when you're not alone. Maybe get a class action going.'

'I made a promise on his deathbed.' She hung her head.

'It's okay. You'll keep that promise when you can.'

Chapter 6

Her pitch team sat around the table, eyes focused on her. She stood, they sat. Serena summed them up in a few seconds. Nearest her, Carl, the ad director: rolled-up shirt sleeves, foot tapping under the desk, confident swagger. He would challenge her. The art director next: slick, perfectly styled hair, goatee, lolling back in his chair so far he was almost horizontal. Lazy. The copywriter: anxious, poor sleeper, fidgeting. Needed coaxing. A couple of account executives and assistants: suited and attentive, they looked terrified. They'd heard about her reputation.

'I'm Serena Swift and I'm the new pitch director for the Mitsubishi account. I guess you know of me but here's a brief rundown: ten years ago I started with McCann Erickson. I won them Fairfax Media, Apple and Mitsubishi. So I know Mitsubishi's business backwards. I even spent two years in Japan.' She paused to allow this to sink in. 'For the last four years I've been with Rooneys London. I won them Sony, American Express, Barclays, Apple, and Sainsbury's among others. Now I'm back and I am going to win Mitsubishi for Rooneys Sydney, with your help. I've read your CVs and you're a great team. I'll drive you hard, but you already know that. So let's talk about where you are up to. Carl, over to you.'

She sat down. Carl stood and picked up a number of A2-sized storyboards. Each one depicted a sequence of sketches that illustrated the key scenes from different ideas they'd been testing. He placed them

22

on a stand, the backs of the boards facing those assembled, so the sketches couldn't be seen, and stood to the side.

'Thank you, Serena,' he said and nodded at her. 'We've been working on this pitch for six months. Its focus is the repositioning of the Mitsubishi brand as the car manufacturer of the future. Green, environmentally-friendly, and so on, but still offering the power, the acceleration, the style. So the focus is on the launch of the hydrogen car. As you'd expect, Serena, we've explored every angle on this. Everything from futuristic space-age technology to kids breathing clean air, the green car company angle, to the beauty of the design and its unique features. And this is where we've got to,' he announced, turning over the first board so the sketches could be seen.

He continued, 'Matt said the brand needed a point of differentiation and we picked its futuristic technology. Here we have a UFO following the new hydrogen car. The aliens can see inside to its hydrogen fuel cells. They nod. "Hydrogen technology, *we* don't even have that yet," an alien says. The others nod approvingly. The shot zooms in on the happy family in the car, smiling kids in the back. "And no pollution. I want it!" says the alien. Then we go to the voiceover, "Mitsubishi cars – everyone wants one." And it ends.'

Carl folded his arms and waited for praise.

'So you all think this is the way to go?' she asked, looking at each face in turn. All eyes turned to Carl, who nodded. The team then said yes in unison.

'Matt clearly didn't do his homework,' said Serena. 'Take a look at this.'

Her smartphone lay on the table. It was the latest model, the Tbyte, and only the top executives at Rooneys received one. It had a smartdoc keyboard, a terabyte of flash RAM onboard, a GPS, blazingly fast wireless connectivity for networking and peripherals, and could even project holographic images, although these were still a bit grainy. A few years ago, she would have carried her laptop around to meetings like this. Now all she needed was her smartphone. Her team watched her click her phone into the keyboard slot so that it stood upright. She pressed a few keys, searching for a file on the network. She found it and then pressed another key, linking her phone to the wall-mounted monitor. It showed another storyboard, with aliens commenting on the technology. But this time it was for Apple computers.

'This was one of the ideas I pitched to Apple six years ago. Same theme. Almost identical. It was one of three. It wasn't the one we recommended, thank God. The vice president of marketing hated it. Thought the aliens were ridiculous.'

'But this is a different account. Hydrogen cars are space age. I mean, all they emit is water. No carbon,' argued Carl.

'If it's shot well, it'll be very powerful,' said the art director. 'Yeah, the aliens idea has been used before but that doesn't mean it can't be used again, in a different context.'

'But we're talking Mitsubishi. We'll be pitching to the VP of marketing. Do you know who that is?'

The team looked at each other, confused.

'Is that a trick question?' asked the copywriter. 'Of course we know who we're pitching to. Aki Shimamoto. Born Japan, educated in the US, worked in Europe and now in Japan.'

'Aki was the VP of marketing at Apple when I did the pitch. He moved to Mitsubishi two years ago. Do you see? He's seen the aliens' idea before and hated it. Loathed it. We are not going to present this idea to him again.'

Stunned silence. 'Shit!' said the art director.

'I'm a pitch director because I know these things. I make it my job to know the client and I know Aki well. We're karaoke buddies. I know what he likes and hates. I know he's very much the American playboy in his personal life but in front of the GM of Mitsubishi, he'll be traditional and restrained. You know, all that Japanese ceremony. He won't comment on our pitch because the Japanese don't like to be confrontational in meetings, but he'll phone me afterwards and tell me what he really thinks. I'll win us this pitch but you'll have to trust me.'

She looked around the room. They nodded.

'Okay, show me the other boards. What other ideas did you come up with?' she asked.

Carl talked through each of the seven boards and explained the ideas presented in each.

'Board seven. I love it. We can play around with the letter H. H the symbol for hydrogen. What else does H stand for?'

'Happiness?' an assistant suggested hesitantly.

'Perfect. Happy people, loving their cars. No guilt, no pollution. Good. What else?'

Back in her office, Serena tried to focus on Mitsubishi but found it hard to concentrate. She shot off an email in Japanese to Aki Shimamoto, her software translating the characters into kanji. But she couldn't get out of her mind the argument in the foyer yesterday. Gene-Asis was one of the top ten companies in the world. You'd have to be mad to assault the global CEO. Or desperate. She remembered her death-bed promise and knew that simply by working for Rooneys, she was betraying it. But the deed was done. Or was it? She wouldn't go near Gene-Asis but there was nothing stopping her checking out the professor. Where was the harm in that?

She typed 'Dr Fergus McPherson' into the search engine and pressed 'enter'.

Over fifty hits came up. One was a link to his résumé.

Born in Glasgow. B.Sc. in physiology, with first-class honours. Ph.D. in biochemistry. Professor of Biochemistry at Edinburgh University. Founded the Audrey Walters Institute of Genetic Research. Professor of Plant Pathology and Genetics at Harvard. Professor of Genetics and Plant Breeding at Arthur Phillip University Sydney. Over 300 primary peer-reviewed papers. Written or edited nine books. His last published book, *Food for a Hotter Planet – how genetic engineering works with climate change to feed the world*, was in 2011. The résumé ended there.

Dr McPherson's credentials were impeccable. It was not the CV of a crank and he appeared to be a steadfast supporter of genetic engineering. But Serena could find nothing after 2011. He was not in the university's Genetics Department staff directory. She guessed he must have left or even been fired.

Her mobile rang, startling her. It was John, checking what time she wanted to move in that night.

'I'll drive by your apartment at, say, seven?'

'Great. I haven't much to pack.'

'Baz's on a date, so unless you want to try my speciality, which is grilled cheese on toast, we're having takeaway tonight.'

Serena laughed. 'Takeaway's fine,' she said. 'John?'

'Yup?'

She checked her door was closed and then filled him in on the altercation in the foyer the day before and her research on Dr McPherson.

'Don't you think it's … well, a bit strange that his life's work seems to suddenly stop?'

'So you haven't let Gene-Asis go?'

'I have. I'm just curious, that's all.'

The momentary pause told her he didn't believe her.

'How old was he?' asked John.

'I'd guess Dad's age.' She felt a tightening in her chest.

'Sounds as though he didn't like what Gene-Asis was doing. If it's bugging you, why don't you call the uni and ask? It could be he just hasn't published anything lately.'

'I guess a phone call can't hurt. Anyway, thanks. See you tonight.'

'No worries.'

Serena put her handheld down on the desk without docking it. She leaned her chin on her palm and stared at the phone's shiny black surface. She spun it around a few times, undecided. Then she quickly dialled directory assistance before she could change her mind and was put though to Arthur Phillip University.

'Hi, can you tell me if Dr Fergus McPherson is still working for the university?'

'Er. There's no Dr McPherson on my list. Do you know which faculty he's with?'

'Genetics and Plant Breeding.'

'I'll put you through.'

The classical hold music nearly deafened her.

'Genetics,' said a clipped female voice.

'Oh, hello. Can I speak to Dr Fergus McPherson, please?'

'Who, sorry?'

'Dr Fergus McPherson.'

'Oh, him. I reckon he left years ago.'

'Do you know where he is now?'

'No idea.'

'Did he leave a contact number?'

'If he did, I couldn't tell you. I can't give out personal information. Look, I've got another call coming in. I must go.'

With that, the line went dead.

Chapter 7

John's shirt sleeves were rolled up and Serena noticed a tattoo on his arm. He hadn't had that four years ago. She could only see part of it but could make out that it resembled a fish's tail. Her suitcases were in the hallway and John was giving her a guided tour of the flat. They stood now in his home office. The white louvre shutters were closed tightly, giving the small room the feel of a dark cave. The only light came from the glare of the monitors, arranged in two rows of three. Three were attached to the wall and three were on the glass-top desk. Cabling coiled like a nest of red-bellied black snakes to the power points. All six screens were on: Serena identified chat rooms on two screens but the other four streamed numbers that made no sense to her. His desk was scattered with memory sticks, empty energy drink bottles and coffee cups, some back-up discs and a football.

'I often work through the night. I prefer to do it here than at the office.'

'Why do you work nights?'

'To catch hackers, you need to be active when they are,' John said as they left the room. He led her into his bedroom. He had his own balcony and through the glass doors she noticed a surfboard leaning against the wall.

'When did you get into surfing?' she asked.

'Couple of years ago. When I moved to the beach.'

'Baz is right. You have changed. First banking and now surfing. I guess a lot can happen in four years.'

He opened the balcony doors wider to let more of the sea breeze through.

'We haven't exactly stayed in contact.' John said 'we' but Serena was the one who'd ignored his emails and phone messages.

'And what made you get into surfing?' she asked, changing the conversation back to a safer topic. She followed him onto the balcony and gazed across the rooftops towards Coogee beach.

'I don't know,' he said, leaning his elbows on the balcony wall. 'It was something different, new. I mean, we both learned to swim at the town pool, but nothing beats those pounding waves and that salty taste. And it keeps me fit.'

Serena glanced at him. It upset her that she no longer knew her childhood best friend. They had always been so close.

'I'm proud of you,' she said.

He grinned his slightly lopsided smile that gave him a roguish air.

'Why, thank you, Miss Swift,' he said cheekily.

When they moved inside, Serena noticed a framed photo on the bedside table. It was of an attractive blonde woman, smiling, with her head resting on John's shoulder. He saw Serena looking at it.

'That's Kat.'

'Oh. You didn't tell me you had a girlfriend.'

'Yeah, well, you didn't ask,' he said, a little defensively. He then recovered himself. 'This is a bit weird. I think we need to … talk.'

She shook her head. 'No, John, please. With Dad's death, it's just too much right now.'

He shrugged. 'Okay.'

Serena glanced back at the photo. 'So, when am I meeting Kat? She looks lovely.'

'She died five months ago.' His eyes had never left her face and when she looked into them, she could read his devastation. She recalled his email from a few months ago, which she'd immediately deleted. If only she'd read it.

'John, I'm so sorry,' said Serena. She put her hand on his arm.

'It was hepatitis S. By the time they worked it out, her liver was gone.'

'I'm so sorry. I had no idea.'

He shrugged again. 'That's what happens when you don't stay in touch.' There was no accusation: he was simply stating a fact. He paused. 'They couldn't even bloody well tell us how she got it, let alone why I didn't,' he said, his face screwed up with bitterness.

'It must have been terrible, watching her ...' Serena paused. 'I feel bad, John. I wish I'd ... I wish we'd ...'

John looked at Serena, calmer now. 'Yeah, well, what's done is done. Baz was the best. He was really there for me, put up with my moods and, God, I was shitty.' He dropped his eyes to the floor. 'Wishing won't bring her back.' He looked at Kat's photograph. 'I made a decision to move on. I have to.'

He walked out of the room. Serena glanced at the framed image, right next to his bed, a daily reminder of Kat's absence. He was still grieving. After a few seconds, Serena followed him to the kitchen.

'I need a drink. How about you?' said John. She nodded.

'So, did you check out the Prof?' he asked, changing the subject.

'Yeah. I called the uni. They said he'd left some years ago.'

He handed her a beer from the fridge.

'This is kinda weird, don't you think? He disappears and then turns up in the foyer of your building and picks a fight with the CEO of Gene-Asis. That's got to be more than just coincidence. I think you were meant to see that fight.'

'I never thought you would go all Zen on me.'

He shrugged. 'I spend lots of time alone, hunting hackers. You know, lots of time to think.'

Serena shook her head.

'The logical explanation is the professor probably worked for Gene-Asis – you know, doing research – and stuffed up. So they fired him and now he bears a grudge, and that's why he went after Bukowski.'

'But didn't he say something about someone being killed? What if he thought a Gene-Asis product had killed someone?'

Serena put her bottle on the table and sat down.

'Oh, John, don't go there. I've been told to stay clear of anything to do with Gene-Asis and my new boss is watching me like a hawk.'

'Okay, whatever. But I think this is your second chance.'

The Genesis Flaw

Serena waved her hand, as if to dismiss the idea. But she didn't enjoy her beer after that – it tasted sour and flat. She sat quietly as her mind ticked over the possibilities. She was hooked, however much she was trying to pretend to John and herself that she wasn't. What if McPherson really did know something incriminating?

Chapter 8

Serena needed to get up to speed on Mitsubishi's recent advertising campaign. She knew Aki Shimamoto, the client, better than she knew her brother, having grown further apart from Keith in recent years as her visits home had grown fewer and fewer. She never forgot Aki's daughters' birthdays: it was her job to remember. But she'd forgotten her niece's birthday last year and Keith had been furious. So, knowing the client well enough wasn't a problem. What she lacked was knowledge of the local advertising campaigns. She checked the file of television commercials, or TVCs, as they were called, and sighed when she realised that last year's were missing. As Jodi wasn't at her desk, she decided to pay her art director a visit.

Gloria was working in a temporary office diagonally across from Serena's. Gloria's PA, Caroline, was standing to attention in front of Gloria's desk as her boss shook her head. Caroline looked distressed. Serena couldn't hear what was being said, but Caroline's face was glum as she returned to her own desk.

'You all right?' asked Serena.

'Yeah,' Caroline replied, eyes down.

'And I need it in an hour,' ordered Gloria from her doorway.

'Yes, sir,' said Caroline under her breath, too annoyed to worry about what Serena thought.

'Can I just ask if you know where Jodi is?' asked Serena.

'No idea, sorry.' She then covered her face with her hands, as if she were about to cry.

Serena gave her shoulder a reassuring squeeze.

'I know Gloria can be a bit abrupt but don't let it get to you. It's not worth it. Why don't you grab yourself a cup of coffee and take a breather for five minutes? You'll feel a whole lot better.'

'Good idea,' she replied, her eyes watery, 'I might just take a quick break.'

The PA raced off. Something on her monitor caught Serena's eye. In her haste to leave, Caroline had forgotten to minimise the document she'd been working on for Gloria. It was the running sheet for the Gene-Asis product launch in New York. What had grabbed Serena's attention were the words 'Project New Dawn'. She leaned on Caroline's desk to take a closer look. So how did Dr McPherson know about such a top-secret launch? And why did he think it would make things worse? Now her interest was piqued.

'Serena, what are you looking at?'

Gloria was striding towards her.

'I'm looking for the latest Mitsubishi TVCs. Have you seen Jodi?'

'No, I haven't and where's Caroline?'

'Don't know, sorry,' she replied, strolling back to her office. She flicked a look behind her and caught Gloria minimising the document.

She stared at her keyboard for a while but her fingers didn't move across the keys. Apart from Project New Dawn, something bothered her about Gloria's presence in Sydney. Why was she here at all? The launch was in New York, so why waste her time in a country where the market for Gene-Asis products was so small? Gloria might be a bitch but she was a PR guru, so there had to be something critical to manage. And it had to be linked to Bukowski's unexpected arrival. Serena would have to wait for an opportune moment to collar Caroline. If there was one thing she had learned during her career, it was that PAs were a font of all company knowledge and if you could get them on side, you'd be one step ahead of the rest.

Absent-mindedly, she rubbed her middle finger over the diagonal scratch on her watch face. A week ago, when she'd been sorting through her father's clothes, she'd found his watch. Battered from years of use, she noticed a tiny piece of dirt behind the face. God knows how it had got inside. It said everything about her dad:

hard-working farmer and father who sacrificed a lot for his children. She'd asked a jeweller to make the strap smaller so she could wear it.

'Well, Dad, what do you make of that? Something's not right, is it?' she said to herself. She gazed out of her window at the view. She believed that T-Speed caused her dad's lung cancer. It was one of Gene-Asis' Supercrops. New Dawn was the code name for their next Supercrop range and McPherson clearly thought there was something wrong with it. Could it be the same thing that had killed her dad? Her eyes wandered to her monitor, where myriad files lay open, begging for attention.

'I've signed a contract,' she said aloud. But it made no difference. She had to know more. With one slow, deliberate motion, she minimised the files. Mitsubishi could wait. She grabbed her bag and took the elevator to the ground floor. She'd guessed correctly: there was Caroline sipping a cappuccino in one of the leather armchairs, toying with her mobile phone.

'Ah, back so soon,' cried the café owner, a little too loudly for Serena's liking. 'A long black?'

She was impressed he remembered.

'I'll take the juice, thanks,' she replied and went to join Caroline. The armchair next to her was empty, so Serena took it.

'Feeling any better?' asked Serena, opening her juice.

Caroline looked up. Her eyes were still a little pink along the lids.

'Yes, thanks.'

Serena leaned forward conspiratorially.

'Look, I know I'm new here but I've worked with Gloria before and she's like that with everyone. Try not to let it get to you. And she's only here for a few more days, isn't she?' Serena asked.

Caroline sat forward and looked around to see who might be within earshot.

'She's so, well, bossy. I mean, she talks to me like I'm an idiot.'

'Yeah, but she'll be gone soon.'

'Yeah, but I don't know how long she's here for. That's the worst of it. And she's giving me loads of work and I have to do all Nathan's as well. I can't do it all.'

Serena took a sip of her juice, not wanting to appear too eager.

'So, why is she here?'

Caroline looked around again.

'Something to do with a suicide they want kept under wraps. The top guy.'

'Oooh, that'll be a tough one,' cooed Serena. 'How on earth can they keep the CEO's suicide quiet?'

Serena's punt it was the CEO paid off. Caroline nodded. 'Yeah, I know, it's all a bit freaky. That Mr Bukowski wants it kept out of the press, and Gloria's moving heaven and earth to keep it that way.'

'Ah, because they don't want it to eclipse New Dawn.'

Caroline's dark eyes blinked in surprise. 'How do you know about that? It's all meant to be hush-hush.'

'Like I said, I've worked with Gloria before; I hear these things. But don't worry, I won't say a word.'

Caroline looked worried as she wriggled from her slippery leather seat.

'I'd better get back. Um, you won't say anything to anyone, will you?'

'My lips are sealed.'

'I'll see you up there.'

Serena pulled her phone from her bag and checked the internet for information about the Gene-Asis Asia-Pacific CEO. According to the latest reports, Tony Mancini was hugely successful and, more significantly, alive and well. The news hadn't leaked yet. So why would Bukowski and Gloria fly to the other side of the world to deal with this? Yes, it wouldn't be good publicity but she was still surprised by Bukowski's intervention.

She took another sip of the sharply acidic orange juice and then glanced at one of the elevators, indicating it had deposited Caroline onto the nineteenth floor. Surely the professor would know what was going on. It was risky but she hoped nobody would miss her if she disappeared for an hour.

Chapter 9

Serena drummed her fingers on the steering wheel as she waited impatiently for the traffic lights to change. As she drove into the campus, she couldn't help but notice the eclectic mix of elegant sandstone buildings, seventies monstrosities and ultra-modern facilities, projecting at odd angles over the site, as if keeping a watchful eye on the students.

She searched for signs to the genetics department but found none and approached a student lying under a tree, typing on his laptop. He gave her directions to the Reilly building. She was shocked at how young he looked. She was only in her early thirties but felt old enough to be his mother.

After several wrong turns, Serena found the dull two-storey building that housed the Genetics and Plant Research Faculty. A brass plate on the wall informed her it was, indeed, 'The Reilly Institute'. From the outside it looked like an abandoned hospital; the red bricks were grimy and the windowsills needed a new coat of paint.

Serena put a hand out to push open the double swing doors, then stopped. Her boss's warning replayed in her head. She took several deep breaths. 'Come on,' she said to herself. She opened the door and found herself in a long corridor with a light grey linoleum floor and many dark wooden doors stretching off into the garishly lit distance. She saw and heard no one. There was no reception desk. She walked towards the first door; her heels clomped loudly and she felt conspicuous in her suit. A door opened and a man and woman stepped out, deep in conversation. They wore knee-length lab coats and each had a pair of goggles balanced on their heads.

'Excuse me,' called Serena.

Their conversation stopped and they drew apart slightly.

'I was looking for someone and wondered if you could help me.'

'I've got to go. See you later,' said the woman to her colleague as she disappeared through another door.

The man took a few steps towards Serena, his rubber-soled trainers squeaking. Though he looked to be in his twenties, he still had acne.

'Who you after?'

'Dr McPherson.'

He blinked.

'Aw, he left years ago. Sorry.'

The man began to walk off and Serena followed.

'Do you know where he is now?'

He stopped.

'Who wants to know?'

A bead of sweat glistened in the cleft of his top lip.

'I was one of his students at Edinburgh Uni. I've moved to Sydney, so I thought I'd look him up.' Her cheeks burned at the lie.

'Look, he left some years back. I didn't know him, so I can't help you.'

He sped off, his trainers squeaking in rapid bursts.

'Can you tell me where he lives now?' Serena called after him. 'Please, he's an old friend.'

He stopped and chewed his lip nervously.

'Try Shelleyman Bay. I heard he moved there and became a recluse.'

'A recluse? What do you mean?'

The female colleague reappeared and bore down on them.

'I don't know,' he replied.

'Is there a problem here?' asked the woman.

'I'm trying to find Dr McPherson, and I believe he left here a few years ago?'

'Dr McPherson brought disgrace on this faculty and we have no interest in his whereabouts. We can't help you.'

'How did he bring … ?'

'I must ask you to leave now.'

The woman was ushering Serena through the entrance doors. Meanwhile, the young man had vanished. The double doors swung shut and Serena walked away from the Reilly Institute, unsettled by their unwillingness to help, and curious about what the professor had done to bring 'disgrace' upon them. She turned her head just enough to see the female researcher using her mobile. Their eyes met and Serena knew she was talking about her.

Chapter 10

Serena raised her arms above her head and stretched, then she walked over to her office window and surveyed the view. The sun was setting and the city was bathed in a blood-orange wash; the sky above, a darkening blue. Outside, the lights in the offices and apartments glittered. It had been a long day – made even longer by her desire for it to end.

Her visit to the Reilly Institute had done nothing to abate her nagging feeling that the professor knew something incriminating about Project New Dawn. And, most tantalising of all, in an office across from hers, Gloria was preparing its media launch.

Serena fiddled with her earring, as she paced in front of the window. Torn between action and inaction, she dropped heavily into her leather chair, and swung it from side to side as she stared at the ceiling. She knew that if she did this and was caught, her career was over. The risk was huge. But next door lay the answer. This was her chance to make amends for her failure to act previously.

Serena remembered the very first time she'd heard her father's rasping cough. He'd phoned her, as he always did on Sundays. He'd sounded out of breath as he spoke. His cough was deep and went on for a long time, and he had to hand the phone to Keith while he recovered. She remembered asking Keith if Dad had the flu. 'Probably, but he won't see a doctor,' he'd replied. Her father continued working in the fields, which were pungent with canola pollen. The canola was a new variety called T-Speed.

She frowned and forced her mind back to her dilemma. It was 8.10 pm. Eighteen people had desks in the department and only three of them were still working. Gloria was one. Questions and doubts ping-ponged through her mind, but she stayed put. Every five minutes or so, she looked to check if the desks outside were empty, but there was still movement. Just after 8.30 pm she heard Gloria's door click open and shut and, turning in her seat, saw Gloria walk out of the department. Grabbing her mobile, Serena popped her head out of her office and into a fug of Channel No. 5. At the water fountain, she filled a plastic cup and sipped from it. She looked around the room. She was alone at last. A solitary radio played in the empty department.

She chewed the rim of her plastic cup. Should she do this?

Throwing her cup in the bin, she wandered along the corridor, looking in other department offices. Marco and Gav were throwing a football to each other. They didn't notice her, as they were brainstorming the new strapline for the Mitsubishi campaign, which she'd asked for by tomorrow. Nathan, an account director, was shut away in the boardroom with his team of seven, working on the Woolworths' pitch. *They'll be in there all night*, she thought. Right down the other end of the corridor, she heard the whirr of a vacuum cleaner.

When she returned to her department, she found the lights had been turned off, probably by the cleaners. She left them off. Serena had made up her mind. Her hand shook so much, she dropped her handheld. She picked it up, her heart about to burst through her chest.

'Coward,' she said to herself. She glanced at the empty corridor. She then strolled to Gloria's office and checked the door, fully expecting it to be locked but hoping it wouldn't be. It slid open, sensing her presence. *Too easy*, she thought as the door shut quietly behind her. She stood in semi-darkness, with only the muted glow from the office building opposite to guide her. She surveyed the desk's surface. There was nothing of interest in the in-tray, except a confirmation letter and schedule from Channel One, detailing New Dawn's advertising spots. She flicked through it. Channel One serviced Australasia and was, without doubt, the biggest TV channel servicing the region. New Dawn's launch was so hush-hush that the project name, rather than the actual product names, was being used till the very last moment.

The Genesis Flaw

Serena went through Gloria's desk drawers and then turned her attention to the filing cabinets. She found drop files and the occasional plastic folder, inside which were USB drives. The light from the office block opposite was too dim to enable her to read the file names, so she moved Gloria's cordless desk lamp across to the top of one of the filing cabinets. She almost dropped that too. Her hands were clammy with perspiration.

She switched it on and her face lit up like the moon. Startled by its brightness, she instantly hit the switch and was plunged into semi-darkness again.

Pull yourself together, for God's sake. Just get on with it.

She turned the desk lamp on again, and her eyes quickly adjusted to the brightness. Her hot hand flicked through one file after another. She was down to the third drawer when she discovered 'New Dawn'.

No paper, just a USB key, which she placed in her Tbyte's drive, then turned the lamp off and crouched on the floor behind the desk. She pressed 'play'. Her screen came alive and she scrolled through the contents page of the 'Supercrop Ultra' product range.

Every year, Gene-Asis Biotech brought out a bigger, better product range. They marketed it heavily, encouraging farmers to buy the latest genetically engineered seeds and livestock. Serena knew this because her dad, anticipating bigger yields, had insisted on buying the new Supercrop wheat and canola each year.

For a fleeting second, she wondered why, with all their money, Gene-Asis couldn't come up with a more inventive brand name than 'Supercrop'. The contents page listed 124 new additions to the product range, all with the same launch date – in five weeks' time.

Serena skimmed the pages. The first product range was 'Frost Resistant': twelve fruits and vegetables, including tomatoes and grapes, which carried an 'anti-freeze' gene from an Antarctic fish.

'Bruise-free' fruit had been developed using animal-derived copper peptides, the same substance found in skin creams used to reduce the appearance of wrinkles. Gene-Asis claimed that the 'Bruise-free' range 'can survive unscathed the rigours of harvesting and transporting both to the food outlets/supermarkets and then on to the consumer's home'.

Next, 'Long-life Meat'. Seventeen standard breeds of cattle, chicken, pigs and sheep had been genetically engineered with an inbuilt preservative so that their 'meat will have twice the normal shelf life'.

Then, 'First To Market' crops, which had a human growth hormone implanted into their DNA. They grew '14% faster than the previous range of Speed products'.

Their next two ranges were completely new. The first was 'Extra-fruity Fruit'. Because people were complaining that genetically engineered fruit tasted of nothing much at all, Gene-Asis had created a new range in which the flavour component of the plants' DNA had been ramped up. They acknowledged that the fruits' sugar content had now increased, and warned that diabetics should exercise caution.

The second was 'Vitrboost', which was neither plant nor animal. It was a completely new genetically engineered virus, which killed the dangerous giardia parasite in the water supply. Vitrboost also contained an immune system booster, which they had sourced from the DNA of chimpanzees. Gene-Asis claimed it boosted the efficiency of human T-cells, 'which act like foot soldiers in the body's fight against infection'.

She quickly flicked through the rest of the range. There was nothing unexpected: Gene-Asis had always mixed a scary array of plant, animal and human genes in their products. She sighed; the document didn't tell her anything useful. She noted the names of the four scientists credited with these innovations: R. L. Singh in the US, Xiao Xu in China and Edelgard Koch in Australia. The fourth was an epidemiologist, Dr P. Munroe, also based in Australia. Serena hadn't seen Dr McPherson's name anywhere.

She scanned the next file, 'Press releases for science media'. There were eight prepared press releases, but their scientific jargon was baffling. Serena needed time to study the file properly, and the more time she spent in Gloria's office, the more likely she would be caught. All Serena needed to do was copy the documents onto her phone, so she could then view them at her leisure. She pressed the 'copy' command. Her Tbyte beeped loudly and 'Permission Denied' popped onto the screen. She swore under her breath.

Serena leant her head back against the desk drawers and took a deep breath. Scrambling to stand, she checked the next drop file and discovered the press releases had been printed but placed in the wrong drop file. Her only option was to copy the printout but that meant stepping into the department, which she didn't like the idea of at all. What if somebody walked in?

Returning the USB key to its plastic sheath, she took the printouts and sped to the photocopier, only to find someone had turned it off. Great!

'Photocopier on,' she said aloud.

The copier responded to her voice, lit up like a carousel at a fairground, whirred loudly for a few seconds, and then went silent. A bead of perspiration trickled down the back of Serena's neck. She leaned on the machine, willing it to speed up. Little images appeared on the display panel and 'ready to copy' illuminated her anxious face. Finding the feeder tray, she took the bulldog clip off the report and placed the documents in there.

'Copy. Double-sided. A4. Go.'

It began copying, the only noise a scratching sound as the paper moved through the machine. Serena's temples ached. She paced in front of the photocopier, willing it to go faster. Finally, the last page was done and, like a starving woman offered a meal, she grabbed the upturned photocopied report.

'Working late, Serena?' said Martin.

She froze, too terrified to turn and face the end of her career.

Chapter 11

Her survival instinct kicked in; she had to talk her way out of this. Serena could feel his presence behind her, almost feel his body heat. But had he seen what she was photocopying? Still unable to find the words to explain her actions satisfactorily, she slowly retrieved the originals from the tray and held them face down, close to her chest. She turned to look at him and forced the twitching muscles of her mouth into what she hoped appeared to be a relaxed smile.

'Why work in the dark?' he asked.

Martin's arms were crossed. There was no smile of idle curiosity.

'Been so busy I hadn't even noticed the lights were off. Seems like we're both working late, Martin.'

His eyes dropped to the papers. He stood so close, she could smell garlic on his breath.

'Serena.'

She felt her cheeks burning and hoped he couldn't see this tell-tale sign. Her mind was searching for an answer: what would she do if he asked to see the papers?

'Yes, Martin?'

'How are you going with the pitch ideas?'

'It's done. I'm presenting initial concepts to you tomorrow, aren't I?'

He nodded.

'Why don't you give me a sneak preview now?'

'Now?'

'Yes, now.'

'I would love to but I …'

Martin was already walking in the direction of her office. Serena followed and glanced at Gloria's desk lamp, illuminating her filing cabinets. Would Martin think it strange?

Inside her office, she placed the pile of papers, face down, next to some Mitsubishi files. She daren't dock her phone, as Gloria's files would appear on her monitor. Instead, she picked up some A3 storyboards scattered over her desk. Martin stood in the corner.

'It seems to me that Mitsubishi currently owns no brand platform. It's a "me too" brand. It needs to own something tangible, something people want and find attractive, something they care about,' she began.

Martin's eyes were glazed: he wasn't listening.

'One sec, Serena,' he said, leaving her. She watched in horror as he entered Gloria's office and stood in the desk lamp's glare, like a circus ringmaster in a solitary spotlight. She dared not move. Had she shut the filing cabinet or left it open? She'd closed it, hadn't she?

Stupefied, Serena stared across the darkened floor, the empty chairs and abandoned desks looking like debris from a night shipwreck. He strode back to her office, leaving Gloria's lamp still on. Serena swallowed. Had the light simply distracted him? If so, why hadn't he turned it off? She knew from the look on his face that something was wrong.

Martin walked straight past her and picked up the pile of papers she had so carefully placed face down on her desk. He took one look at the upturned pages and frowned, his thick brows forming one dark line across his forehead.

'What the fuck are you doing with these?' he yelled as he slapped them back on the desk. Serena wanted to disappear but she knew the best course of defence was attack. If she were to save her career, she had to bluff. She straightened her back, raising an eyebrow.

'Martin, how dare you yell at me like that!' she said, indignant. 'That stuff was printing when I got there. Gloria had just left: she must have forgotten about it. I was going to leave it in her office, and then you turned up and wanted to see the storyboards. I simply forgot I had it in my hand.' She had both knuckles on her waist, her elbows wide apart. She looked genuinely insulted.

'Give me a fucking break, Serena. I wasn't born yesterday. This is all about Gene-Asis,' he said, nodding at the pile of fanned-out paper. 'You went into Gloria's office and copied confidential information, despite your contractual agreement to have nothing to do with Gene-Asis.'

'I did no such thing.'

He raised his arms in exasperation. 'Give me your phone,' he ordered.

'I will not. What's on that phone is my business.'

His hand swept down onto it and he was checking its small screen before she could stop him.

He grunted. 'Ah ha!' He turned the phone round so she could see the screen. 'Gloria caught you snooping around Caroline's desk. She said you wouldn't be able to resist. You'd have to know about New Dawn. And she was right,' he said, triumphantly, holding up the phone as if he were a statue of Justice, holding up scales.

She'd been caught red-handed. Her face and neck were covered in blotches of agitation and her heart was racing but she was barely breathing, which made her light-headed. She had to remain calm and fight her corner if she had any chance of coming out of this with her reputation intact. She forced herself to take a few deep breaths.

'I want to know what's going on, Martin. Why did McPherson assault Bukowski and what's wrong with the new range? It's faulty, isn't it?'

Martin stepped forward, shaking his head at her, the veins on his neck visibly bulging despite the semi-darkness.

'You stupid, paranoid bitch. You've just chucked your whole career down the dunny for nothing. There is nothing wrong with Supercrop and there never has been.' He stepped closer, his chin jutting out. 'And even if there was something wrong, it's none of our business, you hear?'

'We have a moral responsibility …'

'Oh, get over yourself. The advertising business is not about moral judgements. Our job is to sell; sell anything. Sell sand to the fucking Arabs, if needs be. We're not paid to worry about clients' products. We're paid to advertise them. End of story. You've been in this game long enough to know that, so don't give me this moral crap.'

He flicked on the light switch in her office. She squinted at him. Time to switch tactics.

'Martin, I've made a mistake. I'm sorry, truly I am,' she said, her voice soft, her head bowed submissively. 'But it is all going to be made public in a few weeks. So can we just forget this happened?'

'Are you completely out of your mind? You abuse your position by stealing confidential information, and if Gene-Asis ever hears about it, we'll lose our twenty-billion-dollar global account. Unbe-fucking-lievable,' he said, shaking his head.

'But if it's so confidential, why didn't Gloria lock her door?'

'I asked her to leave it unlocked.'

It dawned on her then that she'd fallen into a trap.

'You never wanted me here, did you, Martin?'

He grinned triumphantly.

'You're fired, Serena Swift. And if I have anything to do with it, you'll never work in this business again.'

No more submissive tone. Serena had to fight.

'How dare you, Martin! I've been at Rooneys four years and I've never put a foot wrong. I've won this company new accounts worth thirty billion. Thirty billion! Nobody else has my client contacts, my connections. If I go, so does your hope of winning Mitsubishi and that will make you look bad. Very bad.'

Martin slumped into her chair and joined his hands as if in prayer, his middle fingers tapping his chin thoughtfully.

'Okay, here's a deal. You win us Mitsubishi. You'll work offsite; we'll set you and your team up somewhere else. Then you resign, giving whatever reasons you like. Otherwise, I fire you tonight and I'll tell everyone you were caught stealing confidential information.'

She moved closer and perched on the edge of her desk so that she was looking down on Martin. The Swift family temper had kicked in: she was not going to be shafted, especially not by this little rodent.

'Martin, I know you're not going to tell anyone that. You won't want Gene-Asis knowing I've seen this stuff. I mean, me, of all people. Gene-Asis would fire Rooneys like that.' She clicked her fingers. 'No, you're going to want to keep it quiet. So, here's *my* deal. I resign tonight, so I can spend time with my family. You'll pay me a year's salary and my full bonus, and sign a glowing reference, which I'll write.

You will never blacken my name because, if you do, I'll tell Gene-Asis that confidentiality at Rooneys is non-existent and documents leak like a bucket full of holes.'

Martin looked like he'd been rugby tackled from behind.

'And Mitsubishi?'

'I'll phone Aki and put in a good word for you, and tell him you'll be looking after him personally.'

Martin opened his mouth to object and then apparently thought better of it. He held out his hand. 'Your phone.'

She hesitated but it was Rooneys' property.

'And you will sign a gagging order guaranteeing you will not discuss anything relating to Project New Dawn, Dr McPherson or Gene-Asis for five years, with the media, or with anybody. If you break this agreement, Rooneys will sue you. Your life won't be worth living.'

'You have a deal.'

This was the second time she'd made a deal with her employer over Gene-Asis. But this time, she had no intention of keeping to it.

Chapter 12

Serena placed her wine glass on the coffee table and collapsed back into the sofa cushions. She raised her right hand: it was still shaking. She'd felt physically sick when she'd arrived home. John and Baz were out, so she'd started drinking and the bottle was now two-thirds empty.

There was the sound of a key in the front door and John walked in.

'Honey, I'm home,' he called in an American accent and then appeared, grinning, in the lounge doorframe. Serena looked up, her face pallid and drawn. He carried his suit jacket nonchalantly over his shoulder and he'd removed his tie: the end of it dangled like a striped snake from his pocket. He dropped his jacket on a chair and sat next to her.

'What's happened, Seri?'

She shook her head. She couldn't look at him.

'I've stuffed up big time.'

'How?'

She told him.

'Ah,' he said, 'that's not so good, but you turned it around. You got a great payout and a glowing reference. I gotta say, you've got balls, standing your ground like that.'

'I was shaking like a leaf, John. But I had to do something. Martin would've loved nothing better than destroy my reputation. He never liked the way Lenny pushed him into employing me. At least he knows now that if he trashes me, I'll make sure he loses his biggest client. And he can't afford to risk that. He'll do anything to hush it up. I'll just lie low for a while and then get another job.' Her tone was bullish. She paused. 'But I feel so ashamed. Caught like a common thief. God, if Dad'd been alive …' She shook her head and continued, 'he'd have been gutted, knowing I was fired for stealing.'

Serena had sunk further into the deep cushions and looked like a little girl who'd just received a parental reprimand. Her chin rested on her chest and she didn't look at John, just stared at the polished floorboards.

'I feel bad,' he said. 'I encouraged you. I'm so sorry.'

'I decided to snoop around. It's not your fault.'

'Yeah, yeah. I've always got you into trouble.' He leaned forward, placing his elbows on his knees and ran his hands through his wavy hair. He paused, with his hands on the back of his neck. Serena noticed that his cufflinks sported the ace of spades, and remembered him explaining years ago that it was a hacker thing and symbolised taking a gamble. He'd always been a risk taker. 'Even now I'm Mr Corporate, toeing the line, I still manage to drag you into a mess.'

Serena's face broke into a smile. 'Not for a while, you haven't. I think the last time was over Gary. Gary Shorten.'

John looked across at her and smiled back. She'd seen that wicked grin so many times before. 'I enjoyed that one,' he said.

She leaned sideways and shoved him in the shoulder. 'Poor Gary. He'd gone all out to impress me and booked dinner at Tetsuya's, and you had to go and hack his bank account so his credit card was rejected. He was mortified I had to pay the bill. I never heard from him again, thanks to you.'

'Come on, Seri, I did you a favour. He was a complete dick. A rich dick, but a dick, nonetheless.'

Serena shrugged. 'Maybe. But he really liked me and I haven't exactly had much success with relationships since.'

Their momentary light-heartedness faded as they each withdrew into themselves, remembering an incident they would both rather forget. John broke the silence. 'So what happens next?'

'With all this spare time on my hands, I investigate New Dawn.'

John's head shot up in surprise.

She continued, 'Don't worry, I'll be careful. Do it quietly. I'm fully aware of the implication of the gagging order.'

The concern on his face morphed into open-mouthed admiration.

'Now who's turned into the rebel? Who'd have thought it? But be careful, Seri. If Gene-Asis gets wind of you asking around, they'll come down on you like a tonne of bricks.'

'I know.'

'Hold on. It could make life difficult for Baz. He does recruit for them and you're living with us.'

'Yeah, I know. Maybe I should move out?'

'That's crazy. You've only just moved in. No, I'll talk to him, see how he feels. He'll probably say it's cool, as long as he has no idea what you're doing. You'll need to keep him out of this.'

'No problem.'

'So, what's next?'

'Finding McPherson. I'm going to Shelleyman Bay.'

John frowned. 'He may not want to be found.'

'I know but I'm good at networking, remember? I'll ask around.'

'I'll come with you. You know, just in case.'

'Just in case of what?' she laughed. 'Look, John, I'll be fine. I can look after myself,' she said, slowly and deliberately.

When Serena had made up her mind, nobody could change it.

In her bedroom, she switched on her monitor and dialled Tracey Pollack's number at the UK's newspaper *The Post*. Serena had first met Tracey through a colleague at Rooneys London and they'd become the best of friends.

'What?'

'Trace?'

Serena's screen was blank.

'Uh-huh.'

'It's me, Serena. Turn on your monitor. I can't see you.'

'Hello, darling! How are you, mate?' Tracey squealed in her cockney accent, rapidly followed by a big sniff.

Her image filled Serena's screen. She was hunched over her messy desk, with a thick red scarf coiled around her neck. Her short platinum hair was gelled into spikes.

'Sorry I was a grumpy old fart when I answered. I've got the worst cold. Hold on, let me grab some tissues.'

Serena waited as Tracey noisily blew her nose.

'All right, I can talk now. So, how's it going, twinkle?'

'Not so good, to be honest.'

'Oh God. Is that Gloria bitch giving you a hard time?'

'How did you know she was here?'

'Word gets around. You know the Rooneys' grapevine. I meant to tap you an email to warn you but I've been up to my neck in work … anyway, so what've you gone and done then? Hey?'

'Got fired.'

'Bleeding Nora! How on earth did you manage that?'

'My boss caught me photocopying a confidential file on Gene-Asis.'

'Oh, bloody hell! Are you out of your mind?'

'Probably. I've blown it at Rooneys. At least I've negotiated a good severance deal, but I just hope I get another advertising job.'

Serena leaned forward, her hair partially obscuring her face, eyes downcast.

'Rubbish. Of course you will. Where's my feisty friend, Serena Swift, gone? You're a fighter, missy, and don't you forget it.'

'Yeah. And I've been all brave in front of John but I'm secretly wondering what the hell I've just gone and done.'

'Aw, mate, I wish I could give you a hug. I know it's been hard for you,' Tracey said, stretching out her hand and touching her monitor.

'Thanks, Trace.'

'So what made you do it?'

Serena knew the journalist in Tracey couldn't resist wanting to know more. 'I saw Al Bukowski attacked by a geneticist in the lobby. This guy was screaming about Project New Dawn, saying it would make things worse and it wasn't too late to stop it, whatever "it" is.'

'What's Bukowski doing in Australia?'

'I have no idea.' Serena hesitated. 'But I have a theory.'

'Come on, mate. You can tell me.'

'If I tell you, you have to promise me you won't act on the information. I've signed a gagging order. I'll end up in serious hot water if you do.'

'Mate, you know I can't give you that promise. But I will give you my word I'll never reveal my source.'

Serena, sitting on the edge of her bed, pulled up her long legs and crossed them. Tracey had become her constant companion in London, in many ways filling the void left by her losing touch with John. Serena trusted her totally but at the same time recognised that if she confided in Tracey, an exceptional journalist, she had to accept that the news hound within her would pursue the story.

'The word is the Asia-Pacific CEO has committed suicide and Bukowski wants Gloria to keep it quiet.'

'Now, that *is* interesting and, let's face it, not a good look for Gene-Asis. I haven't heard anything, so I'll do some digging. Now, who assaulted Bukowski? A relative of the suicide?'

'No, I don't think so. It was a Dr McPherson. I've looked up his bio and he's a plant geneticist. But not just any old researcher. Department head at Harvard. Poached by Arthur Phillip uni. Then nothing since 2011. The university said he'd disgraced the faculty.'

'Oooh, I love a bit of disgrace. Let me have a quick look at this bloke and see if I can find out anything. Keep going,' Tracey said as she tapped away at her keyboard.

'They really didn't like me asking about him and no one would tell me where he was. They're obviously hiding something.'

'Those instincts of yours are going to land you in trouble one day, my love. Here we go, Dr McPherson. Yes, he does seem to have vanished, doesn't he! I wonder why? Nothing in the media about being disgraced. Oh, hold on, what's this?'

'What?'

'Looks like he tried to publish a paper in December 2011 in *Bioscience Journal*. It was about to go to print when it was pulled. He then tried *The Lancet* and *Scientific American* and was turned down. I've got some quotes here from peers criticising his methods and saying his findings were invalid. Odd, though, I can't find the actual research anywhere. It's usually available.'

'What was the paper on?'

'Doesn't say, but there was a big barny over it. A Dr Munroe really slagged him off.'

'P. Munroe?'

'Yeah, Philip, how do you know him?'

'He's one of the four scientists behind Project New Dawn. He works for Gene-Asis.'

'And?'

'And … maybe McPherson worked on New Dawn too.'

'Maybe. Maybe he didn't make the grade, or he cocked up somehow, and got the boot. He could just be holding a grudge.'

'Maybe.'

'Well, it's worth sniffing around. But don't get your hopes up, my love. I mean, what's more likely – that he's got a grudge or that one of the biggest companies in the world is covering up selling dangerous stuff to millions of people? That kind of story only comes along once in a lifetime.'

'Come on, Trace, you and I both know Gene-Asis funds every research lab they use to verify product safety. If they want scientists to say their products are safe, that's what happens. What about that researcher who was fired for claiming their GM potatoes caused stomach cancer in rats? Why was he fired? Because Gene-Asis funded his faculty. So, instead of making people sit up and take notice, his research sinks without a trace. Not even *The Post* ran the story. Why not?'

'I'd rather not comment on that.' Tracey looked away, sheepishly.

'Precisely, not even the media can stand up to them.'

'Mate, why are you doing this to yourself? It must be torture. Why not move on, build a new life? Your dad would have wanted that.'

'I can't now. Not when I'm onto something.'

'You know more than you're letting on, don't you?' she asked, smiling her characteristic tight-lipped grin; Tracey didn't like her teeth. 'Come on. Fess up. What were you copying?' Tracey clicked her pen very fast, as she often did when she was excited.

'The press releases on New Dawn.'

'Jesus, tell me about them.'

'But, Trace …'

'I promise I won't print even a syllable. Not unless I can verify it from another source. You have my word.'

Serena took Tracey through what she'd read in Gloria's office, which wasn't very much.

'Hmm. That Vitrboost sounds huge. But there's nothing that rings alarm bells.'

'I know.'

'So what are you going to do now?'

'I'm going to find McPherson.'

'Jeez. You *are* obsessed.'

'Maybe,' said Serena, 'but what have I got to lose?'

Serena fixed herself a quick snack of cheese on toast and a cup of tea. The phone rang.

'Mate?'

Serena turned on her screen and there was Tracey staring at her.

'Trace. What's up?'

'I think I've found something interesting in last week's *Australian*.'

'What?'

'You know you said that Dr Munroe worked on New Dawn …'

'Yes.'

'And you know you said that Dr McPherson has done a vanishing act.'

'Yes. And?'

'Dr Munroe is filed as a missing person. He was last seen arguing with the Australasian CEO of Gene-Asis.'

Chapter 13

Serena had caught the red-eye flight from Sydney and then hired a taxi for the forty-minute trip to the remote Shelleyman Bay. Blinking away tiredness, she drew back the wooden shutters of her Balinese-style accommodation. She then placed the new Tbyte she'd bought at the airport in her handbag. She'd paid cash for the phone and faked her name and contact details on the sales document. She was keen to ensure her phone calls remained private. Call it paranoia or intuition, but she felt safer that way. On the plane, she'd set up a new Hotmail address under a false name.

Walking down a narrow path to the beach, Serena felt the cold, damp sand beneath her feet turn scorching hot as she stepped from under the trees' shade. Out at sea, about twenty surfers faced the horizon, waiting for their wave. One approached, and she watched one young surfer bend and contort his body like a Play-Doh man, riding the crest till the bitter end. A matted, sun-bleached head disappeared into the foaming surf as the surfer's board shot skywards.

A few minutes later, Serena meandered through the beach's car park, settled herself at the first café she could find and ordered a Sunrise. It was baking hot already, but her freshly squeezed juice arrived beautifully pink and cold. A large blue umbrella provided shade from the sun as she sat outside The Three Sisters café.

Tanned holiday-makers strolled by wearing very little, bar baseball caps, shades, swimmers and the occasional well-worn daypack. She could smell sun lotion on the breeze. Life seemed relaxed here. The town had a friendly vibe and Serena was confident that people would be willing to help her.

She went to the counter, where a cappuccino machine spluttered. A dark-haired woman making the coffees was clearly one of the sisters; Serena recognised her from a huge surreal painting hung behind the counter. In it, the three women were sitting on the back of a whale drinking tea.

'That'll be four dollars, thanks.'

'Lovely juice.'

'Glad you enjoyed it.'

As Serena handed her the money, she asked, 'I'm looking for my old uni professor, Dr McPherson. Do you know him?'

The woman had her hand in the till, retrieving Serena's change. She toyed with the coins, staring fixedly at them.

'No, sorry. Have a good day.'

She gave Serena the change and turned back to the cappuccino machine without looking at her again. Dropping a coin in the tip jar, Serena stepped out onto the pavement, wondering who to ask next. She'd try the café opposite. As she walked off, she glanced at the woman she'd just paid. There stood all three sisters, huddled in close-knit conversation. Serena felt their eyes follow her as she crossed the road.

She entered Max's café. Long cushions lay on benches lining the walls, and the smell of lemongrass and ground coffee was delicious. Opera music played in the background and a man sang along to *Carmen* as he cut a slice of cheesecake for a customer.

'Good morning, how can I help you?'

'Hello. I'm an old student of Dr McPherson's and someone told me he'd moved here. I was wondering if you could point me in the right direction?'

He leaned over the counter.

'You're a journalist, aren't you?'

'No, not at all.'

'People round here like to keep themselves to themselves, and we don't like strangers poking around in our business. G'day to you,' he said, turning his back on her.

Taken aback by his hostility, she left quickly and walked around the corner. Spotting the library, she hoped she might find a friendlier face there, but the answer was the same – nobody knew of Dr McPherson. Feeling as unwanted as a leper in a maternity ward, Serena left the library. Next, she tried The Welcome pub. The doors and windows were wide open, and the publican was wiping down tables.

'Don't know him.'

Then she called in at the tiny two-pump garage, and asked the female attendant about Dr McPherson.

'You're a journo, aren't you?'

'No, an old friend.'

'Can't help you.'

Outside, the sun beat down on her head as she considered her next step. Had journalists tried to talk to the professor recently? Perhaps she wasn't alone in believing he had a story to tell. She began to think he was either a total recluse or he didn't live in the Bay anymore.

She noticed a police car parked over the road, with a pot-bellied cop leaning against the bonnet as he chatted to a man she recognised from Max's café. The cop nodded, his pudgy arms folded across his chest. He was wearing dark shades but she was sure he was watching her.

Keen to escape his gaze, Serena headed for a park overlooking the beach and sat under one of the many trees offering shade. Lying nearby, under the same tree, was a man with a tanned chest, bare save for a pigskin waistcoat roughly stitched together. His thick blond curly hair had bits of grass and twigs in it and he lay on his back staring at the tree's branches above. His face fascinated her. A blue tattoo line ran across his forehead and another ran from his ears, down his jawline and across his chin, and disappeared in the reddish-gold tufts of his beard. His green eyes looked at her.

'Isn't it magic?' he said.

'Yes, the beach is beautiful.'

'No, I mean the tree.'

His eyes peered up into its branches again. He was staring at a Norfolk pine. She looked up for a few seconds and saw tiny shards of sunlight piercing the dark underside of the tree's canopy. When she looked down, he was sitting cross-legged next to her, so close she could see the smooth blond hairs on his arms and smell his unwashed body.

'Where are you from?'

'Er, Orange.'

She leaned back to create some space between them.

'How long are you here for?'

'Just a few days.'

'Shame. All you'll see are the money-monkeys … the shops, the cafés, the bars. You won't see the real beauty of the place. You won't sense its spiritual beauty, its energy. Hey, if you like, I can show you the real Shelleyman Bay.'

'I'd love that,' she replied politely, 'but I'm here for a reason, and I don't seem to be having much success.'

He leaned back on both arms, his eyes dropping momentarily onto Serena's sun top.

'Why do you have to be here for a reason? Why can't you just be? You should try it some time. Why don't you come to our camp at Kin Kin? You can chill out there and just be yourself.'

'Thanks, but I have to find someone.'

Serena stood, keen to get away from him. His directness unnerved her and she didn't like him eyeing her body.

'Who do you need to find, apart from yourself?'

She frowned at him, annoyed by his presumption that she hadn't already found herself. She knew exactly who she was and felt like telling him so. But, bereft of any leads, she decided to play along with him.

'Dr McPherson.'

'Ahhh, the poor professor,' he nodded.

'You know him?'

'Poor bastard. Lives alone in the hills. I don't know what he did but the cops keep a close eye on him; hassle him and shit.'

She sat down.

'I used to be a student of his … and I really have to see him. It's very urgent.'

'You're not his student. I can tell you're lying but that doesn't matter. I can see there's good in your intentions.'

'Will you help me then?'

He lay on his back with his hands behind his head.

'I could do, depending on how much you would appreciate the information.'

She understood immediately.

'How about a donation to help fund the camp?'

'Yeah, that could help. When the cops raided us and pulled up all our "tomato" plants, they left us with nothing to sell. So, times have been a bit tough lately.'

Serena handed him a twenty-dollar note. He took it and placed it in his waistcoat pocket, and propped himself up on an elbow.

'There are forty of us to feed.'

She gave him another twenty dollars.

'That's all I have,' she said.

'Do you have a pen? It's kinda hard to find, so I'll draw you a map.'

She never carried a pen, relying on her smartphone for everything. 'You can draw it here,' she said, pointing to the tiny screen.

'Nah, nah. I can't be doing with that techno shit.'

Serena spotted a woman sketching nearby and asked her if she could borrow a pencil. Picking up a discarded paper bag, she tore off a strip and handed both to the tattooed man. He drew a map to Leatherback Point.

'It's the one with the big "Private Property" sign,' he said.

Chapter 14

Serena sat in her rented car, studying the sketched map and the local street directory, and then set off along Bendigos Way. Lush green bush shrouded the road, and the sound of birds squawking and whooping seemed amplified by the tunnel of tall trees. Bendigos Way came to an abrupt end at a busy beach car park. She must have missed the turn-off. She did a U-turn and slowly drove back up Bendigos Way. A police car went by. Serena couldn't see the driver and wondered if it was the same cop who'd been eyeballing her earlier.

Distracted, she almost drove past a narrow turn-off to the left. It was unsigned but she guessed this must be the route: tattooed man had warned her it was an unmade road. As her Volkswagen Beetle swayed from side to side, bouncing up the rocky road, she remembered the car rentals manager warning her not to take it off-road. But it had been the only car left for hire, so here she was, bouncing and revving it up the hill. The tree's branches intertwined into a thick canopy. When the sunlight broke through, its rays illuminated the dust that swirled behind her. Loose stones twanged against the side of the car. She looked at her mobile on the passenger seat. It had no reception.

The dirt track narrowed, and wound like a snake into a tighter coil. A battered four-wheel drive zoomed around a corner and passed her without slowing, leaving behind a dust cloud so thick she had to slam on the brakes. When it cleared, she continued, the road levelling out, and to her left she caught glimpses of a turquoise blue ocean through low trees. Three cars covered in thick layers of brown dust were parked at the side of the track. Someone had written 'C U 2nite' on the filthy windscreen of an old sedan. A path disappeared down the cliff, which she guessed led to a beach.

At a fork in the rough road, she came across a dilapidated sign made of two planks of wood with 'Private Property' painted on it in black. The Beetle protested loudly as she accelerated up the steep and deeply gullied road. Densely tree-lined, the branches hung so low they clawed at the roof. The track cleared to reveal a wooden cabin raised on stilts, surrounded by trees, which kept it permanently in the shade. A huge deck appeared to go right around the house. A dusty old Land Rover was parked under a torn green tarpaulin strung up between trees and a water tank. To the left of the house was a thriving vegetable garden, and a chicken coop. And, standing in the doorway, behind the flyscreen door, a man watched her.

Serena got out of the car and smiled nervously as she walked towards the house. The figure didn't move from behind the flyscreen. Going up the rotten porch steps, she could just make out a man in his early sixties, with John Lennon–style glasses and an ungroomed beard. He wore only shorts. She couldn't see enough to be sure of his identity but the shadowy face resembled the angry person she'd seen in the Rooneys' lobby. As her shoe touched the creaky deck, he spoke.

'What do you want?'

'Are you Dr Fergus McPherson?'

'Who wants to know?'

He spat the words out in a guttural Scottish accent that she recognised as the professor's.

'My name's Serena and I want to talk to you about Project New Dawn.'

'Go away. Now.'

'I saw you confront Bukowski in the Rooneys' building. I heard what you said and I …'

'Go away. This is private property!' he bellowed.

She took a few steps nearer. He stood squarely behind the flyscreen, blocking the entrance, his hand on the door handle.

'You're Dr McPherson, aren't you?'

'Leave me alone. Haven't you people tormented me enough?'

'No, you don't understand. I need your help ...'

A car rumbled up the track towards the house and, through the gathering dust cloud, Serena saw a police car. The man immediately disappeared into the dark recesses of his house.

'No, wait, please; I just want to talk.'

Two policemen got out of the car and she recognised the big-bellied one. The other was younger, with a rugby player's build. Neither approached the house.

'Can you come down here, please, ma'am?' the rotund one called, arms folded across his chest.

Serena did as she was asked.

'Can I see your ID?'

She handed him her driver's licence, which the younger one took and placed in his scanner. He looked at the screen.

'So, Serena Swift, what're you doing on this here private property?'

Instinctively, she knew that to tell the truth would be unwise. They must have followed her all the way from the town. Why would they do that?

'I'm an old student of Dr McPherson's, on vacation, and wanted to look him up for old time's sake.'

'See here,' said the older cop, as he leaned forward and pushed his pug-like face into hers, 'this is Constable Bob Grimes and I'm Senior Constable Anthony Heffernan. You're trespassing on private property, so we are asking you to leave.'

'But I'm a guest. I'm not trespassing.'

'Don't seem like an invited guest to me. So, be a good girl and get in your car and drive away,' said Heffernan.

Serena saw red but bit her tongue. Now was not a good time to have an argument.

'Look, I've flown a long way to see him. He probably doesn't recognise me, it's been such a long time. Just let me have another word with him. I'm sure he'll invite me ...'

Grimes looked at Heffernan and grinned.

'Sounds like she's refusing to leave.'

'Yup, sounds like it to me,' responded Heffernan.

Grimes stepped forward. She caught a whiff of his sweat and noticed the damp stains under his armpits.

'I'm asking you nicely to leave the professor's private property. If you refuse, you'll be coming with us to the station. Choice is yours.'

Serena looked from one to the other.

'I'm going, officers. I didn't mean to cause any trouble.'

'And,' chimed in Heffernan, his breath a pungent mix of bad eggs and cigarettes, 'I don't want you coming near the prof again. He wants to be left alone. If I hear about you hassling him, I'll be on your back so fast you won't know what's hit you.'

'I'm going now,' she replied and hurried to her car. As she turned the key in the ignition, she saw the cops amble back to their car and get in. Serena scanned the house windows for any sign of the professor. He'd disappeared. The cops tailed her all the way back to her accommodation in Shelleyman Bay.

Chapter 15

Serena locked the apartment door behind her. The heat and humidity were stifling, so she opened the balcony doors. A blistering wind engulfed her, even hotter than the interior of the room. She scanned the walls for any sign of air conditioning and realised there was none. Beads of sweat trickled down the back of her neck as she removed her sodden T-shirt and shorts, hoping to feel a little cooler. It didn't help.

She took a bottle of sparkling mineral water from the fridge and gulped it down, leaving the fridge door open. Serena crouched in front of it, enjoying the feeling of the cool air on her body. The little fridge's motor clicked in and rattled loudly as it tried to generate its programmed temperature. She closed the fridge door and leaned against the balcony doorframe as she stared out to sea.

The cops' behaviour was really odd. Excessive, in fact. What was it all about? Why did they want to keep her away from the professor? Who were they protecting? The professor or someone else?

She finished off the water, but continued to hold the bottle in her hand, not moving. She watched people swimming and surfing, and heard squeals of delight from children on the beach.

Well, she sure as hell wasn't going to let some small-town thugs push her around. One thing her dad had always taught her was to stand up to bullies. But how could she speak to McPherson without Grimes and Heffernan knowing? The town folk appeared to act as their spies. Serena ambled to the bed and lay, arms and legs splayed, trying to stop hot skin rubbing against hot skin. She was too overheated to think clearly. So, she donned her bikini and headed for the invitingly cool waves.

It was seven in the evening. As she retraced the route along the tree-lined roads to the professor's house, she kept an eager eye on her rear-view mirror. Nervous, she'd been unable to eat anything all day and her empty stomach growled. There hadn't been a police car outside her apartment when she'd snuck out, and she'd taken care to find a back road through the town. On seeing the 'Private Property' sign, she accelerated hard and skidded up the track.

As it dipped, she entered a thick canopy of trees. She only had to turn the corner and she would see the professor's house. Her mouth dry as rice paper, she sped around the blind corner. Hurtling towards her was a dirty green Land Rover. She swung to the left, the Land Rover to the right. Her wing mirror cracked. She slammed on her brakes and screeched to a halt. The front of her car was buried in lantana bushes. The Land Rover stopped a bit further down the track in a dust cloud and McPherson got out. He was incredibly thin; his chest concave, his ribs protruding like xylophone keys. He wore only a faded pair of blue denim shorts. He strode barefoot towards her.

'What the hell do you think you're doing?' he shouted, waving his arms in the air.

Serena got shakily out of her car.

'It's you!' he said. He was barely a metre from her. 'Leave me alone. Do you understand?' he yelled and stomped back to his car.

'No. Please wait.'

She chased after him until she touched his bare shoulder. He swung around, furious.

'Who the hell do you think you are? Get off my property or I'll call the police.'

'I'm not a journalist. I just want to talk to you about Gene-Asis.'

'I'm calling the cops.'

'Please don't do that. Please.'

He turned away from her but she managed to grab his arm. He wrenched it away.

'Did Gene-Asis' products kill your wife?'

Desperate to hold his attention, she took a punt that the woman Gene-Asis had supposedly 'killed' was his wife. If she'd slapped him, he couldn't have looked more startled.

'I have nothing to say.'

She looked into a pair of sunken blue eyes and sensed his desolation.

'Please help me. I've lost my job because I believed what you said about New Dawn. I think Gene-Asis' products are unsafe. I think you think so too. Please talk to me.'

'I know nothing about it,' he growled.

The professor got into his Land Rover and turned the ignition. It fired up loudly and, shutting his door, he jammed the gear into first and began to move away from her. She hung onto the door handle.

'Yes, you do. You said it will make things "worse." I heard you. What will get worse?'

He accelerated and Serena ran faster.

'Let go, you idiot!' he shouted.

The dust was blinding her. She coughed up dirt. But she wouldn't let go.

'They killed my dad,' she screamed, as she slipped and tumbled to the side of the road. The Land Rover continued down the track. She had fallen hard and cut her knee, the blood trickling down her dirty shin. She didn't move, her head in her hands. She felt a complete fool. She had lost her job for nothing. He wouldn't even talk to her. She stared at the ground in disbelief. The bush went quiet, save for the wind in the trees. Head bowed over her knees, she was not aware of his presence until she noticed a pair of dirty feet, one toenail black with bruising. His hand touched her shoulder gently.

'What happened to your dad?'

She looked into the professor's eyes again.

'Lung cancer. He was a farmer. Used T-Speed canola, and I know it killed him.'

He leaned down, his skeletal hand still on her shoulder.

'I'm so sorry. When someone you love dies, it's like a part of you dies too.'

'Please help me. You gave me hope. Hope you know something, anything ...'

'Don't let your guilt take over your life. Let it go. I know. I lived and breathed my guilt, wallowing in my own self-pity. And look what I've become.'

She watched a dark shadow pass across his face, as if he were reliving some horror.

'Why won't you talk to me?'

'What's your name?'

'Serena Swift.'

'Serena, I can't talk to you. Please go home and forget what I said to Bukowski.'

'But why won't you talk to me?' she persisted.

'Because I'm a coward.'

He stood up and offered his hand to help her stand. Hobbling up, she winced at her painful knee.

'Are you able to drive?'

She had to have one more go. 'Project New Dawn is the code name for Supercrop Ultra. Did you work on it?'

'You need to get out of here, quickly,' he said looking around.

'Professor, I am not going anywhere until you tell me why nobody wants me to talk to you.'

He shook his head.

'Serena, don't ask questions, for your own sake. These are powerful people. They discredited me and destroyed my life. Even in this tiny town, where I hoped to disappear, they control my every move. Those two mongrels you met are paid to keep an eye on me.'

He stopped speaking; listening to the sound of a far-off car engine. 'Don't do this, Serena. Take it from me. The price you'll pay is too high.'

He looked around nervously. Serena noticed his long Roman nose was bent. It had clearly been badly broken.

'Hurry. Let's get you in your car. They mustn't know you spoke to me.'

He took her arm and helped her back to her Beetle.

'Professor, if Gene-Asis are selling products that hurt people, you have to stop it.'

'I tried once and paid for it dearly. Too dearly. And to this day, I wish I never had.'

He let go of her arm and walked away.

'Don't ever contact me again. For your own sake.'

Serena went after him, wincing as she hobbled.

'What do you mean, "paid for it"?'

He turned sharply.

'We were treated like pariahs. Even colleagues turned on us. The stress of it brought on her stroke. My poor wife … my poor wife never recovered.'

'I'm so sorry for your loss. What you've been through is terrible. But I have to know what's going on. Please tell me, why were you treated so badly?'

He looked at her intently through his grubby glasses.

'You never give up, do you?' He paused and she waited. 'I'll meet you tomorrow if only to persuade you to drop this. You have no idea of the danger you're in.'

'Where and when?'

'You mustn't tell anyone, or call anyone, or email anyone about this. No one. If you suspect you're being followed, don't meet me. Turn around and never call on me again. Do I make myself clear?'

Chapter 16

The white sand was cool and caked her feet as she left lonely footprints on a near-deserted beach. A solitary surfer rested on his board way out to sea. She had driven slowly to the rendezvous, checking for any signs of a tail. When she'd arrived at the designated beach, some ten kilometres out of town, the sun had just risen.

As the professor had directed, she walked two kilometres along the beach and then turned away from the sea and followed a stream's winding path inland. The meandering stream had cut sharp-edged banks into the sand, which crumbled as she passed by. Soon she could barely hear the sound of crashing waves. As she neared the bush, the sound of the sea was drowned out by the birds' early morning chorus. The stream doglegged to the right and became wide and murky, stained by something dark.

McPherson had said she would find a path. All Serena could see was a wall of dense vegetation. She searched along the thick foliage, holding back branches to peer into the trees. The grass next to a large gum tree appeared flattened. She ducked under several branches and found a line of crushed vegetation, which formed a rough path.

Stepping gingerly, she ducked and wove her way along the barely visible track. Twigs cracked behind her. She looked around. The bush was so dense she couldn't see the stream any more and could barely see a few metres behind her. A bird above her guffawed loudly and then she heard a splash to her right. She moved forwards, each step softly placed to make as little noise as possible. The crushed grasses became a more defined track of dirt and twigs and, to her right, the trees gave way to tall reeds. A mist hung suspended among them, ebbing and flowing. She caught glimpses of water. Then she stumbled upon a gap, and the ground gently sloped to the edge of an enormous lake, the likes of which she had never seen before.

It was completely surrounded by impenetrable bush. A halo of mist floated between the reeds at its edges but never ventured out into the open water. The reeds were dense and spiky, and acted like the walls of a fortress, barring entry. The only access point was where she stood. But it was the lake's colour, like black tea, that amazed her most. Ripples broke the smooth surface of the water; the professor was swimming towards her. He rose from the water, beard wet and glistening, his eyes scanning the bush behind her.

'You found it, then.'

'It wasn't easy.'

'I know. Are you sure you're alone?'

He stood knee deep, his feet totally obscured by the dark stain of the water.

'Yes.'

'Let's swim to the lake's centre. There's no way we can be overheard there.'

She hesitated.

'What's with the water?'

'It's tea-tree oil. It's good for you.'

He began to swim away from her with jerky strokes. She followed, expecting the water to be cold, but was surprised to find both the sandy mud of the bank and the water very warm. The professor trod water for a while, waiting for her to catch up.

'This lake is surrounded by tea-trees, which release their oil into the water. It's believed to have amazing healing properties. There's a story that a local man who was dying of skin cancer was brought here by a healer and told to bathe in it every day. It's said he's now cancer-free.'

He swam off again towards the lake's centre. The professor was a fast swimmer and Serena was not. He glided through the water easily; she followed awkwardly. As she swam, she noticed the silence of the lake. No bird sang. It was eerie.

Still ahead of her, he stopped swimming and raised himself out of the water until he was walking on its surface. Was she hallucinating? She trod water, open-mouthed. He was beckoning her towards him, like a bearded holy man walking on water. Serena swam and, as she kicked, began to feel mud beneath her feet. She was touching the bottom, which sloped upwards. The professor was standing on a sandbank in the middle of the lake that was just wide enough for the two of them. They both sat silently for a moment, taking in the mystical tranquillity of the place. Then he spoke in hushed tones, his eyes constantly searching the lake's leafy perimeter.

'Way before white men arrived, this place was an ancient Aboriginal birthing lake. Sadly, no more. Aboriginal women used to come here when it was their time. They would bathe their newborns in the cleansing water. No men were allowed here then. Even to this day, this lake is a well-kept secret. That's why I come here. It's one of the few places I can be alone. You see, Serena, there is always someone watching me.'

'Who is watching you, Dr McPherson?'

'You know the answer to that question.'

'Okay, so why is Gene-Asis watching you?'

He sat crossed-legged.

'I hoped my work would lead to great things. I was adamant that genetically engineered foods could save the world from starvation. You have to believe me, Serena. I thought I could solve world hunger.'

He looked at her imploringly. It was the first time he had looked directly into her eyes since arriving at the sandbank.

'I do believe you.'

'When the world's leading biotech company approached me and promised to fund my research if I worked at Arthur Phillip University, I was overjoyed. The research facility was the best I'd ever seen.'

'It looked pretty shabby to me.'

'You've been? No, that's a façade. Inside, the equipment is state of the art. The deal was they would direct my work, and I agreed because they said their mission was to solve the problem of world hunger. I thought we had one and the same goal. After a number of breakthroughs, which they then launched onto the market,

The Genesis Flaw

I was sent to Zimbabwe. I managed the largest and most in-depth human food trials ever conducted. We tested newly developed genetically engineered plants. For five years, I subjected those innocent people to ...'

He paused and looked down at the water lapping at their feet.

'Oh God,' he whispered.

Serena waited for him to continue and when he didn't, she prompted him.

'What happened?'

He removed his wire-rimmed glasses, smudged with lake water, and rubbed his eyes. A scar ran along his cheekbone where the rim of his glasses had rested.

'I'll never forgive myself.'

He shook his head and then suddenly grabbed her arms.

'I was trying to help people, Serena. Please understand!'

'Yes, I do, of course I do. But what happened?'

He stared at the horizon.

'To tell you would lead to my death.'

'What? Are you trying to say they'd actually kill you?' There was a hint of mockery in her voice, which she instantly regretted. Fortunately, it went straight over his head.

'Serena, nobody can stop them. Go home and forget all this.'

Serena couldn't quite believe what he was saying. While she suspected their products were unsafe, she couldn't imagine people at Gene-Asis actually murdering anyone.

'So, why are you still alive?' she challenged, doubting his sanity.

'Me? Because I'm no threat to them now. The world thinks I had a mental breakdown. Who would believe a crazy old goat like me? Ah, but they didn't expect me to turn up in Sydney, did they? Oh no. Heffernan and Grimes would have had the shit kicked out of them for that.'

He almost smiled. 'Did no good, though.'

'So why are they victimising you?'

'Because I tried to tell the truth. I tried to publish my Zimbabwean research.'

'Were you developing Supercrop Ultra?'

'No, one of its predecessors, Supercrop 13.'

'Thirteen! But that's been sold for years! My God, what's wrong with it?'

He stood up abruptly, peering down at her short-sightedly, his glasses still in his hand.

'Do you have any family, Serena?'

'Yes. Brother, niece …'

'Let this go and enjoy them while you still have them.'

Serena stood, her feet sinking into the soft mud.

'I can't. I owe it to my dad. I have to know — could T-Speed canola have caused his lung cancer?'

The professor placed his hand on her sunburned shoulder.

'Yes, it's possible. We had many problems with it, as we did with the rest of Supercrop 13. But the problems — well, they got buried.'

She took a deep breath.

'I'm sorry, Serena.'

Eventually she spoke, her voice small. 'How does it bring on cancer?'

'Through breathing the pollen. Our lab tests on rats showed the foreign DNA caused abnormal thickening of the lungs' cells, which could lead to cancer.'

Serena straightened, her face pale. 'So, Gene-Asis knows it causes cancer?'

'It depends what you mean by "knows". You have to realise Gene-Asis does the absolute minimum in terms of testing before release. They don't want to discover a problem: they simply want the product out on the market.'

She swallowed. It felt like she had a stone stuck in her throat.

'And Supercrop Ultra? What's wrong with it? Will it cause cancer too?'

He placed his glasses back on his nose and, tight-lipped, stepped into the water. 'No, I'm not going there.'

'Stop! Please,' she called.

He paused and looked around fearfully.

'They're trying to cover their tracks, to hide the truth …'

He stopped.

'I've said enough.'

'The truth about what?'

He touched his dripping beard, tugging at it, agitated.

'You haven't listened to me, have you? You'll get hurt. All I'll say is that Supercrop Ultra is a finger in the dyke. It's only temporary. It's a band-aid, not a cure.'

'A cure for what?'

He smiled ruefully.

'Remember, Serena, I'm crazy.'

'When did you hand the report over to Gene-Asis?'

'Sixth of December 2011; I remember it well,' he said, sighing loudly, head down, staring at the water lapping around his ankles.

'So who would have a copy?'

'If one exists, it will be in a maximum-security file.'

'But surely if Supercrop Ultra is a cover-up for earlier errors, then the scientists who developed the latest range would have to use your research as reference?'

'I don't know,' he said, wringing his hands.

'Yes, you do! Help me! There are four scientists behind Supercrop Ultra. They're Singh, Xu, Koch, and Munroe, who's gone missing. Surely they had access to it?'

'Philip Munroe is missing?'

'Yes. He criticised your work, didn't he?'

'He worked with me in Zimbabwe. He was in charge. If he's gone missing, I guess the poor bastard must've stepped out of line.'

'You think so?'

He nodded. Serena watched him for a moment as he kicked at the lake's surface. Despite the sun's first rays on her body, a cold dread chilled her. 'You think he's ... dead?'

'I hope not,' he answered.

Serena stepped into the water so that she could face the professor, trying hard to control her mounting fear.

'Would these scientists have seen your original research?'

'Possibly. Yes, probably.'

'Would anyone else in Australia have seen it?'

'Yes, the Asia-Pacific CEO.'

'Who else?'

'Al Bukowski, of course.'

They stood in silence. The mist among the reeds had cleared and the sun beat down on them. Apart from their voices, there was not a sound; not a ripple on the water, not a crack of branches, not a bird song.

'I've said too much. I must be mad.'

He swam off, fracturing the still water like it had been rent into shards of broken glass. A cloud moved across the sun, plunging the lake into shadow, and a magpie swooped over her head, forcing her to duck. She ran into the water after him, asking him to stop. He ignored her and reached the lake's shore.

'Wait!'

He paused, shivering in the trees' shade. She dragged herself out of the water. He glared at her.

'Never come near me again. Never! I want nothing to do with this.'

Red-faced with rage, he shoved her away. Shocked at his sudden mood change, Serena silently watched him disappear into the trees.

Chapter 17

Serena wanted to get out of Shelleyman Bay fast. It was clear that the two cops were not protecting McPherson but were in the pocket of Gene-Asis. They probably received a nice little kickback for guarding the poor man. As soon as she had mobile coverage, she called the airline and brought her return flight forward to eleven o'clock that day. This left four long hours before she could find herself in the comparative security of the plane.

Serena parked outside her holiday apartment. Four backpackers laughed loudly, jostling for pavement space as they walked by. The cars parked along the street were empty. Except for the woman who owned the units, who waved at her from her kitchen, Serena couldn't see anyone watching her. There was no police car in sight.

Serena raced up the steps to the second floor and unlocked the apartment door. A salty sea breeze blew through the rooms; her balcony door was wide open. Had she left it open this morning? She thought she'd locked it but, in her agitated state, couldn't be sure.

Heeding the professor's warning, she took a kitchen knife from a block of six on the workbench. She stepped quietly through the open-plan lounge/kitchen. Nothing had been disturbed. The bedroom door was slightly ajar, but not enough to see inside. She opened it, slamming the door against the wall. The horizontal window slats were open, as she had left them, and the orange muslin curtains of her four-poster billowed softly in the breeze. There was no sign of an intruder. Lastly, she checked the bathroom, and then returned the knife to its block. She took a very deep breath and released it slowly. She noticed a trickle of red down her knee: the swim must have opened up the wound. She found a Band-Aid in her toiletries bag, which she placed over the cut.

'A band-aid. Not a cure.' A cure for what?

She threw her overnight bag onto the bed. Something rectangular and flat moved on the pillow. She hadn't noticed it this morning. No, she was positive it hadn't been there. From where she stood, it looked like a very old photograph. Moving a few steps closer, she picked it up.

It was indeed a photograph, in colour, of two people on a dusty track: a man and a woman arguing. His arms were raised in anger. One corner of the photograph had been burned away, leaving the edges charred and brown. Serena examined it closely, and her eyes widened in horror as she recognised herself and McPherson on the track outside his house. It had been taken yesterday afternoon. As a result of the burned corner, half of Serena's body had disappeared from the picture.

She spun around, dropping it on the bed, eyes darting around the room. How had they got in? Serena was certain she'd locked the balcony doors, so had they forced the lock? Or had they been given a key to the apartment? Serena shuddered. Grimes and Heffernan must have followed her back to the professor's house and taken this photograph yesterday. What if they'd seen her this morning?

Terrified they might turn up at any moment, she threw her clothes and toiletries into her bag. Tempted to tear up the photograph, she decided to keep it. If anything happened to her, it might be a clue. Picking it up as if it were a poisonous insect, she dropped it in her bag. It landed face down. On the back were five words written in thick black marker pen:

'LOVED ONES ARE SO PRECIOUS'.

Sucking in air, she stared at the words. Her hand shot up to her mouth. Then, yanking the bag from the bed, she ran to her car, leaving the apartment door wide open.

Chapter 18

Serena stared out of the airplane window at the tropical storm clouds below, repeating to herself that she was safe. Pressing the button on her control panel, she asked the flight attendant for another glass of white. *To hell with it.* Once he returned with the wine, Serena tuned into the latest news coverage. She tried to focus on the screen in front of her, keen to forget the last twenty-four hours. But her mind was on overdrive.

Serena had what she'd longed for: confirmation from a Gene-Asis scientist that T-Speed should be taken off the market and investigated. But instead of feeling victorious, she felt only sadness that her dad's death could have been prevented. She remembered the phone conversation with him shortly after he'd bought T-Speed: how excited he'd been about the promise of this fast-growing canola which meant an additional crop each year. With the extra money, he was going to visit the UK and spend time with her.

She shook her head: the memories were too painful. She tried to focus on what she'd learned about the Zimbabwe research but the image of the photograph on her pillow kept returning. The professor had called himself a coward, but she now understood the paralysing nature of fear. The photograph had done more to disturb her than had any verbal threats. This was no longer just about her; her family had become involved. How much did Gene-Asis know about them? She had stumbled across Gene-Asis' Achilles heel – the professor's incriminating report. But she couldn't track down this report if it endangered her family.

Through her headphones, the news reporter's voice cut into her thoughts. Two huge fires had broken out on the Central Coast and 300 fires were burning in country Victoria. Another fire in the Royal National Park had forced road closures, and the evacuation of Bundeena and Engadine. Firefighting resources were stretched to the limit. It was depressing viewing.

'We have just received news that the body of Tony Mancini, CEO and Senior Vice President of Gene-Asis Asia-Pacific, was found hanging in his office …'

Serena sat forward and gawped at the screen.

'The exact timing of his suicide is unclear, but we do know that his body was found by his PA, Karen Connelly. We understand there was no suicide note but his death is not being treated as suspicious. He leaves behind him a wife and a three-month-old son. A private funeral was held yesterday at Beauty Point Catholic Church, attended only by close family.'

The image on screen then cut to Mr Mancini's brother, Marco, standing outside a suburban house.

'We don't understand why. He was so happy. He couldn't get enough of Tom, his son. The day before he died, he was telling me they were planning to have another kid. So why would he commit suicide?' Marco broke down and sobbed.

There was another cut, to a crowd of baying reporters. They surrounded Al Bukowski outside the Gene-Asis building in Sydney, barking questions at him, shoving microphones in his face. He raised his hands, hushing them, and the reporters quietened. The camera zoomed in on his face and, for the first time, Serena could study his features. Two dark-brown eyes, deep-set into a heart-shaped face, looked into the camera. He appeared sombre, and spoke slowly and deliberately, with a firmness that denied any weakness and forbade interruption. He betrayed nothing of the fury that Serena had no doubt he felt over the leak.

'I am greatly saddened by Tony Mancini's death. He worked tirelessly to feed the Asia-Pacific region, to help farmers increase their yields. He passionately believed, as I do, that, despite climate change and our growing population, Gene-Asis can win the war on hunger. But he was more than CEO of our Asia-Pacific operations: he was a good friend of mine. I will be doing all I can to comfort his grieving widow and family. And, on their behalf, I ask you, the media, to respect this family's privacy. That's all. Thank you.'

As he turned to enter the Gene-Asis building, a reporter from the *Sydney Morning Herald* yelled at him, 'Mr Bukowski, who will be taking over operations here?'

Without a moment's hesitation, he replied, 'I personally will be running the Asia-Pacific operations for however long it takes to appoint his successor.'

'But what about the launch in New York?' persisted the same reporter, clearly surprised that the Global CEO was staying in Australia.

'I will, of course, be attending it, Ms Harvey, as I hope you will be. This is our most exciting product launch yet.'

He smiled the whitest, broadest smile Serena had ever seen. The reporter was apparently speechless, shocked and flattered that he knew her name. His charisma was undeniable, his confidence unwavering. Even Serena had to admit he handled the situation well. Plain-clothed bodyguards began escorting him into the Gene-Asis building, barring the entrance. 'Is it true he was worried about product safety?' shouted a *Daily Telegraph* reporter.

Bukowski looked back, his eyes narrowed. 'Not at all.'

'But why hang himself at work?' the reporter persisted.

Bukowski ignored the question and disappeared into the building.

Serena didn't hear the next news piece – her mind was racing. The Asia-Pacific CEO had hung himself in his own office! No wonder Bukowski hadn't wanted it to leak. It was as if Mancini were making a statement: he couldn't go on with his work. Perhaps she was leaping to conclusions but Dr Munroe had been seen arguing with Mancini just before he disappeared. Over what? Safety issues? Supercrop Ultra? What if Munroe had been part of the team trying to 'correct' the safety issues in the Ultra range, the very same issues that Dr McPherson had identified in his 2011 report? And now Munroe was missing, Mancini was dead and McPherson was terrified witless.

She quickly tapped out an email to Tracey:

Hey there. This is my new email address.

There is out about Mancini but I guess you already
know that? There has to be a connection between
Mancini's suicide (in his office!), Mancini's argument
with Munroe and the prof's concerns about Supercrop
Ultra, which Bukowski is determined to launch in a
week's time. Any thoughts? And any news on Munroe's
whereabouts?

Serena added her new mobile number and pressed 'Send' – her
email would go when she landed and had synched her phone. She
needed Tracey's detective-like instincts on this.

She took a few more sips of her wine and peered down at the dry red
earth below. The sunlight poured in through the tiny window and, like
stage footlights, lit up her face. At first she smiled, her eyes bright with
excitement. If recent events were linked, as she believed, there was a trail
of Gene-Asis cover-ups waiting to be unearthed. She crossed her arms,
her glass still balanced in her right hand. Unearthing them would be a
challenge, but she'd spent the last ten years chasing and winning business
from some of the most demanding clients in the world and she felt up to
it. She knew that information was king, and she'd managed to discover
details about her prospective clients that had given her the edge over her
competitors. She would find the professor's report.

Her fair eyebrows creased into a frown and she felt a twinge in
her stomach as anxiety began to well up inside her. She could only
continue her investigations if she found a way to protect her family.
Keith, his pregnant wife, Kerry, and their little girl, Katie, meant
everything to her, despite the fact she'd neglected them over the last
few years. Swift Farm now belonged to Keith. Keeping a watchful
eye out for unwanted visitors over 443 hectares would not be easy.
Keith would be out in the fields all day and Katie at school, which
left Kerry alone in the house fairly often, except when she popped
into town. If the threat were real – and after seeing the professor's
fear she believed it was – then someone would need to patrol the
farm. What would her dad do?

The Genesis Flaw

She glanced down at his old watch and ran her finger over its scratched face. Her father had been much loved by the local community. He'd coached the local junior footy team for years and was always willing to help out his neighbours: one year, he'd raised money for Mary Keane when she'd lost everything in a house fire. Over a hundred people had turned up for his funeral, including a number of officers from the local police force. Senior Sergeant Shane Weston had, with Sergeant Jim Evans, stood apart from the rest of the group, their heads respectfully bowed, in full uniform. Her dad had taught them to play footy when they were boys. Could she call in a favour? After all, if Gene-Asis could use Heffernan and Grimes to intimidate McPherson and anyone who came near him, why couldn't she ask Shane to keep a protective eye on her family?

Serena nodded and swallowed the last drops in her glass. She'd talk to Shane and Keith after she'd landed. But how to get her hands on McPherson's report?

She glanced at the woman next to her. She was reading a book. Serena's eyes absent-mindedly scanned the first few sentences on the page as she grappled with her problem, and saw the words 'multiple personality disorder'. It gave her an idea. If Keith said yes, she knew exactly what to do to discover the truth about Gene-Asis. She would re-invent herself. It was time to meet her alter ego.

Chapter 19

Back at the Coogee apartment, Serena phoned Keith's mobile. He answered with his usual 'Yep?' She could hear a thumping sound in the background; someone was hammering in a fence post. She could see him in her mind's eye: a big man with a slow and steady-as-she-goes walk. He'd be wearing his wide-brimmed, sweat-stained hat and probably using his handkerchief to wipe the sweat off his forehead.

'Keith, it's me.' He wouldn't recognise her new number.

'Hey, how ya goin'?'

'I'm okay. Keith, I need to talk about T-Speed.'

She waited. He was a man of few words who never rushed his response, which could lead to some uncomfortable pauses in conversation.

'Go on.' His tone gave little away but Serena recognised a cautionary note.

She described her visits to Dr McPherson and what he'd said about T-Speed. She knew better than to expect an instant emotional response from Keith, even though this product could have killed their father.

'So, you were right all along.'

'I don't have any proof yet, only his word, but I want to get it.'

Serena then explained her plan to unearth McPherson's damning research document.

'Sounds like something from a movie, sis. But, I guess, if anyone can get away with it, you can.' He exhaled loudly. 'Those bastards! They knew.' His voice was barely a decibel louder but she recognised its angry edge. Some years back, when a developer had tried to pressure their dad into selling the farm, Keith had shown the men off the property, his shot gun casually draped over his arm. There'd been the same edge to his voice then as she heard now. 'If you can't get 'em your way, I'll find this Bukowski and wring his neck myself.'

'I'll make it happen, Keith. Trust me. But there's one obstacle and I have a plan about how to overcome it but I need you to be comfortable with it.' She explained about the implied threat of the burned photograph and the words 'LOVED ONES ARE SO PRECIOUS' as well McPherson's, perhaps far-fetched, belief that Gene-Asis might kill people that got in its way.

'If anyone comes near my family, they'll regret it.' This time he actually raised his voice, and the thumping noise in the background stopped. Whoever was with him – and Serena guessed it was Bernie – must have been taken aback.

'Keith, these guys mean business. I want to prove T-Speed and Supercrop are killing people but I can't if it puts you guys in danger.'

'We'll be right. I got Bernie-the-brick-shithouse here. Hey, Bernie,' he called, 'fancy kicking the shit out of some thugs?' Serena could hear Bernie laughing. 'Let me at 'em,' she heard Bernie say.

'Keith, I'm going to ask Shane and Jim to keep an eye out, to drive by the place regularly. I need to know you're safe.'

'Nah, we don't need them. Don't get me wrong, they're good blokes, but I can take care of my own.'

'If Gene-Asis know the police are watching the farm, they'll think twice. Please, Keith, let them help out. They'll want to. For Dad's sake.'

Another exhalation, this time slower and calmer.

'Right-e-o then. Give 'em something useful to do, I guess. I'll talk to the school as well, ask 'em to keep an eye on Katie.'

'I'll call Shane now. He'll probably drop round to find out what's going on. Can you keep Gene-Asis out of the conversation?'

'No worries. You know me and so does Shane. Stubborn as. I'll maybe hint those developers are back.'

Serena couldn't help but smile: stubbornness was definitely a family trait.

She immediately called Shane. She only told him enough to ensure he and Jim would drive by the farm regularly and watch the school. He began asking probing questions and she told him she simply couldn't tell him any more. He said he'd accept that for the present but if any threats were made directly to her family, she would have to file an official complaint.

Her head was pounding by the call's end. She'd drunk too much wine on the plane and was very dehydrated. She gulped down some tap water and swallowed a couple of painkillers. Her phone rang. Perhaps Shane had changed his mind?

'Hello, my love. How are ya?' It was Tracey. Serena docked her phone and turned on the monitor. Her friend was wearing pink pyjamas with black skulls dotted across them. Her platinum hair was still ferociously spiky despite its owner's pallid weariness.

'It must be the middle of the night there?' said Serena.

'Yeah, you know me: a night owl. Got your email. Something's very fishy – Bukowski's hiding something big. Now, tell me, how did you go with McPherson?' Tracey fired out each sentence without pausing.

Serena's head throbbed. She covered her face with both hands.

'My darling, what's happened?'

Serena uncovered her face and looked at her hands. They were shaking. While she'd been calmly practical when speaking to her brother and Shane, the full enormity of her task had begun to sink in. She was taking on a global corporation with more power than most governments.

'Trace, I need your help. I can't do this alone.' Serena's voice trailed away like a wave lost back to the ocean. Tracey was one of the few people with whom she could let her guard down.

'What's happened?' asked Tracey again, her voice full of concern. She leaned closer to the screen, the stud in her nostril now apparent.

'I … I'm going to nail Gene-Asis. I know how to do it. But …
Trace, I gotta admit, it scares the hell out of me.'

'Tell me what's happened. What's shaken you up?'

'If I tell you, I could be putting your life in danger.'

Tracey paused, studying Serena's drawn face. 'You're not joking, are ya?' Her over-plucked, pencil-thin eyebrows creased into a frown.

'No, I'm not joking.'

'Well, I can't help ya, if you don't tell me, now can I?' Tracey smiled but her hands betrayed her tension: she was clicking her ballpoint pen on and off repeatedly. 'I'm a journalist. I live dangerously. Come on, tell me.'

Serena told her every detail of her trip to Shelleyman Bay, repeating word for word her conversations with McPherson and ending with the burned photograph.

'Bloody hell. Bloody … hell,' was all Tracey could say for a while. 'Mate, this is frigging nasty stuff. I'd think long and hard before you do anything.'

'I have. But now I know T-Speed's dangerous, I can't let it go. I've made my decision. I'm going to find McPherson's report.'

'Serena, mate, these people have threatened your family,' said Tracey, clicking her pen at break-neck speed.

'I've talked to Keith. He wants me to do it. And I've called in a favour with the local police. They'll keep a close eye on them.'

'Okay.' The frantic pen clicking stopped. 'But how you gonna get close enough to Gene-Asis to find evidence?'

'I need to get a job there.'

'I see where you're going. Sort of like espionage. But, you know, spying is incredibly dangerous and Gene-Asis is anal about security. Are you sure?'

'Trace, *I* won't be getting a job there. It'll be someone else.'

'Huh?'

'Okay, here's my plan. Tell me if you think it'll work. I change my identity: new name, a fake résumé that'll win me the job. The new me will have an unassuming personality, be the kind of person people work with every day but tend not to notice. And see this hair,' she said, lifting some strands from her ponytail, 'this is changing colour. Serena Swift will be no more.'

Tracey spat out a laugh like she was spitting out burning hot soup. 'Give me a break! They're the most security-conscious company in the world. They'll spot a fake ID before you've even crossed the threshold.'

Serena shook her head. 'No they won't. This ID will be the best there is, because I know one of the best hackers in Australia and I've seen him create fake IDs. He hasn't been caught out.'

'Who?'

'John Flynn. My flatmate.'

'Oh, that John.'

'Yes, that John,' replied Serena, blushing.

'The same John who kissed you just before you came over here? The guy you ignored for four years?' Tracey was grinning from ear to ear; Serena's face was a lovely shade of beetroot.

'Yes, Trace, that John. The same guy who slept with someone else the very night he kissed me.' Serena's tone was sharper than she'd intended. 'Sorry, Trace. I didn't mean to get snippy. Now, can we get back to my new identity?'

Tracey nodded but Serena could tell she was suppressing a smirk. 'Sure,' she said. 'But why would he do this for you? It could land him in prison.'

Serena glanced around the room, searching for an answer. 'We go back a long way.' She paused, thinking it through. 'And if he won't, I'm sure he'll know someone who will.'

'It better be damn good.'

Serena nodded and, deep in thought, fell silent. Tracey chewed her pen and said, 'Okay. Let's say the ID is good enough. How are you going to get a job there?'

'I thought about asking Baz, John's brother, to help, but that'd be asking him to lie for me and I draw the line at that. And, anyway, I think Baz's company only recruits scientists and technical roles. I can talk my way into most things but a scientific job isn't one of them.'

'Ah, you don't want to compromise Baz but you're happy to involve John.'

Tracey had a knack for going for the jugular. Serena blushed at her own double standards. 'I guess it's because he's encouraged me to take on Gene-Asis, whereas Baz doesn't know anything about it. And John always used to be the bad boy. He loves to live on the edge.'

'So it's got nothing to do with how close you two were?'

'Tracey, you're unbelievable!' exclaimed Serena. 'I've checked out Gene-Asis vacancies. Here, take a look.' She shared her screen with Tracey so that she could see exactly what Serena saw on her monitor. 'Their Sydney office employs over 600 people.' She tapped through the Gene-Asis job vacancies on the internet.

'Here we go. Researcher, biophysics. Nope. Accountant, nope; I'm shit at maths. Ah, this is it: Executive Personal Assistant, with Cantonese and Japanese language skills. I can do that.' Serena screwed

The Genesis Flaw

up her nose. 'Well, almost do it. I know enough Japanese to get by.' She continued reading the details aloud until Tracey stopped her midsentence.

'Oh my God. It's the new CEO's PA. Which means you'll be reporting to Bukowski.'

Serena nodded. 'Until the new CEO starts, by which time I'll be out of there. I'm hoping I'll only need a week or so.'

Tracey wasn't leaping up and down with excitement. She was chewing the end of her plastic pen again. 'What's up?' asked Serena.

'Mate, that's too close. I mean, that's like putting your head in the lion's jaws. Nah, find something else.'

'No way. This is perfect. I'll see his emails, hear his calls, make his appointments. It's exactly what I want.'

'Serena, you know me, I always tell you how it is. Well, this is how I see it. Yeah, perhaps Gene-Asis have cut a few corners and not tested all their products properly. And, yeah, Mancini topped himself. And some dodgy cops tried to scare you away from McPherson. But welcome to the big brutal world of global corporations, my love. It doesn't necessarily mean Bukowski has crossed the line. But, and this is a big but ...' She paused to gnaw at her pen, which she cracked with her teeth, and then continued. 'If you think he has gone too far, then he'll be watching out for anyone sniffing around asking the wrong questions. And if he catches you, God knows what he might do.'

Serena leaned back, pulled her ponytail out of the scrunchy and shook out her hair. 'It's too good to miss, Trace. I'm going to get that job.'

Tracey threw up her hands. 'Okay, okay. Have it your way. I'm in whatever. So, you said you needed my help. What help?'

Serena leaned closer to the monitor. 'I need you to fly to Zimbabwe. Talk to the participants in the food trials. Gather evidence and check out McPherson's story. Take a video camera if you can, make a documentary. Can you do that, Trace?'

'Hmm. I got some leave owing so, yes, I can do it. But the story is exclusively mine. Right?'

'Trace, it'll be all yours. I'll need you to get the truth out. This battle won't be won in the courts; it'll be won in the media. We need public opinion on our side.'

Tracey leaned back with her hands behind her neck. 'This story could make me famous. This could be bigger than Watergate, Enron, or the Madoff scandal.'

Serena nodded. 'You can have all the fame. I just want the truth.'

Tracey had opened a small ring-bound notebook and was jotting down some notes. Unlike many of her peers, she still liked to make notes the old way. 'First up, I'm gonna contact our man in Zimbabwe. If he can find out where the trials took place, I'm flying out there. Did the prof give you any clue? A name of a town where they did the tests?'

'He didn't say.'

'Can you see him again and ask?'

'No. He'd freak. You should've seen how terrified he was, and I mean, terrified. He won't speak to me again.'

'All right, what about writing to him? We need to know places, names, more precise dates; that sort of thing. Otherwise, I'm looking for a needle in a haystack.'

'I'll find a way. Leave it to me. But can your man be trusted?'

'It's all right, he's an ex. And, don't worry, I'll tell my editor I need a break and I'm going somewhere exotic for a week or two. I won't tell him what I'm up to, otherwise he won't let me go.'

'And I'll find the document. Together with your interviews, we've got Gene-Asis in the bag. But we need to be thorough. If we don't get enough evidence, they'll bury the story and us with it.' Serena paused, chewing her lower lip. 'Are you sure your editor will run the story? Let's face it, Tanning owns *The Post* and he's good mates with Bukowski.'

'Mate, with a story this big, I bet you a billion dollars Charlie will run it front page. Once it's run, how can Tanning fire him – or me, for that matter? Circulation will go through the roof! He'll have broken the biggest story in corporate history.'

Serena was silent, taking it all in, then said quietly, 'Let's do it.'

'You're on.'

'One last thing, Trace. I think we should use secure phone and email lines. I think I'm pretty much okay but I'll double-check with John. You may need someone to help you secure yours. We need to be sure they can't eavesdrop on us.'

'Let's hope they haven't already started.'

Chapter 20

Serena had been waiting nervously for John to come home and now that he had, she wondered if her plans were about to unravel. His body language was not positive; his arms were crossed and she wasn't sure if his frown was one of concentration or anger. Serena had told him about the threatening note, her conversations with the professor and her plan to work at Gene-Asis using a fake ID. John had initially been reclining nonchalantly on the sofa, sipping at his beer. Now the drink sat on the coffee table, forgotten and warm, sweating in its glass bottle, as he leaned forward.

'So, I guess you're really glad I moved in, huh?' she said, trying to get him to look at her.

He didn't reply straightaway, but shook his head once, not in answer to her question, but as if he were trying to wake up.

'My God, Seri, are you out of your mind? The cops, the note. These people mean business. You can't do this.'

'What? Only a few days ago, you were egging me on, telling me that I'd get another chance to go after Gene-Asis, and now I'm doing something about it, you're saying I'm out of my mind.'

'Seri, this is different. You're planning on doing something criminal. I meant challenge Gene-Asis through your lawyers, not break the law.'

'This is the only way. I have no evidence and I have to get that evidence. You said I'd get a second chance to prove they killed Dad. Well, this is it.'

He shook his head slowly and then looked straight at her.

'Seri, I know where you're heading with this and I'm not going to do it.'

Serena looked into his eyes: they were steely. She could see that he was ready to walk out, so she leaned forward and took his hand. It was surprisingly cool; hers was warm with desperation. She needed John on board or her plans would collapse. 'Please, John, just let me explain.'

'I'm *not* helping you hack their system,' he said. 'I don't do that anymore. Just keeping up with hacker friends is problematic enough. And I'm not creating your fake ID.' He pulled his hand away and stood up, then leaned on the windowsill, his back to her. She walked up to him and sat on the sill so that they were side by side, one facing in, the other out.

'Please, let me explain. I can't work there as Serena Swift. The cops in Shelleyman will have fed my details back to Gene-Asis by now. And you're the best. I've seen you do it. Please, John.'

He looked sideways at her. 'That was a long time ago and it was only a bit of fun. This would have to withstand rigorous security checks. You'd need a passport, driver's licence and tax file number, at the very least. It's a serious crime.'

Serena pictured an angry teenager with short brown hair and sapphire-blue eyes creating a fake driver's licence so that he could drive to a party some distance away and buy alcohol on the way. John had been fifteen at the time. He'd then progressed to setting up a mate who'd just left prison with a whole set of fake IDs.

'But you've helped friends out before. Stu, when he left jail and wanted to start afresh. You even got into Parliament House once; you were pretending to be a senator, weren't you?'

He smirked. 'That was fun. But again, that was before I worked in InfoSec.'

She knew she was badgering him. She knew she shouldn't ask. But, like a terrier, she had the scent and wouldn't give up.

'When did you become such a wuss? What happened to the guy who loved challenging authority?'

'He grew up.'

'Well, if you won't do it, can you find me someone who will?'

He shook his head.

'Where's all your, I don't know, get up and go gone? You were the one who always got me doing things I never would have.'

'Seri, it's there, believe me, but it's like being an alcoholic. If you've stopped drinking, you want nothing more than to have another drink but you don't. You don't dare or you'll never be able to stop drinking. I can create you a fake passport, a fake anything, but I'll get a taste for it and want to test myself with something more challenging. And, before I know it, I've been caught out and, bang, I'm in prison.' He blinked rapidly, confused. 'I thought you'd prefer me this way; you know, law-abiding, salaried.'

He stood up and turned his back to her.

'I didn't expect you to have a go at me for getting my shit together.'

She stood too and touched his shoulder gently. She'd gone too far and felt bad.

'John, I never meant it that way. I'm very proud of you, I really am.'

He remained silent, his square shoulders tensed, his back to her. She placed both arms around his waist and leaned into his back, placing her cheek against his right shoulderblade. She did it instinctively, having done this many a time when they were young and John was unhappy. She felt the muscles in his back relax and he placed his hands over hers, which were clasped across his stomach. They stayed silently like this for several seconds.

'I'll give you a name. That's all,' he said softly. 'There'll be no hacking of Gene-Asis files.'

'You wouldn't be hacking. You'd just be coaching me on how to get through security. I'd never implicate you.'

He pulled away from her embrace, angry again.

'Of course I'd be implicated. I live with you. Seri, think this through. God, this is so you.' He threw up his hands in exasperation.

She frowned.

'What do you mean, "so me"?'

'You decide what you want and nothing will stop you. You won't listen to anyone. Even your dad didn't want you to do this. You're prepared to ruin my life because of something *you* want to do. Well, not this time, Serena.'

It was as if she'd been slapped. She was speechless, and felt her stomach plunge as she recognised her selfishness but then, a split second later, she recalled why she was driving John so hard.

'John, I have to do this. Every day I see Dad on his death bed and every day I know, deep down, that he should still be alive. And I know he didn't want me going after Gene-Asis because he thought I'd never win. But I know I can get them now. And I'm a big girl. I can look after myself. So, forgive me, but I'm going to do this with or without your help. Please don't try to stop me.'

He was calmer now. 'I wouldn't dream of trying to stop you, Seri. I mean, who could? And Baz? You're not getting him involved?'

'No, I'll get a job there without his help.'

'What job, exactly?'

'PA to the CEO, which means Bukowski, while he's in Sydney.' Karen, the PA who had found Mancini dead, had left the country to recuperate.

'Bukowski? He's no fool. I've read articles on him: brilliant, ruthless. It's too risky.'

'The risk is worth it.'

'No, it's not,' he said loudly, 'God, we're going round in circles.'

'Okay, John, tell me this. Why did Mancini commit suicide only a few weeks before Supercrop Ultra's launch? What was so bad he couldn't bear to live with it anymore?

'What is so critical that Bukowski, the global CEO, the single most important man in Gene-Asis, has to stay in Australia?

'Why has Munroe suddenly disappeared?

'Why was McPherson so terrified he didn't want to talk to me? If he'd just wanted to cause trouble, he'd have blabbed away happily. And why was his research report never published?

'Why did I get warned off by those two cops? And what about the burned photograph, with the threat on the back?

'And why did my healthy dad suddenly die of lung cancer only a year after first using T-Speed, another Supercrop? Is this just coincidence or is something very strange going on?'

John nodded. 'Okay, I agree. It's probably all connected somehow. But go to the police and let them find the evidence.'

'Come on! By the time the police get access to the building, the evidence will be destroyed. You know as well as I do that complaints against Gene-Asis get swept under the carpet. Do you remember when a New South Wales farmer was taken to court by Gene-Asis because their GE canola blew into his organic fields? Gene-Asis claimed he stole their product. I mean, how could he have stopped the wind carrying pollen? They destroyed him in court, poor guy.'

'So what do you expect to achieve, Seri? How can one person make a difference?'

'One person can slip under the radar.'

Chapter 21

In her bedroom, Serena flicked through an ancient photograph album. She turned the pages rhythmically, like windmill sails, until she stopped at a photograph of herself as a skinny, twelve-year-old, arm in arm with John and Baz. It had been John's birthday. Serena was in the middle, then as tall as John, and Baz was making a silly face. John was looking sideways at her, while she laughed into the camera. Their relationship had been so uncomplicated. Now she was unsure what kind of relationship they had. It was like they were in a no-man's-land, wandering blindly. And the tension in the house tonight was like an electric current strong enough to power the CBD. She and John had never disagreed so profoundly on anything before, and it made her unhappy.

Shutting the dog-eared album, Serena pulled out a sheet of paper and an envelope, and began to compose a letter to McPherson. She hadn't been able to find a phone number or any internet-based address for him, so this was her only option. Pressing the pen onto the paper felt strangely old-fashioned. After several drafts had ended up in the bin and her hand ached, she finally had a letter she was happy with:

Dear Dr McPherson,
Remember me? I was one of your undergrad students at Arthur Phillip University
(BSc). I wanted to tell you how truly inspiring I found your lectures. Despite

your well-intentioned warnings about the difficulty of my chosen career path, I have decided to pursue my ambitions of conducting research overseas, and I was wondering if you could give me some guidance? Are there any particular countries or places you would recommend I conduct food trials? I am very grateful for any advice you can give me.

Kind regards,

Neresa Slow

She hoped that the letter wouldn't raise suspicions if anyone read his mail. As for the sender's name, she had no doubt the professor would see through it instantly. She was equally sure Grimes and Heffernan would not. Tomorrow, as a precautionary measure, she'd get a post office box so the letter wouldn't be traced back to the unit.

Her Tbyte beeped. It was an email from Tracey:

Hey! What do you think about this? I've been checking news headlines for 2012 to see if anything new, strange, or unusual happened that could be linked to eating Supercrop 13. One thing stood out: a new hepatitis virus, first recorded in the US in August 2012. They called it hepatitis S. Since then, over 20,000 people worldwide have died from it. No cure's been found, and it's a mystery how it's being transmitted.

Give me a call. Trace.

Serena dialled Tracey's number immediately.

'It's possible they're linked,' said Serena. 'But how can food cause a new virus?' She watched Tracey in the monitor: slumped forward, hand propping up her head.

'Well, I've looked into this. Say a Gene-Asis scientist used a virus closely related to the hepatitis S virus as a promoter gene in a plant. And then, let's say, this plant, containing this promoter gene, is eaten by someone. Then say this virus manages to transfer through the person's intestine into the rest of the body, there's a possibility this could trigger an ancient hepatitis virus.'

'What do you mean, ancient virus?' Serena leaned closer to the screen, unaware that Tracey was getting a close-up of her cleavage.

'Hey, you're suffocating me with your bazookas.'

Serena leaned back, smiling. 'You're so easily distracted. Go on.'

'Well, our DNA goes back to the birth of humankind. And over the centuries, we've had to fight off viruses and the survivors pass on their immunity. So our DNA is embedded with dormant viruses rendered harmless, unless something triggers them again.'

'That's creepy. And when you say "related" to hep S, do you mean from the same family of viruses?'

'Exactly. There are lots of viruses related to human hepatitis, including HIV. So, what I'm saying is, they could have used a virus related to hepatitis S, but one not known to affect people.'

'But what's a "promoter gene"?'

Tracey tapped her nose several times with a pen. 'Okay. Say I want to place a gene into a potato to stop pests. First, I'd use what's called a vector to transfer the alien gene. But the potato doesn't know if it should switch the new gene on or not. So scientists equip the new gene with a promoter which is like a light switch permanently set to "on".'

'Why would anybody in their right mind use a virus linked to hepatitis or HIV?'

'For a promoter to work, it needs to be aggressive and force the host into accepting the alien gene. And a virus is very aggressive – simply put, it bullies the plant into turning on the new gene. I'm not saying anyone would use the human hepatitis S virus in plants, but it could be any one of a number of viruses *related* to hepatitis S.'

'And then the virus enters the human body through the stomach?'

'It's possible, but horizontal gene transfer has been vehemently denied by all biotech companies. They claim it just doesn't happen. But there's mounting evidence it does occur.'

'Let me get this straight. It's possible that a virus used to genetically engineer a food product could be absorbed via the stomach lining into the bloodstream?' asked Serena, shocked.

'Yes, but there's nothing conclusive yet.'

'So why is hep S untreatable?'

'That, I don't know.'

'Well, your theory's sounding more and more likely.'

'It *is* just a theory at this stage.'

Serena pondered this information until she remembered John. 'I've talked to John and it didn't go well. He reluctantly agreed to put me in touch with someone for the ID but he's not going to help me find the file.'

'That's a bummer. Does he know anyone who's got hep S?'

'Why?' asked Serena, but she already knew where Tracey's thoughts were going and she didn't like it. 'Yes, his girlfriend recently died of it and, no, we're not going to use his grief to get him to help. No way.'

'But what if you tell him Supercrop 13 could be linked to the outbreak?'

'I can't do it, mate. It feels wrong, like blackmail,' she replied.

'Up to you.'

After finishing the call, Serena lay on her bed. No, she'd asked enough of John. All she needed was an introduction. She pondered her new identity: what would be her new name, how would she look and what should her résumé say? Serena vaguely registered the phone ringing in the lounge and John talking. Some time later, there was a knock at the door.

'Come in.'

John sat on her bed, his face drawn.

'Are you all right?' she asked, sitting up.

'Your friend Tracey called me.'

'What?'

'She thinks Gene-Asis' food started the virus that killed Kat.'

'She shouldn't have told you that. It's only a theory.'

'But is she right?'

'I honestly don't know, John. Nobody seems to know where this virus came from, and the timing fits in with the release of Supercrop 13. And the professor was talking about a finger in the dyke, trying to hold something back. It could be the virus.'

He stood up and walked towards the door, pausing in the doorway, his back to her.

'Okay, let's get your Tbyte secure and I'll call my mate who can help with the new ID. And I'll advise you on corporate security – within reason. I draw the line at hacking.'

Chapter 22

In the shower, Serena leaned her head back as far as possible without losing her balance. The water, like hot pinpricks, stung her forehead. The rich copper hair dye trickled down her face, shoulders, back, stomach and legs, forming an orange question mark at her feet before it disappeared down the drain. Her hands slid down the recently-cut strands of her sleek bob to her exposed neck. The last time she'd had hair this short, she'd been ten.

The steam was too thick for the tiny ceiling fan that was trying to suck it away. She stepped out, took a black towel and dried her hair and body, then wiped the mirror. She stared at her reflection. It wasn't Serena Swift she saw in the glass. The vibrant red hair made her skin appear paler, her hazel eyes greener. The sharp edge of the cut formed a horizontal line just below the ears, which accentuated her slender neck. *Not bad*, she thought.

Yesterday had been difficult; she hoped today would be better. John had told Baz of her plans and, to her surprise, Baz had been on her side. It had led to an argument between the two brothers.

'Guys, please. I'll move out,' she'd said.

'No,' both brothers had said in unison.

Baz had looked at John. 'I don't know what's got into you,' he said, turning his gaze to her, 'Seri, I know the recruiter, I can put in a good word. As far as I know, you're whoever you tell me you are. Just give me a name. I'll put in a call on Monday.'

The Genesis Flaw

John had left the flat, slamming the door behind him. Some hours later, he'd returned with a slab of beers, opened three of them, and it was as if the argument had never happened. She knew full well she was asking too much of her childhood friends but was determined to seize her chance to get Gene-Asis.

Putting on her black silk bathrobe, Serena opened the door. Steam escaped from behind her, like a ghost released from its tomb. From the music coming from the lounge, she guessed John must be in there. As she was about to enter, he opened the door and stared at her.

'My God, you look amazing.'

'Thank you.' She stretched out her hand and shook his. 'Pleased to meet you. I'm Bukowski's new PA,' she said presumptuously.

John nodded, mesmerised.

'Oh no, wait. One more thing.' Serena ran into her room and reappeared wearing black rectangular-framed glasses. While the style was simple, the brand was Dolce & Gabbana.

John found his tongue. 'If you hadn't just stepped out of my bathroom, I wouldn't have known you. The red hair makes such a difference. And where did you get the glasses? They're very librarian.'

'They're mine. I got them in England and wore them once or twice, and then forgot about them. I prefer contacts.'

There was an awkward silence. John stepped to his right to let her pass but she didn't move, blocking his passage. 'Any luck finding someone to do the ID?' she asked.

He shook his head. 'God, Seri, you'll be the death of me. Come with me.'

He led her to his office and shut the door. Of the six monitors, only one was on. It displayed a hackers' chat-room conversation. Green letters on a black screen – the time, the person and the comment.

'Interesting,' said John, as he read the last few lines. 'They're talking about legal intercept, the capability of governments to intercept the communications of people at home. Anyway, take a seat,' he said, pulling up a chair. 'Okay, let's be clear about this. I'll help you with the fake ID but only because I don't want the cops knocking on our door. I have the contacts, I know who should be trustworthy – you don't. But you need to understand that, as this is a rushed job, it'll be risky and expensive.' Serena opened her mouth to thank him but he continued, 'So what security checks does Gene-Asis do on new employees?'

'I have to produce a driver's licence or passport, and three work references.'

'Right. Do you have a fake CV yet?'

'Yes, and I have in mind three friends who'll give me references. I can get away with giving Gene-Asis mobile numbers, which means my mates can pretend to be anybody I ask them to be.'

'Great. I'll leave that bit to you, then. You'll also need a bank account for your salary and a tax file number.'

She nodded and then cupped her hand under her chin, leaning towards him and resting her elbow on her crossed leg.

'Let's park those for a moment. I want to focus on the driver's licence and passport.' He leaned way back in his Herman Miller Aeron chair; so far back, in fact, he was almost horizontal. It was as if Serena and John were the two parts of a yin and yang: as she moved forwards, he moved backwards. He then tucked his hands behind his head to consider the obstacles. 'The passport is too hard. The licence is easier.'

As John was on a roll, Serena refrained from asking why.

'So how do you get a driver's licence in someone else's name? Well, first up you need a birth certificate and the best way to get a fake birth certificate is to use a dead child's identity.'

Serena's head shot up. 'Dead child?' she asked frowning, finding the concept distasteful.

'Yeah. This isn't very nice, Seri, but what you're about to do isn't exactly kosher. So, get with it or forget the whole idea.' John had leaned forward, the chair back following him. His eyes were like blue ice. 'Do you want to know more or shall we stop this now?'

Serena leaned back, wishing to get away from John's severe stare and harsh tone. Yin and yang.

'Go on,' she said firmly.

'Visit graveyards. Find a little girl buried there who was born around your birth year. You'll need to take her identity.'

'I see. Go on,' she said, trying not to betray how uncomfortable she felt.

'You'll also need to find a girl whose mother or father is dead too – so you'll check Births, Deaths and Marriages – because when you apply for a birth certificate, you need proof of a parent's identity. I can fake that for you, as long as they're dead.'

'Is there any other way?'

He tilted back again. This time, she didn't move. Without realising, she had clenched her hands into a tight ball.

'Not that I know of.' He waited.

She knew he was testing her, gauging how badly she wanted to go through with it. Serena let her eyes wander around the room for a moment as she wracked her brain for another idea. 'What about the birth certificate of a dead friend? I mean, asking the mother if we can have it?'

They both leaned forward in sync, so that their faces were almost touching.

'You mean Amber. Amber Crosby. She was, what, fifteen?' said John.

'Yes, Amber.'

Amber Crosby had been Serena's best friend at school until she died in a car crash. Serena still visited Amber's parents, who ran a popular hardware store, popping by whenever she was in town. Jill and Tim regarded Serena almost as an adopted daughter.

'But why would her parents let us have her birth certificate?' quizzed John.

'They'll do it for me. Amber and I were very close, and Jill and Tim trust me. I'll tell them it's for something important, something Amber would be proud of, but not to ask any questions, as what I'm doing isn't legal.'

'You'd risk telling them that?'

'Yes I would. And Amber would be proud. She was always doing e-campaigning; you remember? Fighting some kind of injustice. I reckon she'd be cool about this.'

John grinned. 'I think you could be right, and if you can get the certificate off Jill and Tim, that saves me a whole heap of effort.'

'I'll get it,' she said, feeling less like a thief.

'Good,' said John, clapping his hands together in a loud smack and standing. 'Once you have the birth certificate, I can help you with the driver's licence. To get one, you'll need two forms of identity. We'll have the birth certificate but we'll need one other and I suggest we go for a utility bill.'

'And you'll create the utility bill?'

He nodded. 'They want it for the address. I'll do an electricity one. The question is, what address we put on it?'

'It can't be this one. If I get caught, I don't want you implicated.'

John laughed. 'Nice thought, Seri, but they'll work it out. I'm implicated either way.'

Seri stood, arms folded. 'No, not this address. I noticed a vacant apartment near the bus stop. I'd prefer to use that.'

'Suits me,' shrugged John.

'But won't the RTA want proof of a driving test or something?'

'That's a bit tricky but your stint in the UK could help. You'll either have to apply for a learner's licence, which is a bit unusual at your age, and means keeping a driving log and all that crap, or you apply with a UK driver's licence.'

'Which I have!' Serena replied excitedly. She had been permitted to drive in the UK on her Australian licence for the first year, but had then had to apply for a UK licence.

He clicked his tongue twice. 'That you do. But it belongs to Serena Swift, so we'll have to do a bit of work on it. Someone I know can change the name over to Amber's and replace the photo of the good-looking blonde with one of a stunning redhead.'

She ignored the compliment, keen to learn the next step. 'So, I have a UK driving licence in Amber's name. Then what?'

'You pass an eyesight test, you sit a written test and then a driving test. If you pass those, you go into an RTA branch, show them Amber's UK licence, birth certificate and electricity bill, and you get yourself an Australian driver's licence with your face on it. You will have become Amber Crosby,' he announced in the manner of a magician pulling a rabbit out of a hat.

'This is incredible,' Serena said. 'I didn't think it would be this easy.'

'Easy? Forging a UK driver's licence isn't easy. And the guy will want payback some time. It's the payback I'm worried about.'

'He'll have a hold over you?'

John nodded.

'But it's for me, not you.'

'No offence, but I'm the hacker, not you. I think he'll be more interested in my skills.'

She sighed loudly. 'That's not good, John. I can't let that happen—'

'Serena, if you want to do this, I have no choice.' His tone was a touch sharp and she noticed that he'd used her full name. 'So, are we doing this or what?'

She stepped gracefully towards him in her black silk robe, resembling a geisha. She took both his hands and held them between hers. 'Yes, John; we are doing this.'

He nodded silently for a while before he spoke. 'Right, then. We've got to consider a few more things: the bank account and tax file number.'

He gently pulled his hands away, but stayed close to her. They stood in the centre of the room, totally engrossed in their conspiracy. 'Once you have the Australian driver's licence as well as the birth certificate, you have the hundred points you need to get a bank account.'

'What about the TFN?'

'That's where I come in again. I'm going to have to hack the tax office and create a tax file number and all the tax return history you'd expect a working woman like Amber Crosby to have.'

'Shit. The tax office?'

'Yup.'

'That's serious shit.'

John nodded. 'That's jail time if we're caught.'

Chapter 23

'The kitchen's on the left; help yourself to tea, coffee, energy drinks …
and the ladies' toilets are back down the corridor on the right.'

Serena peered down the corridor from behind her black-framed
glasses. She had dressed as conservatively as possible, in a black skirt
and an olive green top, but could do little to hide her curves and
long legs. She smiled sweetly at her new colleague.

As Amber Crosby, she had just arrived for her first day at Gene-
Asis Asia-Pacific's head office, in the heart of the CBD. The fifty-
five floors stretched up into the sky and, in its exterior design,
resembled the Osaka World Trade Center, with a viewing and
entertaining platform at the very top. In red letters, as tall as three
storeys, the illuminated company name shone day and night over
the city, except during Earth Hour. Serena had discovered that
Gene-Asis made a big noise about its environmental sustainability
program and was proud of this highly energy-efficient building,
complete with cogeneration and solar panelling on the roof. But
she doubted that the company's responsible stance was much more
than a veneer.

Serena was following a heavily pregnant woman in flat pump shoes
along the brightly lit corridor of the fifty-fifth floor. Liz was PA to
Henry Peng Loh, the chief financial officer. She winced and paused
for a second.

'Are you okay? Do you need to sit down?' asked Serena.

'No, I'm fine, thanks. It's my ankles. They swelled up even more over the weekend and my back's killing me.'

'When's the baby due?'

'In five weeks.'

Liz continued walking, one hand on her stomach.

'Oh, before I forget, Amber, here's your ID card back. It's been cleared.'

'Thanks,' replied Serena, exhaling a little too loudly with relief.

Following Liz through thick frosted glass doors, she found herself inside the executive office area. Everywhere she walked, she'd spotted 'spy-eyes': tiny cameras like eyeballs that were movement sensitive. There was one covering the entrance to the executive suite but, she was relieved to find, none inside.

A wall of flat screens was silently playing Gene-Asis' TV commercials and news interviews. There were eight screens suspended randomly at varying heights on a maze of steel wires, each one showing a different image. With the Gene-Asis advertising budget in the billions every year, they could have run their own twenty-four-hour network if they'd wanted to, but buying advertising time gave them much more leverage with the media. To her left were four glass-fronted private offices, and one huge suite at the very end, which, she guessed, belonged to the CEO.

In the middle were the PAs' desks. Designed as one flowing workstation, the desks curled in and out like a wave, each pod set up with two computer screens suspended from a T-bar, a keyboard and a mouse that caught Serena's attention. A red beam of light swung repeatedly from one side of it to the other. Embedded in the far wall were filing cabinets, which locked automatically when the drawers closed.

'This is where you'll sit. Your system has the foreign language software. We don't. You're fluent in Japanese and Cantonese, right?'

'That's right.' Serena swallowed. Over the last ten days she'd done some intensive study. She'd recapped her business Japanese, which was pretty good, but her Cantonese was bare-bones level.

'You can meet Al now. He's been in since seven.'

Something in Serena's stomach plunged, as if a rock had dropped into the muesli she'd eaten for breakfast. She felt her face flush.

'Is that where … you know?'

'Yes, but it's okay. You'd never know.'

Following Liz's swaying figure into Al's enormous office, she found herself standing in front of the very man she believed held the key to Gene-Asis' secrets.

Behind the desk hung a beautiful abstract oil painting in reds, indigos, creams, blacks and whites. She recognised the artist as Sean Scully. Tony Mancini had certainly been a man of taste. A soft cream carpet and cream leather chairs around a coffee table created an atmosphere of relaxation and warmth. But it was Bukowski's office now, and his desk was neat and clear, save for his docked handheld. She could see a digital photo frame to the right, but not the image.

Bukowski looked up, clearly deep in thought. He glanced momentarily at Liz, and then focused on Serena. He struck her as a man who never rushed his movements; each one was deliberate and controlled. The eyes observing her were so dark that she couldn't see where his pupils ended and his irises began.

'You must be Amber. Welcome. Welcome.'

He stood up and walked around the wooden desk to shake her hand. Bukowski was shorter and of slighter build than she'd imagined, but his stature did nothing to diminish his charisma.

Last night she'd searched the Net for information on her new boss and there had been plenty to choose from. It appeared this man was not shy of publicity and the news media couldn't get enough of him. She'd traced his family back to the 1920s, when his great-grandfather had drilled for oil in Cisco, Texas, which had established the family fortune. Bukowski's grandfather and father had continued to grow the oil business into an empire but Bukowski had foreseen the demise of oil. At a young age, he'd correctly predicted that genetic engineering would be the powerhouse of the future, so he'd studied bioscience and business at Harvard. From what she could discern, Bukowski revered his father, a stern disciplinarian and genuine patriarch who had a paternal approach to his employees. Bukowski had joined Gene-Asis' strategy and corporate development team straight out of university. He did a stint in Russia and India, and succeeded in converting the major farming belts of Eastern Europe, India and Pakistan to Gene-Asis' seeds. He went on to tackle the Asia-Pacific region. His biggest coup was converting China, which he had done by negotiating directly with the Chinese Government; three hundred million Chinese farmers were directed to use Gene-Asis' genetically engineered product lines. Developed so that the seeds could never be used more than once, the farmers were forced to buy seed from Gene-Asis every year. With this triumph under his belt, he returned to the United States as president of strategy and corporate development, supplanting his boss. Three years later, Bukowski was appointed global CEO.

In her four-centimetre heels Serena looked straight into his eyes, which made him about 177 centimetres tall. As he smiled, his eyes became narrow slits edged with thick black eyelashes, which made it disconcertingly difficult to read their expression. His smile was very wide, creating dimples in each cheek, and she found herself transfixed by the whitest, most perfect teeth she had ever seen. Distracted, Serena failed to register that he held her hand just a fraction too long before he let it go.

'I'm delighted you're here. At this stage, I'm not sure how long you'll be working for me. I'm hoping to appoint a new Asia-Pacific CEO shortly. Did HR explain this to you?' He extended his 'r's with a Texan drawl.

'Yes, Mr Bukowski. And it's lovely to meet you.' Serena returned his smile. She had to consciously stop herself from warming to him.

He sat on the edge of his desk in a relaxed manner but scanned her face with the intensity of a laser.

'Why, thank you, Amber. Your language skills will prove invaluable. Now, has Liz given you the grand tour?'

'Not yet, Al. I wanted to introduce her to you first and then we'll go through her induction program,' interjected Liz.

'Good, good. Now, Amber, do you know what we do here?'

Was that a trick question? 'Yes, genetically engineer plants and animals so they grow faster, resist disease and taste better.'

'Yes, but we do so much more. We give hope to the starving in drought-stricken Africa; we give hope to flooded and low-lying countries like Bangladesh; we give hope to this country, where the desert is slowly creeping towards the coast, destroying your agricultural land. And how do we give them hope? By using the brilliant minds the Lord has seen fit to give us to improve on

Creation, and by doing so, make people's lives better. The drought-resistant, disease-resistant, flood-resistant crops we develop are all about helping people, Amber, and I'm real proud of that. It's what we call the war on hunger.' His voice rang out with evangelical fervour. 'I'm proud we put food on people's tables and I'm proud that in ten years' time, over eighty per cent of the world's crops will be genetically engineered. By *my* company.'

Serena had heard many companies bang their own drum before and the cynical advertising pitch director within her would normally have groaned at another 'we serve the greater good' speech. The reference to 'the Lord' didn't surprise her: she'd read he was from a United Methodist family. But the conviction with which he spoke did surprise her and it took all her strength not to be moved by his words.

'I'm proud to be here, Mr Bukowski.'

His tone changed as he moved on to practicalities. 'You'll find me pretty easy to handle. I like things done a certain way but Monica will explain all that. Monica is my PA in New York and you'll need to work closely with her. I have two pet hates. The first is paper: it's not necessary in this high-tech age. The second is sloppiness and that includes anything that undermines company security. Apart from that, I'm an easygoing kinda guy.'

He raised his hands, palms up, smiling; amused at the contradictions in his own statement.

'No problem, Mr Bukowski.'

'No, please, call me Al.'

He smelled of musk, citrus and pine trees, and it reminded her of the pungent, untamed forests of the Scottish Highlands she'd visited during her time in the UK.

Liz responded, 'Thank you, Al. I guess we'd better take Amber down to Security.'

'Of course. Now, Amber, I'd like you back here by eight-thirty so I can brief you for the day.'

Serena nodded.

'If you'll excuse me, I have a call I must take,' he said. In the split second before he moved away, his eyes dropped the length of her body, so subtly that Serena mightn't have noticed. But she felt his gaze and it made her uncomfortable.

'Thank you, Al,' said Liz, leading Serena from the office.

'Jane, my dear, how can I help?' Serena heard Bukowski say into his earpiece. Was that Jane Mancini, the widow?

Serena glanced back and caught him watching her, still smiling. She smiled back shly and he nodded his head in acknowledgement. Serena had held her own with CEOs and senior executives all her working life, and Bukowski was the first to unsettle her. She reassured herself it was because of the role she was playing.

'So, how is Karen doing? She must be very shaken up,' Serena asked when they were safely out of hearing distance.

'She's not good. The company's paid for an overseas holiday and counselling but it doesn't help that she's got to hide from the media.' Liz paused. 'She's not coming back, by the way.'

'How have people here responded to Mr Mancini's death?'

'Everyone's very sad. Morale is pretty low.'

'Forgive me for asking, but do you know why Mr Bukowski is staying here?'

'To recruit Tony's replacement.'

'And how long will that take, do you think?'

'I don't know. Why?' replied Liz, giving Serena a questioning look. Perhaps she had gone too far.

'I just like to know who I'm working for, that's all,' she shrugged. 'So, what's Mr Bukowski like?'

Liz sat down at her desk, puffing with the exertion of walking, while Serena pulled up another chair.

'Call him Al. Seriously. He sees the company as one big happy family and he hates formality with his people. You're very lucky: he's a genuinely nice boss. And he's been so lovely to Tony's widow. He's paid for the funeral and giving Jane her husband's salary for as long as she needs it.'

'That's very generous,' said Serena, genuinely surprised at his kindness.

'And he tried to keep the news of Tony's death from the media, to protect the family. He was furious when it leaked out. His PR company got a real serve.'

That would be Gloria, thought Serena. As expected, the Gene-Asis share price had plummeted when news of the suicide leaked.

'Why did he do it? You know, kill himself here? Did he hate his job?'

'God, no! He loved it.' Liz changed the subject. 'Let me introduce you to some people. This is Sue,' she said looking at a woman to her right. 'She works for Chris Mann, Vice-President of Research and Development.'

Sue was watching Al, her fingers hovering above the keyboard.

'Sue, wakey, wakey.' Startled, Sue looked at Liz. 'Sue, this is Amber.' Petite and dark, with large, almond-shaped eyes, and possibly Turkish heritage, she beamed a friendly smile. Liz continued. 'Sal is in with Darko Petrinec, the VP of Strategy and Corporate Development. Amanda Jacobs is VP of Sales and Marketing, but she's out of the office this morning and I can't see Ron – he's her PA – anywhere. He might be getting coffee. And the CFO's interstate seeing banks.'

Serena glanced at Bukowski, who was still on the phone. He was looking straight at her, undressing her with his eyes.

Chapter 24

After the introductions, Liz took Serena to Security, nine floors below, to be retina-scanned and fingerprinted.

In the Sydney office, forty people worked in InfoSec, monitoring and fixing any potential security vulnerabilities. In New York, they were rumoured to employ over 200 people, including some of the world's brightest systems penetration experts. Gene-Asis was one of the most probed companies in the world. Some hackers did it for fun. Some to be able to boast. Some wanted to bring the company down: mainly environmentalists who wanted to stop Gene-Asis' work. Most wanted to steal the company's secrets for money. This meant all new staff were vetted as a security precaution and continually monitored during their employment. Serena presumed this was through the spy-eyes.

As the lift opened on the forty-sixth floor, the atmosphere was very different from the one she had come from: gone were the sunlight and bright glass-partitioned offices. In fact, Serena couldn't spot a window. Liz faced a retina-scanner, which looked like a pair of binoculars protruding from the wall. She placed her face against the retina scanner and the doors slid open. Inside was a corridor of glass. One side was dimly lit but Serena could see row upon row of desks arranged in a semicircle, like NASA mission control; two people to a pod, each of which had six computer screens. The screens were alive with data, wriggling like a giant tapeworm of encrypted code.

'That's system penetration,' Liz said, nodding to the left. 'You're not allowed in there. This is IT, which you'll have access to. I'll leave you with Colin Chang. He's a database administrator and he'll set you up.'

Serena followed Liz into the IT department, which was alive with people talking on phones or rushing around clutching various computer parts. It was a wasps' nest of frenetic activity.

'Over there are the server racks. That's bullet-proof glass, by the way. Only a handful of people are allowed in.'

'Like who?'

Liz gave her a quizzical look. 'You don't need to know that.'

'Sorry. I was just interested, that's all. I've never seen anything like it.'

Serena spotted a spy-eye camera watching the door to the server room and several more spy-eyes inside watching a technician working.

'This is the service desk. God knows why it's called that, 'cause they're not too hot on service,' whispered Liz behind her hand. She then continued aloud, 'And here we have the second line support team, and there are the system administrators.'

Liz walked up to a man hunched over a keyboard.

'Colin. This is Amber Crosby. She needs her bio-stats set up.'

They were standing behind him and he didn't respond. His fingers flew across the keyboard.

'Colin?' said Liz, touching him on the shoulder.

He jumped and knocked his coffee over his desk.

'Shit! Oh, sorry.' He raced off to get a cloth to wipe up the frothy mess. On his screen, Serena saw a number of fingerprint images. Next to each one was a name and a six-digit code.

'So sorry! I didn't mean to be rude. I was listening to music,' he said, wiping his desk clean.

Liz introduced her again, explained what he needed to do and left.

Colin was short, slightly rotund and badly in need of a haircut. Covering his eyes was a thick fringe, which he nervously moved aside and then stood, blinking at her. After a few seconds, he timidly put out his hand, which she shook. It was sweaty.

'Your first day?'

'Yes, I'm very nervous,' she confided.

'You'll be all right. Don't you worry. You've got a good boss.'

'So everyone tells me.'

His fringe had fallen over his eyes again. He pushed it back as he shuffled from foot to foot.

'How long have you worked here, Colin?'

'Six years. Long time.'

'And you manage this database! You must be very clever.'

'You think so? Oh, thank you.'

He shuffled from foot to foot a bit faster, smiling to reveal a crooked row of teeth.

'Colin, you'll look after me, won't you? I'm a bit scared about the retina scan. Does it hurt?'

She did 'female in distress' very convincingly and, in response, Colin puffed out his chest.

'Don't worry, it doesn't hurt. So, you please come with me?'

Colin's English was a little stilted.

'Where are you from originally?' she asked. 'Hong Kong?'

'Very good,' he grinned like the Cheshire Cat. 'You been to Hong Kong?'

'A while back. Great city.'

'Too much noise. Always noisy. I like Sydney better.'

Two workstations down, he introduced her to Sarah, who controlled the retina scanners' database and their maintenance. Protectively watching over her, Colin waited as she was asked to sit. Serena noticed his eyes lingering on her cleavage.

'Okay. All you have to do is keep very still and try not to blink. You won't feel a thing,' said Sarah.

On Serena's face she put a pair of glasses with a cable attached to the computer. And, keeping her eyes open wide, Serena felt a light move across them.

'Good. You see – it didn't hurt,' chimed in Colin.

'All done,' said Sarah, and Colin led her back to his workstation.

'Now your fingerprint. You right- or left-handed?'

'Right.'

'Place the first finger of your right hand on here,' said Colin.

She placed her finger as directed on a minute scanner.

'This is called biometric security,' he said, enjoying the opportunity to show off. 'I'll scan your fingerprint. I will then tell your specific computer mouse to accept your fingerprint as the sole user. No one else can use your computer and mouse, and you won't be able to use anyone else's. You'll have access to three of the four security levels.'

'What are the security levels?'

'Level 1 is Highly Protected information and you won't have access to this. Only top execs and the board see it. Level 2 is Confidential. Level 3 is Internal Use Only and Level 4 is Public information. You'll answer Mr Bukowski's day-to-day emails: the ones he's happy for you see. Some of his emails will be Highly Protected and you won't be able to open them. They're encrypted.'

'And the retina scanner will only let me into certain departments?'

'Yes, exactly. You have access to reception, the executive suite, marketing, accounts, IT, the restaurant, the boardroom, and that's all. And now, I'll show you to a waiting room while I finish your biometric enrolment.'

'Let me watch, please. I find what you do so fascinating.'

Serena looked up at him flirtatiously. Colin shuffled.

'No, I am sorry. This way, please.'

He showed her to a small room with a fridge, tea and coffee-making facilities, and a big screen showing cable-news coverage. As he shut the door, she waved and smiled, and he waved back with a big grin. She knew she had made a very useful friend. She also knew she needed to see how the fingerprint database worked. If she could only use her own computer and had restricted security access, she would never find the professor's report. She would need to bypass the biometric mouse somehow.

Serena quietly opened the door and, walking casually towards Colin's desk, stood behind him. He had his music playing and didn't hear her. She watched over his shoulder as he placed an image of her fingerprint into the database, with her name and a code number. On the screen, she could see eight other fingerprints and names she didn't know. If she could move her fingerprint under Bukowski's entry in the database, then she could access all the Highly Protected files through his computer. Serena watched carefully as Colin worked. Then, backing away, she returned to the little waiting room. In the hubbub of the IT department, no one had thought to challenge her.

'Okay, Amber. It's all set up. Two more things: you must sign our Acceptable Mail Use Policy here,' he said pointing at a one-page document, which she signed as Amber Crosby. 'You also need a password, which I'll set up now. It should be letters and numbers, as many as you like.'

'Peter59.'

'Peter your boyfriend?' he asked.

'No, I don't have one, Colin. Peter was my dad.'

And he was fifty-nine when he died, she thought. She needed to remind herself every day why she might be, at best, landing herself in jail; at worst, putting her life in danger.

Chapter 25

Liz very efficiently took Serena through all the processes and files she would need to use. Being Al's PA was going to be a piece of cake. Accessing his Highly Protected files, however, was not. Serena had also noticed that none of the PAs' computers had DVD drives or USB ports. She asked Liz why that was.

'Gene-Asis has a policy of avoiding disc copies. We can't make disc or memory key copies from *our* computers. A few top execs can from theirs. There's no problem printing copies, but if it's Highly Protected stuff, you'll need authorisation. So, if Al needs you to make a copy of, say, the latest TV commercial, he will give you authorisation via email and the guys in IT will make the copy for you. There are five of them down there. The fastest is Gary.'

'But what about sending files as attachments to emails? Can I do that?'

'Oh yeah, of course. But only Confidential, Internal Use and Public documents. Even if Al wants to attach a Highly Protected file to an email, it will be held in quarantine for ten minutes before it's released.'

'Wow! This must make simple everyday business communication very slow.'

'You'll get used to it,' Liz shrugged.

So, not only did she *not* have direct access to the kind of security files she needed, she couldn't make a copy, or send an emailed copy, without raising suspicion. As the day went on, Serena grew more and more despondent.

That afternoon, Bukowski called Amber into his office.

'I need you to organise a company dinner for Friday night. Five hundred and seventy-six people work here and I want them all invited to the 360 Hotel. I know it's short notice but I expect people to attend. Everyone is understandably upset by Tony's death, but I need my people to rally and get their eyes back on the ball. I'll be thanking them for all their hard work and handing out some awards for people who've excelled recently. So, can you book the venue, get me menu options and organise presentation equipment?'

'No problem. And if the 360 isn't available on Friday, do you have a second preference?'

'Tell them it's for Al R. Bukowski, and there'll be no problem. I'm a guest there. They'll do it for me.'

He emphasised the 'R' as if it stood for Rex; as in 'king'.

He really does think he's king of the world! 'Would you like me to write your speech? I used to do it for my old boss.'

'No, I always write my own. But thank you.' He gave her a single nod. 'I get the feeling you're a very talented woman.'

She heard a distant ringing sound. Bukowski tapped his earpiece; clearly his phone had rung, and he took the call, indicating Serena should wait.

'Yeah, that sounds good. Just a moment; let me log back in and I'll check.'

From the other side of his desk, Serena watched as he turned to his keyboard, which was partly obscured by his screen. He tapped in his user name: ARBukowski. It was the first part of his email address and she already knew this. After the slightest pause, he tapped in what she guessed was his password, which she counted as eight keystrokes. Then another slight pause. He looked down at his wristwatch for a moment. His hand obscured her view but he appeared to move something very briefly. What was he doing? Then she heard him tap ten keys. He scanned his screen.

'Yeah. That's correct. It's okay to go.'

He swivelled round in his chair as he ended the call.

'So, Amber, can you get back to me on this by two? I want invitations emailed by three.'

'Yes, Al.'

When Serena left Bukowski's office, she checked out the email system. She noticed that occasionally emails would arrive encrypted, which only Bukowski could read. She saw the name of the person who sent them, the time they were sent, and the content of the subject box, but the actual substance of the email was complete gobbledygook.

When Bukowski left his office, her eyes dropped to his watch, protruding below his cuff. It appeared to be a normal digital watch, which displayed the time in several countries. Something on that watch had prompted him with the final entry-code of his computer login. And Serena thought she knew what it might be.

'Do I need a key-fob code?' she asked Liz, whose workstation was next to hers.

'No. Al and a few others do. We don't ever see anything confidential enough to warrant one,' Liz replied as she typed.

'My old boss used to have one, except it looked like a key ring. Is that what Al uses?'

'No, it's in his watch, which he never takes off. Apparently, if he removes it from his skin, the code becomes invisible. It only reappears if the watch touches his skin again. Clever, huh?'

So Bukowski had a coded fob on his watch. Without its code, she would never get to see his Highly Protected files. She was in serious shit.

'Must go to the Ladies'. It's the baby pressing on my bladder,' said Liz.

A new email arrived in Bukowski's inbox. It was encrypted. Then the sender's name caught her eye: Dr R. L. Singh. He was one of the four Gene-Asis scientists behind Supercrop Ultra. The email was cc'd to Chris Mann, the Vice President of R&D. The subject box read: 'Delete file ~^1~^G/569/:P`12/6/2011 post PND launch?'

Serena guessed that 'PND' referred to Project New Dawn. But what file would they be destroying after its launch in New York? Could it be the professor's research? The name of the file was meaningless to her. Or was it? The last few numbers appeared to be a date, and 6 December 2011 was when Dr McPherson claimed he had submitted his report.

Elated, she searched her desk for some paper and found none. Desperate to note down the file name, she pulled a tissue out of her handbag and, using her eyeliner pencil, copied the file name carefully, checking no one was looking her way. As she placed it back in her bag, Liz appeared.

A man resembling a plump cocktail sausage on a stick shuffled past them, wiping his forehead with a large white handkerchief.

'Come and meet Chris, VP of R&D. He's lovely,' said Liz, swaying her way into his office.

'Knock, knock. Chris, can I introduce you to Al's new PA, Amber?'

He was slumped in his swivel chair, still dabbing his forehead. Upon seeing them, he grabbed the chair's arms, gyrating his body from side to side in an attempt to stand up. So large was his stomach and bottom that he appeared permanently wedged between the arm rests. Then, like a champagne cork freed from its bottle, he was up and springing towards her.

'Amber? Lovely to meet you ... please sit down ... hmmm ... so, I hear you worked in London?'

He wedged himself back in his chair and glugged down a glass of water.

'Yes.'

'Love London ... ah, the Royal Albert Hall ...The London Symphony Orchestra ... couldn't get enough when I was there ... and you can't beat a London curry house. Yes ... used to go to the Tandoori Palace in Soho and have a royal feast. The lamb vindaloo was the best I've ever tasted.'

'I've been there – it's the best. I've been trying to find a curry house in Sydney to match it.'

'Then you must try the Taj Mahal at Darlinghurst.'

'Well, if you ever fancy going there one lunchtime, or after work, I'd love to. It's great to meet a fellow curry lover.'

Chris' cheeks wobbled as he nodded eagerly.

'You're on. And, you know, I think you're going to fit in here very well.'

'I hope so,' she said. He did seem quite friendly for a senior executive, but what she was really hoping was that a night out with the local head of research and development might reveal some of the company's secrets.

'Bukowski's not what I expected,' Serena said, eating dinner with John and Baz that night.

'What did you expect?' asked Baz, tucking into a medium-rare steak.

'I don't know. Someone more hard-nosed, less well-liked.'

'Mancini was like that. I met him once or twice. A genuinely nice guy, a real family man,' said Baz.

'He's doing the right thing by the widow, for sure,' said John. 'But be careful, Seri. Don't let your guard down.'

'No, I wouldn't dare. There's something about the way he looks at people. It's like he's reading their minds. You feel like he knows all about you and you haven't said a word.'

John frowned. 'I don't like the sound of that.'

Serena continued, 'He has this charisma that draws people to him and I'm convinced several women in the office fancy him. A PA called Sue can't keep her eyes off him.' She decided not to mention his interest in her. John was already being overly protective.

'He's got a bit of a reputation,' said Baz. 'I think he's been caught out once or twice with some unwanted pregnancies. Nothing confirmed. Just rumours.'

'But he's religious, right?'

Baz raised his hands in mock defeat. 'I'm just telling you what I heard.'

Serena swallowed her last mouthful. 'My problem is their security. It's unbelievable. They really are paranoid.' She looked over to John. 'I really wouldn't mind talking it through with you.' Too much was at stake. She had to persist. He left the table and rinsed his plate before stacking it. Serena glanced at Baz, who winked encouragement. John folded his arms and leaned against the dishwasher.

'I can probably guess, but why don't you tell me about it?' said John.

'You sure?'

'Go on,' John said.

Before John could change his mind, she launched into a detailed description of the security systems she'd seen that day.

'That's some system,' he said. 'Seri, there's no way you'll get through all that. You'll need to get into Highly Protected and you simply can't do it.'

'But why not?'

'Why not? Okay, let's look at the four hurdles you've got to jump.' He held up his hand and counted them off. 'First, the simple one. You have to know Bukowski's user name.'

'ARBukowski.'

'As I said, that's the simple one. Second, you need his password. Apart from actually seeing him tap it in, your only other option is to guess it. If you guess wrong, and you will, you'll activate "password lock-out".'

'But I'll get a couple of attempts before I get locked out, right?'

'Yeah, and then alarm bells go off in IT. It's a bad idea. In fact, this whole thing is a bad idea.' He shook his head. 'I can't believe I'm discussing this.'

'John, I'm sorry. I know this is putting you in a really tough position. But I have to keep going.'

'Since Tracey told me about your hep S theory, I can't stop thinking about it. Part of me thinks the whole idea is crazy and part of me thinks there's a chance she's right. Look, I'll help where I can. Just understand there's a limit.'

'I do,' she replied, touching his arm. He looked down at her hand. Serena instantly withdrew it.

'Okay, let's get back into it. Third, you need to know the ten-digit code on Bukowski's watch fob. That's pretty impossible, unless you are standing right behind him when he brings it up. You can't guess it, and the random numbers will change at regular intervals, probably every few minutes.'

'He and a few other top execs use this code to open Highly Protected files.'

'Makes sense. And even if you do happen to see the code, it'll be useless after a few minutes anyway.'

'But if I do get to see it and I establish how frequently it changes, I might be able to use it?'

'You might. But, as I said, how are you going to see it? And even if you find the professor's report, you can't copy it on your computer. You'll have to use a computer, such as Bukowski's, that allows copies. Then you have the problem of the biometric mouse, which won't respond to your fingerprint, only Bukowski's. There's no way past that unless you break into their system and link your fingerprint to Bukowski's name in the biometric database.'

'But I might be able to persuade the database administrator to link my name to Bukowski's mouse.'

'Serena, I have no doubt you can be very persuasive. But that will take some doing.'

'Or a brilliant hacker could do it easily,' she said, grinning cheekily.

'Yeah, he could, but he won't,' he replied, smiling. 'You don't give up, do you?'

'Not generally,' she replied, laughing.

Chapter 26

As a child, Serena had enjoyed sneaking up on her family and shouting 'Boo' at the top of her voice. She knew if she timed it right there was a slim chance she could walk into Bukowski's office unobserved. She might then see him tap in his password and use his watch fob. She had to try it.

Serena didn't announce her presence and he hadn't noticed her. She was too late to see him enter his password, but saw him turn his left wrist up so he could see the watch face. It simply showed the time in four capital cities. Then he pressed his thumb on the face and it changed to reveal a line of green numbers on a black LCD screen. He tapped in the numbers with ten keystrokes. He looked up, surprised.

'Amber. I didn't see you.'

'Sorry; I knocked but you didn't respond,' she lied and continued, 'I wanted to ask you a quick question, if I may? What time do you want to arrive in New York for the launch? I'm guessing the day before, which means Tuesday? I need to tell your pilot.'

He leaned back in his chair and put both hands behind his head. His shirtsleeves were rolled up to just below his elbow to reveal lean, strong arms.

'It'll have to be around four in the afternoon on the Tuesday.'

'Which means leaving Sydney on Tuesday, because of the time difference.'

'I have a meeting at head office that evening. Have my driver pick me up.'

Serena moved closer so that she stood beside his desk. She'd worn her black wrap-around dress and the fabric brushed his leg. He looked down. She glanced at the digital photo frame, which had just that instant switched from a portrait close-up of a young girl to the same girl on a horse. It was time to find out more about this man.

'She's very pretty,' Serena commented.

He gazed at the photo.

'Jen's my daughter and I think she's awesome, but I'm biased.'

He smiled his wide smile, the rest of his face almost disappearing behind it.

'How old is she?'

'Seven, going on twenty-seven,' he joked.

'And she loves horses. I loved riding as a kid. Couldn't get enough of it. My mum used to despair of me ever doing my homework, always grooming or riding Biscuit.'

'Biscuit? Great name. Jen's mare is called Princess,' he responded, shaking his head in disbelief. He continued. 'Dumb name but Jen's won a lot of competitions on Princess.'

'You must be very proud.'

'I am but, unfortunately, I don't see much of her. She's with Cecile, her mom, in Dallas.'

'That must be hard.'

'Yes, I miss her very much: Jen that is, not her mother. We're divorced.'

'So, is Jen your only child?'

'She sure is,' he replied without hesitation. If this man had illegitimate children, there was no tell-tale response giving it away. 'But with the money she costs me, I'm not sure I'd want another. You know, she rang me the other day asking for her own credit card.'

'Credit card? At seven?'

'Yup. I said no. Then she tells me she wants something called a Shopping Barbie. It's a robotic doll with conversation skills. Barbie talks about the latest fashion items and where to buy them, and even comments on what she sees in the stores.'

'Sounds like Shopping Barbie could end up costing you a fortune!' she laughed.

He stared at her silently for a moment. The irises of his eyes were so dark they appeared black.

'So how are you finding working with us?'

'I'm loving it. It's a great company. And how are you finding Australia?'

'I haven't seen much of it, except from the plane. I don't have time to be a tourist, unfortunately. But I am going to a football match tomorrow. I believe it's very different from American football.'

'Oh yeah. They don't wear all that padding, for starters,' she said, grinning.

'Yeah, but our matches are tougher,' he replied, clearly enjoying her cheekiness. 'Pitch the Dallas Cowboys against your Wallabies and we'd make minced meat of them.'

'Oh, I don't think so,' she laughed.

He looked at his screen. An email had just whooshed into his inbox.

'I'll leave you to get on, Mr Bu ... sorry, I meant Al.'

He looked up at her.

'Nice talking with you, Amber.'

She was almost out of his office when he spoke again. 'That dress suits you.'

Serena returned to her desk, unsure if he'd been flirting with her or if he were simply paying her a compliment. When she looked through the glass partition, he had the photo frame in his hand. A lock of black hair fell forward and he brushed it back into place before placing the frame carefully back on the desk.

Bukowski was proving difficult to fathom. He clearly adored his daughter, and showed compassion and generosity to his employees. Yet, this man was ultimately responsible for ensuring the safety of each and every product released onto the market. He was global CEO. He had to know that T-Speed was dangerous. He also had to know about McPherson's research in Zimbabwe. He personally would be presenting Supercrop Ultra to the world in eight days' time in New York; the very products the professor had said were genetically engineered to 'cover their tracks, to hide the truth'. How could he live with himself, knowing his daughter might be eating foods that could make her sick?

She kept watching Bukowski: he was making big gestures with his arms as he spoke on the phone. Was it possible for a CEO to be unaware he was selling dangerous products? Was this information being kept from him? Serena shook the thought away. This man could have prevented her dad's death and she must never forget it. She mustn't allow herself to get sucked in by his beguiling manner.

'Amber?'

She jumped. Chris was standing in front of her.

'Chris. How are you?'

'Good. Wondered if you wanted a curry tonight? I've got the taste for one.'

It was early morning and Serena found it hard to imagine how anyone could crave a curry at breakfast time.

'Would love to, Chris.'

'Gorgeous day … perfect for a beer first, wouldn't you say?'

'Absolutely. Where do you suggest?'

'The Forresters first, at the junction of Riley and Foveaux. Then on to the Taj Mahal. Six-thirty suit?'

'Done. I'll see you there.'

Chris then manoeuvred his large body on its skinny legs out of the executive suite.

At lunchtime, Sue, Liz, Sal and Ron took her for a sandwich at the local café. They were very friendly, especially Sue, who loved to gossip. As a result, Serena learned a bit more about her boss: his birthday was 2/8/74, which made him forty; his favourite movie was *The Silence of the Lambs*, which she found slightly creepy; he was a God-fearing man and read his electronic Bible every morning; he drove a black Maybach, registration GENSIS13; and the rumours were true that he was a bit of a ladies' man. Ron warned her with a wink that he had a penchant for redheads. As he said it, Serena spotted Liz giving Sue a sideways glance, as Sue stared stony-faced at Ron. If Bukowski found Serena attractive, could she use this to her advantage? She decided to try to put Sue at her ease: if Sue became her enemy, life might become very difficult.

The Genesis Flaw

'God, I'm so not interested. I'd never dream of having a relationship with my boss. And, anyway, I only go for very tall men.'

Sue scanned Serena's face. She must have been satisfied with what she saw, because she relaxed her clenched jaw and chatted happily for the rest of the lunch break.

As they walked back to the office, Serena silently mulled over the information she'd gleaned on Bukowski and wondered if it might help her guess his password. Most people tended to pick one that was easy to remember, such as their child's name or a car registration. Serena was tempted to try one or two possibilities, but, heeding John's warning, decided against it.

As they entered the executive suite, a pale man with thinning blond hair and sharp cheekbones came out of his office. She hadn't met Darko Petrinec before.

'Sal, where is that investment bank submission?'

'I'm sorry, Darko, they were supposed to email it over by lunchtime.'

'I wouldn't be asking for it if they had. Please call them immediately.'

Sal raced off and dialled the contact at the bank. Serena heard Darko mutter 'Fools' under his breath as he returned to his office.

In a whisper, Serena asked Sue, 'Is he always like that?'

Sue nodded. 'Yeah, he's a real piece of work but Al rates him. In fact, they seem to be best mates. I can't work it out myself. I mean, Al is always so, you know, open and charming. And Darko; well, he's just cold and grumpy most of the time.'

They sat back at their workstations. 'So, what does Al see in him?'

'No idea but I know why Darko is so loyal.' She looked around to check that nobody but the PAs were in earshot. 'The story goes that Darko was working for Al when Al was VP of strategy in the Eastern European office. Darko was young and really ambitious. He was running this takeover of a local competitor and it turned out the target's CEO was involved in price fixing and bribery, and Darko missed it in the due diligence. And the local authorities then went after Gene-Asis as the new owner. Of course Al sorted it all out, but it should have gotten Darko fired. Instead, Al promoted him. He's now head of strategy and corporate development for

Asia-Pacific. I think that's a credit to Al, don't you? I mean, giving Darko a second chance.'

You mean, Bukowski has power over Darko. He's bought himself a loyal puppet, thought Serena.

'And what's with the sinister name?' asked Serena.

'Darko means "gift" in Croatian, apparently. Some gift!' she replied quietly, raising her eyes.

Chapter 27

Bukowski was out at a meeting for a few hours that afternoon, so Serena had some time to snoop around. She was almost certain that Dr McPherson's report would be in a Highly Protected file and she therefore wouldn't be able to open it, but at least she could locate it. Serena discovered a Highly Protected folder called 'Gibson Research Lab'. Curious, she tried to open it. Her computer beeped loudly, as 'access denied' popped up on screen. Sue looked her way.

'Sorry, made a mistake. I'll turn the sound off.'

She broke out in a sweat and quickly returned to Bukowski's diary. To Serena, the computer beep had sounded as attention-getting as a loudhailer. As she calmed herself, she wondered where the Gibson Research Lab was in Australia. She knew of the Gibson Desert: hot, remote and isolated. A location like that would ensure absolute secrecy. Could they really sustain a research facility in such a hostile environment?

It was then she noticed that the icons running along the bottom of her screen had changed colour. They were usually on a pale blue bar, which was now pale red. Quickly checking Sal's screen, Serena noted that her icons bar was still pale blue.

'What's with the different coloured icon bars?' asked Serena pointing at Sal's screen.

'If it turns red, you're being shadowed.'

'Shadowed?'

'Means the thought police are reading every word you type,' she announced dramatically.

Serena blushed from her scalp to her chest.

'Who are the "thought police"?'

'Oh, I call them that. Don't look so worried; they're only the guys at the IT service desk. If they suspect a computer glitch or virus, they can check out your files remotely. They sit at their desks and watch everything you're doing on your computer, as you do it. It's a bit Big Brother, I think. Anyway, why do you ask? Is your toolbar red?'

'Yes.'

'They're just checking your system is bug-free. They do that from time to time.'

Serena sat back down. What was she going to do now? Someone would have seen her trying to access the Highly Protected Gibson Research Lab file.

Trying to clear her head, she rested her fingers over the keyboard and took some deep breaths. She needed to find out who was shadowing her, so she rang the service desk line.

'Hi, I'm Amber Crosby, Al Bukowski's new PA.'

'Hi, Amber, I'm Kylie, and I know who you are. I have all your details in front of me.'

'I think I'm being shadowed and wondered if you could tell me who is doing it?'

'Me. I'm checking for any problems in your software. Al asked me to make sure it was running perfectly.'

'What have you found?'

'Seems to be running fine; you're virus-free.'

'Great. So, how long do you shadow for?'

'I'm just about done for today. By the way, you know you can't see Al's Highly Protected files, don't you?'

'I'm so sorry. I'm a bit confused about what I can and can't do, to be honest. This is only my second day and I've never worked anywhere with so many levels of security. There's no harm done, is there?'

This excuse sounded incredibly lame even to Serena but it was all she could think of.

'Shit, hasn't anyone told you that you can't get into his Highly Protected files? It's a big no, no. I'll come up and talk you through it.'

'That would be fantastic. I'm feeling a little lost at the moment,' said Serena pathetically.

Kylie arrived a few minutes later. Short and dark with very hairy arms, she also had some very distracting black hairs under her chin. She ran through all the security accessing issues that Liz had described yesterday. Fortunately, it seemed that Kylie was enjoying showing off her knowledge to the none-too-bright Amber.

'Am I in trouble for this?'

'Nah, look, I won't be dobbing you in. It's an easy mistake to make, but just be careful not to do it again. Next time I'll have to log the incident.'

'Thanks, Kylie; I really appreciate your help.'

'No worries, darl.'

Bukowski arrived back at four o'clock. Serena had worked hard to get all her work up to date, and now waited nervously to see if Kylie kept her word. She watched him unpack his briefcase, dock his handheld and sit. He tapped his earpiece: he was receiving a phone call. He was looking down, nodding. She couldn't make out his expression. After that call, he made another one and then settled down to reply to some emails. There was nothing in his actions to suggest he'd been informed of her activity that afternoon – except an email acknowledging a password change. Why would Bukowski change his password today? Did he do it at the end of every day?

'Are we meant to change our passwords every day?' she asked Sue.

'No. Al and Darko change theirs regularly. I haven't changed mine for weeks.'

At 5.35 pm Bukowski locked his office door and left, saying, 'Good night, Amber,' with his usual big smile. His departure was earlier than usual but there was nothing about his behaviour to suggest he was angry or suspicious. A few minutes later, Serena exited the cool foyer into the heat of the evening. She began walking down the street, weaving in and out of the throng, in the direction of the car park. Her neck and shoulder muscles relaxed as the tension of the day drained from her.

'Amber!'

She barely heard the call over the traffic noise. She was deep in thought and now she'd left the Gene-Asis building, was thinking as Serena.

'Amber!' It was louder this time and the accent stopped her in her tracks. A pedestrian bumped her arm as he narrowly missed colliding with her. A black Maybach had pulled up beside her. The tinted rear window was down and Al beckoned her over. Serena's eyes widened and she had to fight the urge to run. Was he about to confront her? She stood tall, her stride confident, as she dodged the people racing up and down the street to reach his car. He opened the door to reveal rich cream upholstery and she could smell the newness of the leather. She made sure she looked him in the eye.

'Get in. I'll give you a ride.'

She hesitated.

'It's okay. I'd like to talk about Chris,' he said as he shifted across the seat, confident she would do as he asked.

The strangeness of his invitation intrigued her; he could have spoken to her at the office. Worried Bukowski had a problem with her dinner date, she got in. He nodded to the bull-necked chauffeur, who was watching in the rear-view mirror for a signal from his boss. He pulled out into the traffic and the doors locked with a clunk. Serena instantly felt nervous. She recognised the driver as the same man who'd swept Bukowski away from McPherson's attack. He was more than a driver; he was Bukowski's bodyguard.

'I hear you're having dinner tonight?' His legs were stretched out, his tie removed and his jacket hung on a hook. He spoke casually, as if they were friends discussing their evening's plans. Serena wondered how he knew about their date. She suspected Sue.

'Yes. We share a love of curries.'

He opened a compartment to reveal a minibar. 'Would you like a drink?' She refused, desperate for him to get to the point. But he made her wait, pouring a sparkling mineral water into an exquisite crystal tumbler.

'Chris is a brilliant man, one of the best R&D guys I've had. But a gossip. I need you to do something for me.'

His smile reminded her of the wax figures at Madame Tussauds in London.

'Go on,' she replied.

'I worry Chris may be a security risk. He drinks too much and says things he shouldn't. I want you to tell me everything he says about Gene-Asis. I need to know he can be trusted.'

Serena shook her head. 'Mr Bukowski, I couldn't do that. It would betray his trust. Please don't ask me to do this.' The distress on her face was genuine. She wanted to pump Chris for information and had no intention of telling Bukowski any of their conversation.

He slowly and deliberately put down his glass and then leaned forward.

'My dear, I know this is a lot to ask but if I have a traitor in my midst, I have to know.'

Her cheeks burned. She swallowed; her mouth dry. His gaze shifted from her right eye to the left and back to the right, observing her response. She blinked and looked down, afraid he might detect the traitor in her.

'Mr Bukow …'

'Al, please. Just Al.' His face creased into the dimpled smile that had softened so many women's hearts.

'Al, it doesn't feel right. Look, I'm just a PA, this is all too, um, cloak and dagger for me.' She shook her head, pretending to be overwhelmed.

'Amber, if Chris says nothing wrong, there can be no harm in you telling me about it, now can there?'

She was trapped and nodded in acquiescence, but knew she wouldn't betray Chris.

'Good, now let me drop you there. The Forresters, I believe?'

'Yes. How did you know that?'

'I get to know everything.' He nodded in that I'm-the-king-of-the-world way of his and picked up his drink. 'Surry Hills,' he said to the driver.

'Everything? About every product? I mean, I'd heard you're very hands on, but how do you do it? I guess that's why you work such long hours.'

He ran a hand through his thick black hair and glanced at his reflection in the driver's rear-view mirror. His vanity was clearly as huge as his ego. 'I rely on my team of experts, Amber. That's what they're paid for. But, yes, I work hard. You don't get to my position without it. Power is something you have to earn and, once you have it, you have to fight to keep it.' He sipped his water. 'But, let me tell you, it's worth it.'

He'd dodged the question. She tried again.

'So, do you enjoy the science? I mean, do you check the science behind your products?'

He tilted his head to one side. 'Why do you ask?'

'Well, I read up on you before my interview; you know, to make sure I was informed about my potential new boss. You have a degree in business and genetics, so I imagine you like to get involved in the science.'

'As I said, I rely on my team of experts for that. I have enough on my plate. You know, right now, I'm doing two roles, mine and the Asia-Pacific CEO's. That means I cram two work days into one. In a few hours, I start my regular job. I have a conference call with my people in New York at midnight – that's the start of their day.'

'You must be exhausted. You do that every night?'

'Sure do, but I don't need a lot of sleep. I'll sleep for a few hours, then do my work-out, have a bit of breakfast and I'm ready to go again. In my position, Amber, everyone wants a piece of you. My people, the media, government, banks, charities, legal; you name it. You know, back home, Congress won't even consider a new agricultural bill without asking my opinion first. I get more interview requests from the media than I could ever say yes to. So when I do say yes, they lap up every word. My speeches get standing ovations. They love me, Amber. You probably can't imagine how good that feels.'

His condescension infuriated her, but she forced a fawning smile and asked, 'But how do you cope with all the criticism? All those people who say you're contaminating non-GM crops, that they're not safe to eat, that you're bullying farmers, that sort of thing. It must be hard to take?'

'I see you've done your homework.' He nodded his approval and then moved closer to her.

'You've heard that saying, "A butterfly flaps its wings here and the weather changes in China"? Well, when I talk to the Chinese government, their whole agricultural policy changes. Do you see what

I'm saying? My critics can bleat all they like but they're wasting their breath. I'm untouchable.' He laughed and his deep-set eyes became little more than semicircles of eyelashes, resembling two black sea anemones.

Serena had read *The Bonfire of the Vanities* many years ago, and recalled the central character had assumed invincibility and his world had come crashing down around him. But maybe Bukowski really was a Master of the Universe. John's warning finally sank in as she realised she wasn't just taking on a corporation. She was taking on a man who, metaphorically speaking, could part waves.

'And what about you, Amber? I see before me a woman of strength and intelligence. Why are you a PA when you could be so much more?'

She'd have to work harder at hiding her true self.

'You're right. I could do more but I choose not to. The truth is, I want to get married, have kids, have time to enjoy life. The career ladder doesn't interest me.'

He raised his eyebrows. 'I don't believe you.' His mouth was set hard; his stare drilled into her. A red flush spread up her chest and neck to her cheeks. He erupted into a loud laugh. 'I'm sorry, Amber. I don't mean to offend you but I see ambition in you, and I'm usually right about people.'

They were driving parallel to Hyde Park. 'Davidson, pull over. We're getting out.' The driver expertly manoeuvred the car between two buses and stopped, ignoring the angry honking. 'Will you walk with me? Have you time?'

He was leaning forward in his seat, with the eager expression of a little boy wanting to play after school. The sudden switch from narcissist to ordinary man caught her off guard. She stammered 'Sure' and they got out. The driver sped off.

'Where's he going?' she asked.

'He'll do laps around the park till I'm ready. Shall we?'

They wandered along a path under a canopy of Hills Figs that provided welcome shade. The day had been breezeless and humid but a Sydney summer evening nor'easter had begun to blow through the branches, which rustled like water cascading over pebbles. Bukowski was silent for a while, watching the activity in the park. She peered at his face, wondering if Bukowski really wanted to talk about Chris, or had an ulterior motive.

Two children, no more than five or six years old, were standing in the large circular Archibald fountain, splashing water at each other and giggling with joy. Their mother was perched on the wall, arms outstretched in case one of the children fell over. Bukowski laughed as he watched them.

'Reminds me of Jen. She used to love running through the garden sprinklers. That's one thing I regret – not having enough time for her.'

A tiny chink of vulnerability, at last.

'So, the world you're helping to create – you know, one where all plants are genetically engineered – is it going to make a better world for her?'

He turned to Serena and stepped too close: the kind of closeness that happened in a fight or between lovers. 'It'll be a better world because I will have created it; because, through my company, the expanding population will have enough to eat. We're going to win the war on hunger.'

The wind blew several strands of hair across Serena's face. In the sunlight, they shone like polished copper. He lifted his hand and she almost flinched before he gently tucked the wayward strands behind her ear. He was so near she could actually see where his pupils ended and his irises – the colour of dark chocolate – began. 'Thank you for your company,' he said. 'I need to get back to my hotel now. I'll drop you off first.'

Chapter 28

If Bukowski had intended to blindside her, he couldn't have done a better job. She stared blankly down Elizabeth Street at his departing limo. What the hell was that all about? The tiny hairs on the back of her neck prickled. That whole encounter had been out of kilter, especially his presumed intimacy with her. But Serena wouldn't allow it to force her off track. She flagged down a taxi and returned to the city, as she had something important to do before she met Chris. On the way, she called John: perhaps talking it through with him would help. John was saying goodnight to a colleague when he answered. She heard him say, 'I'll silc you later.'

'Silc you?'

'Yeah, a secure internet relay chat.'

'Right,' she replied, still puzzled. 'John, something weird has just happened.'

He was reluctant to talk at first but after she told him about Bukowski asking her to spy on Chris, he was all ears.

'You're right. It could be a trap. If you don't tell Bukowski what Chris says, he won't be able to trust you and you'll be out of there,' said John. 'But why would he be setting a trap for you in the first place? Have you done anything to raise his suspicions?'

'I tried getting into a Highly Protected file and got caught. They were shadowing me and I didn't realise.' She filled him in on the Gibson file.

'Shit. That wasn't a good idea.'

'Well, it's too late now. I played dumb and Kylie, who was shadowing me, said she wouldn't report it. But maybe she did anyway and Bukowski is testing me. I mean, he changed his password as soon as he got back to the office.'

'Bukowski's password change could just be a regular thing.' He paused. She could imagine his far-way look; the expression he always had when deep in thought. 'But it's her job to report you, and it would make no sense to her that you were trying to open that Gibson file. At the very least, you'll be shadowed some more.'

'Anyway, look, if Chris is a gossip, he's exactly what I need. I'm going to pump him for everything I can and only tell Bukowski the safe stuff. Apart from anything else, I refuse to land Chris in trouble.'

'Sounds like he already is. Just be careful not to implicate yourself.'

At the GPO on George Street, Serena opened her post office box. Inside its narrow confines lay a solitary package addressed to Neresa Slow. It wasn't just a letter: the envelope was big enough to hold a book. She felt a sudden surge of adrenaline: had McPherson sent her his research notebook? She jumped when a man next to her opened his mailbox door with a loud clank. Placing the package quickly in her handbag, she locked the box. She walked towards the escalator, scanning the myriad faces of people swarming in and out of the vault-like space. Her box was at the post office backpackers used as a poste restante. She'd selected it deliberately because it was always busy. She passed two postmen piling large grey mailbags onto a trolley. A queue of backpackers waiting to pick up their mail snaked back to the escalator. She went to the ground floor and found a quiet corner in which to open the package. She ripped it open. Inside were two items: a book, but not the one she'd anticipated, and a handwritten letter.

Dear Serena

Thank you for your letter. I am sorry that we did not meet and I hope you will forgive my unavailability. I live a quiet life and do not like unexpected visitors.

You need to know that I am a man of God now, not a man of science. The only advice I can give you is to let God's word show you the way. Read this Bible every day and The Truth will become known to you. I have marked a page for you to begin your reading. Please read it carefully, as I have selected this passage specifically for you. It is beautifully written and will transport you to an exotic land of beautiful, fragile people.

God bless you.

Fergus McPherson

She stared at the letter, frowning, trying to unravel his cryptic message. Perhaps the passage he'd marked would tell her the location of his food trials? She didn't believe for a minute the mumbo jumbo about being a man of God.

Serena opened the Bible at the spot marked by a torn-off scrap of blank paper. It was the Book of Proverbs, Chapter 13, verses 3-6, and he'd marked in pencil a passage with an asterisk. He had also underlined five words; to emphasise their importance, she assumed. She read the passage:

Keep what you know to yourself,

and you will be safe;

Talk too <u>much</u> and you are done for.

No ma<u>tt</u>er how much you wa<u>nt</u>,

Laziness won't help a bit,

but hard work will reward you

with more than enough.

A good person hates <u>d</u>eceit,

but those who are evil cause sh<u>a</u>me and disgrace.

Live right, and you are safe! But sin will destroy you.

Her frown deepened. 'Much', 'matter', 'want', 'deceit' and 'shame' were the words he'd underlined. What did they mean? Otherwise, all she could glean from this passage was a warning to be careful. Was he asking her to keep to herself the information he'd given her? Was he encouraging her actively to seek the truth about Gene-Asis with the line 'laziness won't help a bit'? Perhaps he was referring to Gene-Asis' sin with the words 'sin will destroy you'?

No, there was more to it than that, but Serena didn't have time to think about it, as she was running late for her date with Chris Mann. She rushed out into the street and whistled loudly at a passing taxi, which screeched to a halt.

Chapter 29

She pulled up outside The Forresters and spied Chris immediately, puffing and wheezing like an old steam engine as he walked across the road to the pub.

'Chris!' she shouted as she waved and got out of the taxi.

He waved back, then wiped the sweat on his forehead with an orange handkerchief. The pub was buzzing with people as thirsty office workers sought a cool place to have an after-work drink. They found a shady spot outside and, once they had ice-cold beers in hand, Chris' laboured breathing began to relax.

'Seemed … a bit, er … down today, Amber, my dear. Not getting on top of you, is it? … No need, you know. It's just a job.'

'Been a tough second day. That's all. I'm fine, really.'

The cold beer tasted divine and, before she knew it, she'd drunk half a schooner. Chris had bolted his and ordered a second.

'You can tell me it's none of my business if you like, but Al hasn't … you know … made things awkward?'

She blinked. Awkward wasn't the right word. Confusing was probably a better one.

'No, not at all. He's been very friendly. Why? What do you mean?'

'Inappropriate of me to say, really … great guy, awesome businessman, but not your type, I imagine?'

'Chris, I'm not interested in Al, other than he's my boss.' She decided to play innocent. 'But surely Al would never come onto a member of staff?'

'Hmm, normally not. But he's a bit of a charmer and the women in the office seem to dote on him. He certainly seems interested in you.'

He placed his finger against the side of his nose and tapped it conspiratorially.

'Me? Why would he be interested in me?' she asked.

'Why not? You're a very attractive woman, if you don't mind me saying so, and I've noticed him watching you. Takes a lot to distract Al from his job. I've never met a more dedicated corporate man. It cost him his marriage, of course.'

'How so?'

'Well, he was always being promoted, which meant moving from country to country, and Cecile couldn't hack it. She filed for divorce.'

'So the rumours aren't true? Someone told me he'd had an affair.'

'Ah, you've heard. All I'll say to you is he always gets what he wants and I would hate to see you hurt, like my poor Sue.'

'Sue? Did they have an affair?'

'Oh, my dear. The poor girl fell head over heels for him. From what I can tell, it was one night of passion and then he dropped her like a hot potato. Behaved as if it never happened.' Chris tried to lean forward but his big belly prevented him. 'Look, I shouldn't be saying anything. This is just between us, right?'

'Of course.'

'I'm very fond of Sue. When my wife left me, she was a great friend, helped me through it, although God knows why she'd waste time on a fat old fart like me. Anyway, she did and I hate to see her hurt. It makes me angry. Very.' Chris nodded as he said 'very'. 'And you know what? Damn it. I don't want to see it happen to you.'

'Chris, you are a sweetheart and I will be careful. I promise. But I'm surprised he has time for affairs. Isn't he supposed to be super dedicated?'

'Dedicated! My word he is. I think "obsessed" would be more like it. He'd do anything for the company. Just don't get in his way, that's all I'll say. Oh, excuse me, two more Cascades, please,' he called to a passing barman. Chris was now on his third beer.

'What do you mean, "don't get in his way"?'

'Well, I probably shouldn't go into this,' said Chris, wiping a dribble of beer from his chin, 'but a year ago I resigned from Gene-Asis to join a company called Human Synthetics. They're pioneering the manufacture of synthetic body organs for transplants. Lungs, liver and heart, that sort of thing. They're not in any way competitive with Gene-Asis, so I imagined there would be no problem. I did know it was an awkward time to resign, as we were in the middle of some highly sensitive genetics developments, but I had signed all the obligatory confidentiality contracts, so their secrets were safe with me.

'Anyway, Al offered me all sorts of incentives to stay with Gene-Asis, including a huge pay rise and a holiday house in Port Douglas. But I had personal reasons for wanting to leave, so I stuck with my decision to join Human Synthetics. To this day, I don't know what strings Al pulled, but my job offer was suddenly withdrawn, and no other company would touch me. I was a leper in the industry. When Al offered me my job back, I had no choice.'

'But what makes you think Al put the bad word on you?'

'I *know* he was behind it. I have friends in head office. Apparently, Al went ballistic, saying that Project New Dawn would be jeopardised if I were allowed to leave. He demanded that my departure be stopped.'

'So, what's Project what's-his-name?' She deliberately stumbled over her words.

'Can't tell you, my dear, but you'll know soon enough.'

'Shit! Chris, what you know must be pretty damn important for them to go to all that trouble.'

'What I know … yes … what I know is that I've sold my soul to … a corporation … yes, indeed … anyway, we'll make a move after these beers, shall we? Now, tell me about you.'

Serena tried to manoeuvre the conversation back to this last comment but he steered clear of it. He determinedly focused on her, and her time in England, until they arrived at the entrance to the Taj Mahal restaurant. It was up a short flight of steps and Serena was worried that Chris might go into cardiac arrest. By the time they got to the top, his little legs were about to buckle and he was sweating profusely.

The Genesis Flaw

'Ah welcome, Mr Mann. We are very pleased to see you again. Let me show you to your table,' said the Indian maître d'.

Chris sat down on a red velvet chair, large sweat patches staining the underarms of his pale blue shirt. The restaurant was very small and decked out like an Aladdin's cave, rich in exotic fabrics and copper lanterns, except for the starched white tablecloths, which looked out of place amidst so many colours. On the walls hung pictures of bejewelled gods and goddesses, and stone statues rested on every shelf and in every crevice. The heady aroma of incense and spices filled the air.

Chris ordered ten of his favourite dishes from the menu, and while drinking a bottle of Rosemount Riesling, they munched their way through several poppadoms and pickles, until their dishes arrived.

'I'm sorry to hear your wife left you, Chris. Do you have any kids?'

'Yes, was married … left me when my reputation was trashed by you-know-who … took the kids, of course … like to see a photo?'

He opened his wallet and two blonde-haired, brown-eyed faces beamed up at her.

'They're gorgeous. How old are they?'

'They're ten and seven now. This was taken a few years back,' he said, replacing the photo in his wallet.

'Do you get to see them much?'

'Only every other weekend. Hardly at all, really … I never want to give them back. And it's hard for them too.' Pouring himself another glass of wine, Chris then took a large mouthful of lamb vindaloo, the front of his shirt stained with the occasional splattering of greasy sauce.

'You're single, aren't you?'

'Very single.'

'A word of advice: when you find the right one, hang onto them. Nothing is more important … nothing.' The poppadoms jumped as Chris' hand hit the table. The waiter shot them a concerned look.

'I let my wretched career consume my life. And, believe me, it's not worth it. No wonder she left me. God, I've done things for this job I would never do again, and what do I have for all my hard work? Nothing, except a fat gut and high cholesterol.'

His face was puce as he sucked down his wine.

Serena replied, 'Yes, I've done some pretty stupid things in my time to further my career. And I hated myself for it. I don't want to play that game anymore and I certainly wouldn't further my career by hurting anyone.'

He slouched forward and looked blearily into her eyes.

'You're in the wrong company then, my dear, and I'd leave now if I were you.' His speech was very slurred. He poured himself the last of the wine.

'Gene-Asis aren't the caring-sharing company they seem to be, then?'

With a thump, Chris leaned into the back of his chair.

'Too much, too much ... I've said too much. Wine gone to my head ... best to go home ... waiter, can I have the bill, please?'

'Please, Chris. You can't leave me worried like this. What's going on?'

'No, no. Just forget all this. I'm just a drunken has-been.'

The bill paid, Chris swayed slightly as he got up, steadying himself for a moment by leaning on the table. Putting his weight against the wall at the top of the stairs, he clung onto the handrail with both hands as he descended the stairs. Slowly, he fumbled his way down each step. With only one step to go, he slipped on a shiny, bald patch of carpet, fell onto his bottom, and sat there motionless like a sack of potatoes. Serena ran down the last steps.

'Chris, Chris, are you all right?'

He sat there with his legs splayed out in front of him, his back propped up by the stairs and his stomach rising like a beach ball from his half-open shirt, where two buttons had burst off. With his head hung, he emitted strange sobbing noises as if he were gulping for air.

'I'll call an ambulance?'

'No, no.'

Leaning closer, she saw his red cheeks were wet with tears.

'That poor man,' he sobbed.

'Chris? What man? Tony Mancini?'

'God forgive me. I should have done something to stop it.'

'What man, Chris?'

He looked at her through his bloodshot, watery eyes. Silently, he placed his pudgy finger over her lips.

'Ssshhhh. Not another word.'

The maître d' and a waiter came bolting down the stairs.

'Oh, Mr Mann, what has happened? Let me help you up. Oh dear, oh dear.'

They hauled him to his feet and placed him in a taxi. Chris refused to say anything more. He just hung his head. Stunned, she watched the taxi disappear into the traffic.

What man, Chris? And what happened to him? What have you done?

Was he referring to Mancini, or McPherson, or even Munroe? One thing was for sure: Bukowski was not a man to be crossed. And he was watching her.

Chapter 30

The taxi pulled up outside the block of units in Coogee. Having drunk too much to drive home, Serena had left her car in the car park overnight. As the taxi sped off, she stood under a streetlight, searching for her key: a small square plastic card, which she would place over the sensor at the main entrance. The summery smell of frangipani filled the air, coming from a tree in the front yard. At her feet, the pavement was strewn with many yellow and white flowers wilting on the still-warm concrete.

Finding her key, she looked up and something caught her eye. It was the glare from a computer screen coming from the dark interior of a car. Parked well away from the streetlights, she could see only the silhouette of a man sitting in the driver's seat, head bowed over some kind of laptop. He turned his head and looked at her, but she could not make out his features. He moved the computer from his lap, started the ignition and drove off.

Still feeling jittery from her conversation with Chris, this odd behaviour made her nervous and she quickly walked inside the Art Deco building. Racing inside, she called out, 'Anyone home?' John replied from the lounge, a great cheer erupting from the television, as if the lounge were filled with football fans. She wandered in to find him watching the cricket: Australia was playing England, and Australia was batting.

'Who's winning?'

'Australia. But it's close. How did it go with Chris?' he asked, turning away from the television. Play had stopped.

'Do you really want to know?'

'I shouldn't,' he said, shaking his head. 'I really shouldn't but … oh shit, just tell me. I couldn't focus on the match at all tonight. I kept wondering what was happening to you. And you know how hard it is to distract me from my cricket.'

She filled him in on her evening with Chris. 'It's been a pretty full-on day,' she said, removing her strappy sandals and rubbing her sore toes.

'Bukowski fancies you.' His face was serious, and there was an angry edge to his voice. Serena frowned, taken aback.

'You reckon?'

'Yeah. I've been thinking about your little trip with him tonight. And now you tell me Chris thinks the same thing. That ride wasn't about you spying. I mean, why go for a walk?'

'Maybe he's just testing me. Or warning me. He made it pretty clear how he feels about traitors.'

'Either way, this interest in you is a worry. I think you should get out of there.'

'No way. If he does fancy me, I can use it. Get close. He might let something slip. And if he's sussing me out, I just have to be very careful not to slip up. I can handle him.'

'Seri, this guy's predatory. He's hunting you.'

'I can handle it,' she said, flicking her hand back as if she were swatting away the problem. 'Now, what do you think about what Chris said?'

'Disturbing. Bukowski sounds like a ruthless son of a bitch but I guess we already knew that. Any idea who the "poor man" is?'

'I don't know. I was thinking at first it might be Tony Mancini. But the cops are sure it was an unassisted suicide. So then I thought of the two scientists: McPherson and Munroe. Maybe he had something to do with ruining Dr McPherson's reputation?'

'You said the other one, Munroe, went missing recently?'

'Yes, still hasn't been found.'

John stood up and paced the room.

'You should try talking to Chris again. With a confession, you could go to the police.'

'I can try, but he's pretty cowed. He's given up. It's sad.'

'Try, Seri. If you can get Chris to turn whistleblower, you can get out of there.'

Serena considered it. 'I'll talk to him tomorrow but it'll have to be away from the office.' She paused, chewing a fingernail. 'I could tell Chris that Bukowski asked me to spy on him. That could win him over to our side. And I'll assure him I told Bukowski nothing.'

She glanced out the open window and saw the clear night sky. Should she tell John about the strange car outside? He was already overprotective. 'One more thing. It's weird. Tonight, when I came home, I saw someone with a laptop parked down the street. When I spotted them, they drove off.'

John went to the open window and leaned out. The cars parked outside were empty.

'They could have been tapping into our computers and phone lines. It's easily done.'

Serena felt her stomach plunge. 'You think it could be Gene-Asis?'

He turned his back on the view and leaned on the window ledge.

'Uh-huh. But their hacker would have to be better than me, and I doubt it. He wouldn't get past my security and I fixed your phone so your calls can't be tapped. So they won't find anything.'

'And, look, I'm probably just being paranoid,' she said, trying to convince herself more than John.

He sat close to her.

'Seri, please listen. Don't go back there. They are probably onto you and, regardless, Bukowski's interest in you is not good. I thought you wanted to slip under the radar. Well, you're totally *on* his radar. That's the wrong place to be.'

She shook her head. He half-smiled in resignation.

'You leave me no choice then,' he said.

'Don't try to stop me, John.' She moved back, to place some distance between them.

'No, you've got me all wrong. I can't let you make a pig's ear of this, so I guess I'll have to help you.'

'Really? That's great.' She hugged him.

'I'm going to give you a device that'll allow you to see everything Bukowski does on his computer. It's something I've been developing in my own time. It's not quite ready, but give me a few days.'

'Can you do it in less?' She grinned cheekily.

'You're unbelievable,' he replied, shaking his head in mock exasperation. 'Being a genius takes time,' he joked. Serena poked him in the ribs. He began to laugh as she tickled him. He grabbed her wrists, holding them firmly enough to stop her, but not enough to hurt. She was laughing too. His eyes dropped to her lips and then did a circle around her face. He moved closer. The playfulness instantly switched to a totally different energy. *No, not again*, she thought, *I can't go there.*

'Like being kids again,' she said, sabotaging the moment. He released her wrists.

'Not quite,' he said, looking away, and cleared his throat. 'Okay, why don't you show me McPherson's letter and the Bible? I reckon I can work it out.'

'All right, Mr Genius. There you are,' she said, handing him the Bible. 'He's underlined five words.'

'Not exactly. He's underlined *parts* of five words. That's got to mean something.'

She peered over his shoulder.

'You're right! It spells "Mutenda". That's got to be where they did the food trials,' said Serena, docking her phone and accessing the Net. They both peered at the monitor. 'I'll bet you any money Mutenda is in Zimbabwe.'

She was right: Mutenda was a remote village in the Gweru District of the Midlands Province of Zimbabwe.

'Bingo!' she shrieked. 'I must call Tracey and let her know we're in business.'

Chapter 31

The bus was crowded with morning commuters and she had to stand. The man next to Serena was reading a magazine and kept elbowing her whenever he turned the page. Her Tbyte beeped in her handbag, meaning that she had an email, but reading it would be tricky. She managed to get it out of her bag and, widening her stance to improve her balance, brought up Tracey's email:

> Mate,
> Bloody fantastic work! You and John make a great team, and would make a great couple too, if you ask me!!
> My flight's booked, and I'm leaving tomorrow morning. I should be in Nyrwbsp the following day. I'll keep you posted. Wish me luck!
> Love, Trace

When Serena had emailed the details of Mutenda village to Tracey last night, she'd written the name of the village in a code she knew Tracey would understand, as they'd used it when emailing each other at work. At Rooneys, emails were randomly checked. So, to conceal the name of the person they were discussing, they created a childishly simple, yet effective, code. Looking at a keyboard, they used the letter of the alphabet to the left of the one they actually wanted to spell. If there was no letter to the left, they went up a line and used the first letter on the far right. So 'm'

The Genesis Flaw

became 'n' and 'u' became 'y', and 'Nyrwbsp' was really 'Mutenda'.

Getting off the bus, she walked through the multistorey car park to check her hire car was still there and in one piece. She spotted her black Golf wedged between a white utility and a blue Commodore. Approaching, Serena saw a piece of paper under the windscreen wiper on the driver's side. She guessed it was either a marketing leaflet or a warning from the security guards not to leave her car overnight. Increasing her pace, she pulled out from under the wiper a folded piece of paper clearly torn from a spiral-bound A5 notebook. Someone had scribbled a handwritten note:

I can tell you what's in the Gibson file. Call 0410 555 639.

She did a three sixty. Who knew about her abortive attempt to open the Gibson file, apart from Kylie and herself? Was he or she watching her now? A woman in a white top and beige three-quarter-length pants walked towards her with a small daypack on her back, but continued on. Cars crawled along, as if on a conveyor belt, the people inside peering through their windscreens in search of a parking space. One man seemed to be staring at her. He was in his thirties, with a crew cut, and wearing a baggy T-shirt. Clutching the note tightly, she leaned against the wing of her car as he drove towards her. He gave her a tiny nod and then wound down his passenger window.

'Are you leaving?' he asked, nodding at her car.

She stared at him, uncomprehendingly at first.

'Oh, no; sorry.'

He drove on and she exhaled loudly; she had been holding her breath. Cramming the note into her bag, she checked the doors were still locked and the alarm set. Then Serena walked to work, all the time wondering who had written the note, and if she should call the number on it.

Pausing outside the Gene-Asis building, she peered up at its 256-metre tall exterior, and then down into its 2000 square metre glass and steel atrium. Staff entering the building brushed by her while she stood rooted to the spot. She watched them place their faces in one of the many retina scanners that released the ten massive security doors leading to the elevators. Serena made her decision: she would call the number. But she would have to be quick, as she was running late. The number rang a couple of times before a man's deep voice said, 'Hello.'

She hesitated, then ended the call. *Shit, shit, shit. Why did I do that?* She paced the pavement, and then redialled.

'Hello?'

'Who is this?' Serena asked, sounding more aggressive than she'd intended.

'Who's asking?'

'You left a note on my car.'

'Amber, is that you?'

'Yes. Why did you leave me your phone number? What do you want?'

'I didn't mean to scare you: it just seemed the best way to contact you.' He spoke slowly. 'I didn't want to talk to you inside the Gene-Asis building.' His voice had a baritone richness and an ocker accent.

'Why do you want to speak to me?'

'Because you have an interest in the Gibson Lab, and I know all about that place.'

'I don't understand. What makes you think I'm interested in this lab?'

'Because I overheard Kylie's conversation with you, when you tried to get into the file. That wasn't a good idea, Amber. Try that again and you'll be fired.'

'You sit next to Kylie?'

'Not usually.'

'So, how did you hear our conversation?'

'I told you. My ears pricked up when she mentioned the Gibson file.'

He was dodging the question.

'It was a silly mistake, that's all.'

'As you wish. But if you change your mind and want to know what's in that file, you have my number.'

'But why would you tell me? It's a top-security file.'

'Because ... Amber, I have to be careful to protect myself. I'm taking a big risk talking to you at all. If I've made a mistake, I'm sorry.'

The line went dead.

Serena felt as if the ground had just shaken beneath her feet.

Chapter 32

Racing into the atrium, she bolted past the cafés, restaurants and stores, and lined up at one of the retina-scanner queues. It was like placing her face in a giant camera lens, inside of which were two retina scanners, one for each eye. The security doors slid open, and she passed through the metal and explosives detectors unscathed.

Squeezing into an already packed elevator, Serena shot to the fifty-fifth floor, all the time mulling over her recent encounter. If this man knew of her attempt to access the Gibson Research Lab file, then who else did? Did Bukowski know? No, she doubted it. Serena was sure she'd have been fired by now if he suspected her of spying. So was this note-leaver friend or foe? And how did he know what was in the file? She'd check out the staff list as soon as she could.

At her desk, she could see Bukowski standing behind his, leaning forward on his knuckles. He was looking angrily at a man she recognised from her tour of the IT department on day one. Serena couldn't hear what was said but the IT man's body language was very defensive, while Bukowski's head jutted forward, his fists clenched on the desk. The man nodded and beat a hasty retreat, opening Bukowski's door. She heard the tail end of their conversation:

'I need this fixed now, do you hear? I cannot have the system running this slow.'

'Yes, Mr Bukowski,' replied the man, red-faced with embarrassment. He scurried off.

'Who was that?' Serena whispered to Liz, both of them, heads down, pretending to work.

'Larry Griffiths, Service Desk Manager.'

'What was that all about?'

'I don't know for sure but I think Al is pissed off because the METRO update means his connection drops out all the time.'

'METRO?'

'Yeah. METRO includes our antivirus software, our firewall, and our intruder detection and prevention systems. Last night, Larry installed an updated version and now every computer in the building is running really slowly. And Al's connection drops out. He's thrown a wobbly.'

'Oh,' Serena said, watching Bukowski walk towards her, his jaw clenched. She pasted on a big smile and said, 'Good morning, Al, how are you?'

It was as if, having earlier witnessed a tornado, she were now sitting in the tranquil eye of the storm. He was calm and smiling warmly.

'I'm great. Couldn't be better. And how was your evening?'

'Wonderful, thank you.'

'Can you come into my office, please?' It was expressed as a question but he didn't expect an answer. As she followed Bukowski, Serena noticed Sue watching them out of the corner of her eye.

'So, what did Chris tell you?'

'Nothing unusual, Al. He talked about his divorce, how much he misses his kids. He mentioned he was offered a job at another company but decided to stay at Gene-Asis.'

Bukowski smirked. 'Is that what he said? Go on.'

'We talked about you and your career, but nothing about the projects he's working on or anything like that.'

Bukowski nodded, his fingertips touching to form a triangular shape like the beams of a roof. 'Go on.'

'That's it, really. The rest was about London, curry houses and me.'

'Good. Thank you, Amber. Now, can you get Gav Rayner, the Minister for Agriculture, on the phone for me? You may need to drag him out of a parliamentary session, so just say Al R. Bukowski needs to speak to him *urgently*.'

He emphasised the 'urgently' with a certain severity, yet smiled at the same time, much like a wild bear might appear playful before it swipes you with its deadly claws. Serena rang Gav Rayner's personal assistant, Martine, in Canberra. Yes, he was in the House and would not be available to call Mr Bukowski until the afternoon. With some trepidation, Serena called Bukowski on his internal line and explained the outcome of her call.

'Did you tell her who was calling?'

'I did, Al.'

'I'd like you to give Martine another call,' he said, speaking slowly, 'and explain that our conversation cannot wait until this afternoon. Can you do that for me?'

'Certainly, Al.'

She called Martine and repeated Bukowski's words. Martine sighed and, clearly irritated, said she would see what she could do. Serena didn't blame her.

Checking nobody was watching, Serena scrolled through the staff database and found the list for the Gibson Research Lab. There were sixty-seven names, forty-two were women. This left twenty-five men. But there was no way she could guess the name of the note-leaver.

She glanced into Chris' office. He wasn't in yet. Then Serena noticed Sue clearing up his untidy desk. She looked miserable. Serena ducked her head round the office doorway.

'Hey, how are you?'

'Oh, it's you,' Sue responded, clearly not pleased to see her.

Serena partly closed the door. 'Sue, look, I know you like Al and please believe me when I say I'm not interested in him.'

'Oh sure,' she said sarcastically. Then she shook her head. 'Anyway, I'm not worried about that. I'm worried about Chris.'

'Why? What's happened?'

'Chris is sick.' Sue didn't look at her and continued picking up the paper files messily layered on the desk. Chris was certainly out of sync with the company's 'no paper' policy.

'He looked fine to me last night. What's he got, a hangover?' she joked.

'You saw him last night?'

'Yes, went to the Taj Mahal. Turns out we're both mad about curries.' Serena wanted their dinner date to be out in the open.

'Well, Al tells me he rang in this morning and he's fallen into a deep depression, so he's been given extended sick leave.'

Serena remembered Chris at the bottom of the restaurant steps, sobbing. Her flippancy evaporated.

'That's terrible. I had no idea he was prone to depression.'

Sue leaned closer to Serena and whispered, 'Al told me Chris is bipolar. But I can't see it myself. Yes, Chris gets down sometimes and he found his divorce hard, but my dad's bipolar and Chris has never had the severe mood swings Dad goes through.'

'Why does Al think he's bipolar?' Serena carried two sticky takeaway coffee cups and several empty lolly wrappers to the bin.

'Says Chris has seen a specialist recently, who diagnosed bipolar.'

'Why don't we send him a Get Well card? That might help, him knowing we're thinking of him.'

Sue looked over Serena's shoulder into Bukowski's office.

'Al says we're not to contact him. No phone calls, nothing. I already suggested sending flowers but Al told me not to. He said Chris was being looked after, he'd made sure of that, but it would set him back if we contacted him.'

Serena followed Sue to the filing cabinets.

'So how long is Chris away for?' she asked.

'Indefinitely. I'm being assigned to Lily Phung in the R&D department.'

'What? You're leaving us?'

'Yeah; temporarily, I hope. The word is she's a real bitch. Aren't I the lucky one!'

Serena's phone was ringing and she raced back to her desk to answer it.

'G'day. Gav Rayner here, for Al Bukowski.'

'I'll put you straight through, Mr Rayner.'

As she did so, Bukowski looked up and gave her a salute and his 'I told you so' grin. Well, he certainly had clout. But why would Bukowski cut off contact with Chris when he was ill? She had seen Chris wracked with guilt last night and felt in some way responsible for the onset of his depression. Perhaps their conversation had triggered it? But how could Sue not have known he was bipolar? They'd been working together for years. Checking her inbox, she found an email from HR explaining that Chris was on indefinite sick leave and that his duties would be covered, until further notice, by Lily Phung. Under no circumstances was Chris to be contacted.

Serena was worried. She scrolled through the staff database searching for Chris Mann's home address and phone number:

Fiona Malone

Paul Manning

Simone Manor

Aura Maples

Kenji Maruyama

Chris's name was no longer in the database. It was like he'd never existed.

Chapter 33

Increasingly concerned about Chris' welfare, Serena tried the public phone directory, hoping he might be listed, but he wasn't. Her phone rang and it was Larry Griffiths from IT, wanting to speak to her boss. But Bukowski was in a meeting with the CFO.

'Can I take a message for you?'

'Er, yes, I suppose. Can you tell Mr Bukowski that we have a solution to his problem?'

'Oh, you mean the connection dropping out because of the update. Yeah, it's been a real pain.' Serena winged it, hoping she was saying the right thing.

'Oh, I wasn't sure if he'd informed you. Well, can you tell him we have a solution?' He sighed, clearly not happy.

'And what's that? He's bound to ask me.'

'Really? I don't think I should say anymore – you know, security and all that.'

Serena daren't press him further, so said she'd pass on the message. It was time for a visit to her friend Colin Chang. Nipping out of the executive suites, she made her way to the IT department. The doors slid open and she counted the seconds before it closed again: five. Serena knew that the time of her entrance to the IT department was recorded via the retina scanner, so if she ever needed to enter without being monitored, she would have to piggyback another member of staff, following them in, hopefully without being challenged.

She found Colin peering short-sightedly at his computer screen. He was wearing glasses today but they didn't seem to help much. Serena sat on the edge of his desk.

'Oh, Amber, good to see you.'

The glasses were very thick, and he removed them hastily, placing them on his lap.

'How's your day been, Colin?'

'Busy, very busy. And you?'

'Not bad. My boss has been a bit cross today, though.'

'Oh, we know,' he nodded. 'He gave Larry a real serve this morning.'

'Yes, I heard some of it. It's about the METRO update slowing down all the systems and the connection dropping out, right?'

'Yes, but the problem is that we have to turn METRO off to solve it. That is very dangerous for the company. No METRO means no intruder detection, means competitors can spy on us and we won't know they're doing it.'

'So, what's the solution?'

'We find an alternative to METRO that doesn't slow the system down or cause disconnections. But that will take a few days.'

Serena moved closer to Colin, whose eyes kept darting to her cleavage, visible in her wrap-around sleeveless blouse.

'But you know what Al is like. He'll want action now.'

'Amber, you know I can't talk about this. I will get into trouble.'

'Come on, Colin, I'm his PA. I'm the one who gets barked at when I'm being too slow. I need a little reassurance here. Please.'

She smiled sweetly and placed her hand on his. A trickle of perspiration ran down his left temple and he stared at her hand as if it were covered in diamonds.

'Please,' she begged.

'Okay. I'll tell you but you must not tell anyone, okay?'

'Promise,' she said, withdrawing her hand.

Colin leaned forward.

'METRO will run all night but will be turned off during the busy parts of the day, until we can roll back the update or work out a patch. So, between twelve-thirty and two, we'll turn METRO back on to check for intruders.'

'But in the mornings and afternoons, the system is off?'

'Yes,' replied Colin, shaking his head in disbelief.

'And the evening? When does it come back on?'

'Six.'

'Why would Al risk that? He's paranoid about security?'

'It happens all the time. Senior management gets frustrated and can't wait. Al can't work, so we have to turn it off. At least we'll be able to monitor traffic during the middle of the day.'

'Well,' she sighed, 'at least Al won't be so grumpy with me now.'

Colin gazed up at her, squinting in myopic adoration.

'I hope not,' he said and smiled.

'I'd better get back to my desk. Oh, by the way, do we have any visitors from the Gibson Lab here today?'

'Yes, one's here. Why?'

'How long's he been here in Sydney?'

'Arrived this morning. We very rarely see those guys. We call them the desert rats,' said Colin, chuckling to himself.

'What's his name?'

Colin's eyelids fluttered in confusion. 'Oh, I thought you knew him.'

'No, but one of the girls I work with fancies him. I said I'd try to find out something about him.'

'The Gibson crowd – very strange people. Don't say much. I guess they can't, given all the secrecy around what they do.'

'But you can tell me his name?'

'Don't know. Not seen this one before. Oh, wait a moment. I think someone called him Ben.'

Serena slid along Colin's desk so that she was within whispering distance. 'What do they do out there?'

Colin puffed out his chest, clearly flattered she was asking his opinion; it was rare that anyone did. He looked around to check he couldn't be overheard. 'All I know is, it's like a city in the desert. High security. Lots of big dome-shaped greenhouses. It's our Southern Hemisphere base, where all the new crops and animals come from. I'd like to see it one day.'

'Sounds amazing. Anyway, where's this guy sitting?'

'He's over there.' Colin nodded in the direction of the server racks.

The Genesis Flaw

Across the frenetic IT floor, she saw a big man in jeans and a white shirt sitting quietly at his computer. He looked up from his desk and locked eyes with Serena. He nodded very slightly and then returned his gaze to his computer. She blushed. There was recognition in his stare. This had to be the man she spoke to earlier.

'You know him?' asked Colin.

'No, Colin. Are you sure he wasn't here yesterday?' *If he wasn't, then he couldn't have overheard my conversation with Kylie.*

'I didn't see him, but he could have been. Why?'

'Oh, something one of the girls said. You know.'

Colin nodded enthusiastically.

As Serena took her leave, Colin stood up suddenly, dropping his glasses on the floor.

'Amber. You want to meet for lunch today? Or coffee, maybe? Or …'

'I'd love to, but can we make it tomorrow?' she replied, desperate to get away.

Chapter 34

Alone in the elevator, Serena shouted an exalted 'Yes!' She planned to make the most of the spy ware being off for much of the day. She still didn't know what to make of Ben, but he might also prove very helpful.

Back at her desk, she flicked through the staff database. There was only one Ben listed at the Gibson Research base: Ben Hartstone. And his mobile number matched the one in the note. He was down as 'Information Systems Support Specialist'. At twelve-thirty, she left the building to find a quiet spot to call him.

'Hello, Amber,' Ben answered, 'nice to meet you just now.' He must have recognised her phone number.

'Can you talk?' she asked.

'Yes.'

'Are you Ben Hartstone?'

'Done your homework, then.'

'Ben, why do you think I want to know about the Gibson Lab? I just made a simple mistake.'

'I don't think so. You're clearly a very bright woman and I don't believe you'd make a stupid error like that. You knew you were trying to open a top-security file. Kylie might've fallen for it, but I've been watching you, and you're not dumb.'

'How long have you been watching me?' Serena's voice bristled with anger.

'Since you tried to open the file.'

'Were you outside my apartment last night?'

A moment's pause.

'No. I mean watching you at work. Look, I'm not some kind of stalker.'

'Okay. Why?'

'Why, what?'

'Why have you been watching me?'

'I wanted to work you out. You know. What's your interest in Gene-Asis? Were you someone likely to help me?'

'Help you? I'm just a PA trying to keep my nose clean.'

'Then I'm sorry I bothered you.'

He waited for her response.

'But what you do is top secret. Why would you want to tell a perfect stranger about it? You could lose your job.'

'My job! Like I give a shit about my stinking job. Have you seen the Gibson Desert? Do you know what it's like out there?'

He had raised his voice, startling her. She could feel his fury.

'No, I don't.'

'It's over forty degrees Celsius every day. At night, it's freezing. There's nothing but sand and spinifex, as far as you can see. We live like moles in an underground facility. Only the paddocks and greenhouses are above ground, and I can't go there because I'm just an IT geek. It's shit and I've had enough.'

'So why don't you leave?'

'I am. I've been shat on for long enough.'

'But why offer to tell me the contents of that file?'

'Well, here's my thinking. I tell you what you want to know. And you tell me what I want to know. We just exchange a bit of information, if you know what I mean.'

'I don't …'

'Look, Amber, I can do this with or without you. But if you want my help, call me.'

'No, wait!'

Silence down the other end of the line. She had to take the risk of finding out more.

'Can we meet somewhere?' she asked.

'Sure. How about tonight, at the Cortile bar in the Hotel InterContinental? Say six-thirty?'

'Fine.'

Walking in a daze along the crowded pavements, she wondered, too late, if meeting Ben in such a public place were a good idea. What if they were spotted together? She redialled his number, but his mobile was switched off.

Chapter 35

The hotel bar exuded the elegance of bygone days with floors of black and white checked marble, velvet chairs in a deep burgundy, and a marble fountain with a statuette at its central point. High above, the glass roof on the sixth floor allowed sunlight to pour in. A pianist tinkled softly in one corner as waiters, wearing bow ties and green waistcoats, took drinks orders.

Hovering on the outskirts of the bar, Serena scanned the area for Ben. A woman in her fifties sat alone, nervously fiddling with the straps of her pink sun top, clearly waiting for someone. A group of Japanese businessmen laughed loudly, clinking their beer glasses together. A young couple lounged back in their chairs, smiles on their sunburned faces. But there was no Ben.

Serena sat at a table near the bar and ordered a drink.

'Excuse me, is this seat taken?'

She looked up into the green eyes of Ben Hartstone, who extended his hand. She shook it, his enormous palm dwarfing hers. As he sat, she sized him up. He was a very big man: probably 188 centimetres tall, with a neck as wide as his head. His muscular thighs appeared to be stretching the seams of his blue jeans. His nose was like a ski jump: flattened at the top and turned up at the end. It had clearly been broken. He looked more like a bouncer than an IT person.

Ben ordered a light beer, relaxing his bear-like frame in the cushioned chair.

'Look, I'm sorry I went off at you earlier. I shouldn't have.'

'You sounded upset.'

'I am.'

Serena waited for more details, but he sat silently looking at her.

'About what?'

He leaned forward, his elbows resting on his massive thighs.

'I'm good. I'm very good at what I do. I've worked for Gene-Asis for six years. I've done my time and I should've been made the IS Support Specialist for Sydney.'

His beer arrived, served in a tall glass. Ben took a sip and, as she waited for him to continue, she looked at his face; it was weather-beaten, with deep lines around his eyes and forehead, like the furrows of ploughed fields. His closely cropped hair was the colour of dusty straw.

'So, what happened?'

'I got assigned to that desert shithole. Gary Wang got the job in Sydney and the little runt doesn't know his arse from his elbow. He just blinds people with technical jargon.'

Ben leaned back into his chair, slapping his hand down on one knee with a *clack*. A woman at the next table looked up. Serena sat forward and dropped her voice.

'So you want out?'

'I want out, but with a pay-off. And that's where you come in.'

He took a large gulp of his beer. She noticed his nails were bitten down so far that the fingernails were half their normal length, which seemed at odds with the strength of the man.

'Go on,' she prodded, trying not to betray her impatience. Was he ever going to get to the point?

'I know things. Things Gene-Asis would like kept quiet. Things the press would pay a lot of money for. But it needs to be someone I can trust; someone who won't reveal their source, but who'll pay well.'

He swallowed some more beer. Serena took a deep breath and, needing something to do with her hands, tucked her hair behind her ears slowly and deliberately.

'And you have the right contacts. You can introduce me to the right person,' Ben continued.

Her eyes widened and she felt her face flush. *Does he mean Tracey? How on earth could he know about Tracey? He said he'd been watching me …*

'How so?' she stammered.

'Your résumé. I've seen it. You worked at *The Post*.'

Yes, of course. My fake résumé.

'So what?'

'You'll introduce me to a journo I can trust and I have my eye on that Pollack lady. You know, the science correspondent. I've checked out her stuff. Seems to me she's a journo with real balls, and she'll need balls to publish this story.'

Serena crossed her arms and eyed Ben dubiously. 'You don't need me. If your story's that hot, you can have your pick of journalists.'

'You joking? If the journo dobs me in, I'm in deep shit. These secrets are big and dirty.'

It was her turn to be silent. She chewed her lower lip, considering her response.

'Why not a local journalist?'

'Overseas is good. Keeps the spotlight off me,' he replied.

'And if I decide to help you, what do I get in return?'

'All the files on the Gibson. And I'm telling you, there's some weird shit.'

'Like?'

'Oh no, I'm not telling you a thing until you tell me why you're interested. Come on now, Amber; that's fair, isn't it?'

It was fair, yes. But she couldn't bring herself to trust him, yet.

'What makes you think Pollack will listen to me?'

'She was one of your referees. Of course she'll listen.'

Ben had done his homework, all right.

'I have to go now, Ben.'

He threw up his hands in resignation.

'When do you go back to the Gibson?' she asked.

'On Saturday. I'd need to do the interview before then – phone conversations are recorded at the Gibson. So, think it over fast. I don't have much time. After Saturday, I'm stuck in nowheresville for the next three months.'

'I must go,' Serena replied, standing up. She started rummaging in her handbag for her purse.

'I'll get the bill,' Ben said, standing too. He towered over her and held out his hand. She shook it.

'You might think what I'm doing is wrong,' he said. 'But, you know, everyone gets something. I get cash, you get info, and the ordinary Joe gets to read a few scary stories.'

Chapter 36

Serena had to knock repeatedly on John's home office door. He finally opened it and leaned on the doorframe. His hair was uncombed and he had bags under his eyes. The interior of the room was dark except for the glare from numerous computer screens.

'Hey there. I didn't hear you. I was hanging out in channel with my headphones on,' he said.

'Hanging out where?'

'IRC.'

She shook her head. Sometimes John sounded like he came from another planet. 'You all right? You look tired.'

'Yeah, I am a bit. I've got a problem at work.'

'What?'

'A hacker called Menace has been boasting he's gonna bring down the bank. He's good, very good. I'm trying to find out how he plans to do it so I can stop him, and if I'm going to be up all night, I'd rather be at home.'

'Don't you employ people to do this for you?'

'Yeah, but I like it. It's like a game of chess: working out who will make the wrong move. So, sometimes I get my hands dirty and go head to head with a hacker. And Menace is a real challenge.'

'How do you stop a hacker? He's not going to give the game away, is he?'

'By setting up a dialogue with him. Meet e0n. That's the name I go by in hackers' chat rooms.'

'But surely this Menace guy won't tell you anything?'

'Hackers love to brag about their achievements. He won't tell me what he's gonna do exactly, but I may be able to guess something from a conversation with him. And I'll lay any money I'll find him in #2600.'

'An IRC?'

He nodded.

'Which is?'

'Internet Relay Chat.'

'And how long have you been tracking Menace?' she asked.

John looked at his watch.

'Since last night.'

'So, you haven't slept?'

'Nope.'

'Jesus, John, let me make you some dinner.'

'Thanks. But I can't be away long, in case I miss him.'

'You can keep checking in,' she replied, dragging him to the kitchen. She'd make a quick stir-fry.

'A guy left a note on my windscreen today,' she said, chopping an onion. 'He may lead me to McPherson's report.' John's bloodshot eyes opened in surprise. 'He's an IT guy at their Gibson Lab with a massive chip on his shoulder. He wants out and if I line up an interview for him with Trace, he'll hand me the Gibson file, where, I suspect, I'll find McPherson's research.'

John didn't respond, so Serena stopped chopping and looked at him.

'What?' she asked, as he stared at her silently. As the onion was making her eyes water, she stepped away from it.

'Can you trust him? He could blow everything you've planned.'

'I don't know. But if I set him up with Tracey and he spills the beans, then he may end up doing my job for me. I won't need to find evidence. I won't need to pretend to be Amber Crosby anymore, with that creep Bukowski breathing down my neck.'

'I like that idea but, equally, he may know nothing but gossip and if you help him, you could get fired and we're back where we started – with nothing.'

He was slumped forward with exhaustion. She put the knife down and washed her hands, then began massaging his shoulders.

'That's good,' he sighed.

'The other possibility is that it's some kind of trap. I still don't really know how he knows about me trying to get into the Gibson file. But if Bukowski suspected me, he'd surely just fire me? What would be the point of playing games?' John moved his head from side to side, stretching his aching neck. She could tell he was enjoying her fingers digging into his knotted back muscles. She continued, 'Tracey will be in Zimbabwe by now. I'll give her Ben's number. She can suss him out.'

She stopped massaging and John turned to face her.

'I suppose it's worth a go. I wonder if he'll go through with it and call her?'

Serena shrugged. 'We'll see. And, in the meantime, I'll need your hacking device.'

'You'll have it Friday and it's a B0r3r.' He pronounced it 'Borer'.

'Go on,' she said, sitting next to him. 'How does it work?'

'Menace uses them all the time, but his is nothing like my B0r3r. He used one to steal twenty million credit card numbers from a credit card bureau used by a US bank. He then sold them on the black market to the Mafia and other criminal cartels. Made a fortune. Here's how it works. Menace went to the world's largest banking convention in Chicago, using a fake name. He sat at one of the computer terminals for participants, pretended that his computer wasn't working and unplugged the keyboard cable. He blew on the keyboard port, making out it was dusty, and then slipped a keylogger onto the cable. A keylogger comes in two parts: a transmitter and a receiver. It's Bluetooth with a limited range. The USB Bluetooth dongle …'

'Dongle?'

'Sorry, geek speak. I mean, the transmitter is a tiny device about the size of your thumbnail, which records up to five million keystrokes. That's what Menace attached to the computer. The receiver was plugged into his smartphone. Anyway, this Menace guy then reattached the keyboard with his keylogger transmitter inside, and pretended to be surfing the Net. When he was sure he hadn't been caught, he logged off and then waited for the next person to use the computer.

He simply read the keystrokes of each person who used that particular computer until he found one idiot from this credit card bureau who made the fatal mistake of using an untrusted PC to log in remotely. Bingo! Menace now had this man's credentials.

'When the man had gone, Menace sat at the same computer and logged back in using this man's confidential password. This gave him access to the credit card bureau's network. By using the public-access PC, there was no way he could be traced, you see. He viewed the credit card numbers, which he recorded on a memory stick, and, retrieving his keylogger, he left the convention undetected.'

'This keylogger records every keystroke?' she asked.

'That's right.'

'So I could use one to watch Bukowski's keystrokes. Then I'd know his password and his watch fob code.'

'No, you can't, because Bukowski's keyboard is not detachable. It's part of the dock for his smartphone. You couldn't use a standard keylogger.'

Serena leaned forward, excited.

'But the B0r3r can?' she guessed.

'It can. Let me show you my prototype.'

Serena followed John into her room and watched as he removed her Tbyte from its slot. He then placed a tiny device at the precise point the handheld connected with the dock. Its design resembled the port in every way, mirroring its shape exactly, except it was fractionally smaller. The B0r3r keylogger slotted inside the port, invisible to the naked eye.

'The transmitter has bored its way inside the dock,' said John. He then re-docked the Tbyte. 'Okay. Now you sit here and access your bank account online as you normally do. Maybe move some money around or something. I'll leave the room and, when you're done, log off. Then come and find me.'

She did as she was asked, and then returned to John's room.

'I've placed the second part of the B0r3r, the receiver, into exactly the same spot in my dock. The two parts are hard to tell apart, so remember; the one with the red ring is the receiver.'

John's monitor was a moving stream of data, shooting from left to right and then back again, like an alphabet-soup serpent.

'How is the B0r3r doing this?'

'It's transmitting wireless signals to the receiver in my computer.'

'Does the receiver have to slot into the dock? Can't it be slotted into my smartphone, like Menace did?'

'Possibly, but we'd have to adapt your handheld to take it. And that could delay us.'

'Okay, so how far away can the receiver be and still receive the wireless signal?'

'Approximately thirty metres. And it's not so good through solid walls.'

Serena silently absorbed this information.

John continued, 'When my B0r3r is glitch-free, you'll be able to view anything Bukowski sees on his screen. However – and it's a big however – their IDS, IPS and SIEM will instantly alert them to a keylogger.'

'Hold on, John. What's with all the acronyms?'

'Sorry. They'll have intrusion detection systems, intrusion pro-tection systems and a security information event monitoring system. Probably METRO?'

'Yes, that's it. METRO.'

'That's a big problem.'

'Not anymore. It's now off during most of the day. Only switched back on at lunchtime, to check for intruders.'

'Serious?'

'Serious.'

'Then the only outstanding problem is making a copy. You'll need to use Bukowski's computer to do it.'

'I'm working on that one,' she replied, thinking of Colin.

He guessed. 'But what if Colin won't cooperate? You're asking a lot. And God knows what Bukowski would do if he caught you.'

'If Ben doesn't come up with the goods, then this is the only other option. I need the B0r3r.'

Chapter 37

Colin and Serena sat in the shade of a large umbrella outside the Crown Hotel, having a liquid lunch. It was too hot to eat. Colin nervously sipped his beer, leaving a residue of froth across his upper lip.

'Why are you not married?' he blurted out.

'Never met the right guy, I guess. How about you?'

'Me?' he chuckled at the absurdity of the thought. 'No. I'm too shy to meet girls.'

'But in your role, you must meet absolutely everyone who works here; so, you know, you must get to chat to all the new girls.'

'Most of them are not very friendly. Not like you,' he grinned.

Serena felt a twinge of guilt as she looked at Colin's pale and eager face. She knew she was taking advantage of his obvious crush on her, but she needed his cooperation in order to succeed in her plan.

'Did you know Chris Mann was away sick? Apparently, he's suffering from depression and has been for a while.'

'Yes, I know. I removed his fingerprint from the security database, so I think he's not coming back.'

'Wow! I thought it was only *temporary* sick leave. That's a shame. He's a really nice guy.'

'Yes, nice man. Always smiling.'

'So, he never seemed depressed to you?'

'No, always happy.'

Silence ensued as Colin introspectively sipped his beer. Serena was finding it very hard to keep the conversation going, so downed her lemon, lime and bitters and was about to make her excuses to leave. She was very distracted – Tracey had jumped at the chance to talk to Ben, and Serena was keen to know how it had gone.

'If you don't understand something and need help, you call me. I will help you. It's no problem. You must understand, if you break security rules at Gene-Asis, you are in trouble.'

'Thank you, Colin, but I must be getting back. Got loads to do.'

Colin still sat, looking up at her.

'He's been checking you out.'

Serena sat back down.

'Who has?'

'You are not meant to know this, so please keep it to yourself. Okay?'

'Of course, Colin.'

'Mr Bukowski asked Head of Security to run further background checks on you.'

'Why?' she asked, visibly concerned.

'I don't know. You must have done something wrong.'

He looked at her questioningly.

'Oh dear. Now I'm worried. I need this job.'

'Don't worry. You have nothing to hide, so you have no problem.'

Not quite, she thought. A background check was the last thing she needed. Her ignorance of the service desk's remote monitoring capabilities could have cost her dearly. This meant that time was running out. She had to use the B0r3r quickly and she needed to persuade Colin to breach security protocols. But how could she do this without landing him in trouble?

They returned to the office, both deep in their own thoughts. Neither spoke and they parted company, leaving the elevator at their respective floors. As the executive suite doors slid open, she heard a voice she had hoped never to hear again. Serena took a step back so the heavy doors shut immediately. Had she been seen? In the split second that Serena had been framed in the open doorway, she'd seen a man in a light grey suit and a woman in a cherry red dress talking to Amanda, the Vice President of Sales and Marketing. Fortunately, they'd been facing in the opposite direction, so Martin Delaney and Gloria Philladitis hadn't seen her – yet. Serena turned quickly and collided with Darko.

'Sorry, Mr Petrinec.'

'Amber, what is the big hurry?'

'I, er, left my mobile at the pub. Just remembered,' she spluttered.

He stood, blankly peering down at her. His eyes were palest blue and, up close, his face was harshly chiselled, with protruding cheekbones and sunken eye sockets. He looked as if he were in need of a hearty meal.

'You must have a lot on your mind to forget such a thing.'

He still didn't move, so Serena took a step back. He was in her personal space and his presence was disquieting.

'Yes, very busy. You know – new job and lots to get my head around.'

'Of course,' he said, and smiled.

Darko moved towards the suite's doors, which slid open. Gloria and Martin were heading her way. They were leaving. As fast as she could, she raced down the corridor and stabbed at the elevator call button.

'That went very well,' boomed Gloria a few metres behind Serena.

'Yup, we have one happy client,' replied Martin.

The elevator door opened and Serena raced inside.

'Hold the lift,' called Gloria.

Cornered, Serena had no choice but to do so. They stepped inside, talking. Serena pressed the button for the next floor down, then the ground-floor button, and stepped to the back of the elevator, pulling a tissue out of her bag, and pretending to wipe her nose. She stood behind Gloria and Martin, hoping they wouldn't look around. Engrossed in their own self-importance, they ignored her.

'Fuck, what a dumb bitch she is,' commented Gloria, presumably referring to her client.

'Keep it down,' said Martin, flicking a look at Serena. He obviously didn't recognise her with red hair and glasses.

The confined space filled with the aroma of Gloria's Chanel No. 5. Serena continued to cover her face with her tissue, wiping her nose. The elevator doors opened and she rushed out, heading straight for the Ladies'. Gloria and Martin continued to the ground floor. Diving for a cubicle, she slammed the door and locked it. That was too close for comfort.

Someone entered the bathroom, sniffing. Serena heard the tap run and some splashing. The tap was turned off. Then there was a sob. Serena had never been able to hear someone crying without wanting to comfort them. Flushing the toilet for effect, she opened the cubicle door to find Sue leaning over a washbasin, tears streaming down her face.

'Sue, what's the matter?'

'Oh, it's you,' said Sue, sniffing.

'Let me get you a tissue,' said Serena, grabbing some toilet paper and handing it to her.

'Is your new boss giving you a hard time?'

Sue shook her head and then looked up at Serena through red, swollen eyes.

'He's dead, Amber.'

Sue burst into tears again.

'You don't mean Chris?' Serena asked, praying she'd misunderstood.

Sue leaned over the basin and, turning on the cold tap, began splashing her face. Serena handed her some paper towels and Sue looked in the mirror at Serena.

'Yes. He overdosed on sleeping pills last night.'

Speechless, Serena stared open-mouthed at Sue.

'I just don't understand,' continued Sue, shaking her head violently. 'It doesn't make sense. Chris wasn't depressed. I know he wasn't. The only time I ever saw him down was when his wife left him and, even then, he put on a brave face. He didn't commit suicide then, so why would he do such a terrible thing now?'

The shock forced Serena to lean back on a washbasin. A man she'd had dinner with only two days ago was dead. She didn't believe Chris had ever been bipolar. Nor did she believe he had committed suicide.

Chapter 38

His body glistened as he ran from the surf. The early evening sun was still hot as Serena followed, refreshed by the cool water. Chris' death had really upset her and she'd been listless all day. But the pounding waves had kick-started her energy again. She watched John run up the beach. For a tall man, he was surprisingly muscular, not the skinny rake she remembered from school days. He threw himself onto his towel and closed his eyes.

'What's with the tattoo?' Serena asked, as she towelled her body. Two young men walked by and eyed her approvingly. Her black bikini was skimpy and its top barely held her ample breasts.

'A blue marlin,' John replied. 'I just decided to get it done one day. Guess it symbolises my new life here, living at the beach.'

She stared at him.

'What?' he asked, smiling, his eyes still closed.

'How did you … Oh, never mind. I mean, I feel I know you so well and yet sometimes I feel you're a different person from the John I've known all my life.'

'But I am, Seri. You've been away a long time.' He opened his eyes. 'And what about you? You've changed heaps. Who'd have thought you'd turn into a corporate spy? And when did that belly-button ring happen?'

He laughed and rolled onto his side with his hand propped under his head so he could look at her. She mirrored his posture.

'When I was in Soho. I think I wanted to check I was alive. I've spent my career schmoozing corporate execs, putting on a show for them, being focused on an outcome. I wanted to break the rules, just a little. I know this sounds childish but when they put it in, with the gun, the sting was exhilarating.'

'Suits you.'

'It's funny how life works out. It's like I've gone full circle – left home, gone to the other side of the world, and here I am back in Australia, living with the boy next door. And you know what? It's good to be home. I've missed your company.'

'It's good to have you home,' replied John, resting his free hand on hers. She felt the same electricity she'd felt the night they'd deciphered McPherson's Bible message. She could hear her heart beating so loudly it drowned out the sound of the crashing waves.

'Seri, I'm sorry.' His expression was as desolate as ground zero. At that moment, she wanted nothing more than to lie next to him but her feelings were a distraction she couldn't afford right now.

'I know, John. When this is over, we'll talk.'

He nodded. 'I can wait.'

'Fancy some dinner? We can talk strategy as we eat,' she said, nodding at the sign above the fish and chip shop. It read 'Chish and Fips'.

'Yes, boss. So, tell me, what did your last slave die of?' he replied, grinning. She chased him up the beach to the café.

The weather-beaten hut had a few rickety tables and chairs outside. They ate barramundi and chips. Serena toyed with her food.

'I feel bad about this.'

'Then find that file,' said John, spearing some chips with a plastic fork.

Then, after a pause, he asked, 'Did you see the piece on Munroe in the paper today?'

'No, what did it say?'

'Still missing. Gave a bit of background. He travelled a lot, but was based at the Gibson Lab. Same place as this Ben character.'

'I've got a theory,' said Serena. 'Munroe told Mancini something that could ruin the company and threatened to expose them. He'd linked hep S to their GM seeds; to Supercrop itself, their leading brand. Mancini couldn't bear to live with the responsibility, so he hanged himself. Munroe was now a liability and Gene-Asis had to stop him blabbing to the press. That could then explain what Chris meant by "that poor man". Munroe reported directly to Chris, so he would've told Chris all about it. Therefore, Chris would've been party to any plan to stop Munroe blabbing.'

'Makes sense.'

Her Tbyte beeped. It was a text message from Tracey.

Sorry, love. Your source is a waste of space. He couldn't give me anything concrete. And very evasive. I'd stay away from him. Anyway, I'll get on with my work here and keep you in the loop. Love, Tracey

'Shit,' she said, passing her handheld to John, who read the text.

'Plan B then. The B0r3r's ready. I'll give it to you when we get back.'

'Tomorrow could be my last chance to use it. They're checking me out, Colin told me. If they dig too deep, they might discover my real identity.'

'So, how are you going to get the B0r3r into Bukowski's keyboard?'

'There's a big company dinner tomorrow night. Everyone is going, bar a few security people. I need to time it so that I see Bukowski's watch fob code just before he leaves and before METRO gets turned back on. I'll have till 6 pm.'

'And Bukowski will leave before then?'

'Yup, he's going to his penthouse to change.'

'And the biometric mouse?'

'I just need to organise Colin beforehand.'

'It's very risky. Too risky.'

'I can't stop now. Too many people have died. I'm not going to let them get away with it.'

Chapter 39

Serena had deliberately left working on an urgent document till the end of the day. She watched Bukowski prepare to leave and checked the clock: it was 5.40 pm. Her colleagues were either on their way to the venue or in the bathrooms changing. Pre-dinner drinks started at 6 pm. All day, people had remarked to her on her funky, gold-coloured earrings. Little did they know that they were the two parts of the B0r3r, dangling from little hooks. The thin red line, denoting the receiver, was only visible at very close range.

'You look gorgeous,' said Serena to Sue, who shimmered in a silver full-length dress. She wore a diamanté necklace, bracelet and earrings, complete with diamanté shoes and bag. She looked like a jewellery shop.

'So do you,' replied Sue, with a half-smile.

Serena's dress was dark chocolate, with slender shoulder straps. She wore her hair tucked behind her ears and no jewellery, except for her earrings. The understated look was stunning.

'Get a move on, Amber, our cab's here,' said Ron.

'Go without me. I just need to finish this.'

She'd arranged to meet Colin so they could go to the dinner together. But she planned to persuade him to change the biometric database and leave her behind, with the promise she'd join him later.

'Forget it. Come on, this is your dinner; you organised it,' Ron persisted.

'I'll just be ten minutes. Off you go.'

They left the executive suite, chattering loudly.

'No, you don't,' said Bukowski. 'You go with the others.'

He leaned on her desk and smiled. Immaculate as always, he smelled of aftershave.

'But, Al, I just want to finish …'

'I insist.'

'Please, Al. I'm not good at parties. I'd rather stay here a little longer.'

'Am I going to have to take you there myself?'

'No, Al, I'm fine, thank you.'

'Well, off you go then.'

Thoroughly frustrated, she dropped into IT and picked up an over-excited Colin, who fiddled with his bow tie constantly. They took a cab together and she texted John, letting him know it was all off for tonight. Serena read an email from Tracey, careful to ensure Colin couldn't see it.

Mate,
I'm in the right place, that's for sure, but people are
frightened to talk. Some official geezer keeps turning up,
asking me questions. I've told him I'm doing a piece on
the effectiveness of food and agricultural aid, but I don't
think he believes me. I've met a very brave woman who's
been banished by her family, and she's really opened up
to me. What she's told me has made my stomach churn.
It's terrible. I just need to get it on film. She's taking me
to meet some of the 'aid' recipients today. Wish me luck!

'Everything okay?' asked Colin.

'Put it this way: things are looking up,' she beamed. Her plans might have been thwarted but Tracey was hot on the case.

As Serena stepped out of the taxi, she looked up. The building loomed upwards like a pointed finger scratching the pale blue sky. She'd noticed it before. After all, who in Sydney hadn't? Its twenty-six floors loomed large above Darlinghurst, out of sync with the terrace houses at its base. Like a tall white cylinder made of a child's building blocks, the top two floors rotated 360 degrees every twenty-four hours. This gave the restaurant and suites on those floors an ever-changing view of the city, the harbour, and out to the Blue Mountains. Bukowski's suite was on one of these floors.

As she entered the banqueting room, her Tbyte beeped. It was a message from Ben.

'We must talk tonight.'

Harsh lamps illuminated the hotel's white exterior, blinding her like sunlight reflected off glass. Ben had sent her another message during the course of the evening, asking her to be outside the front of the hotel at eleven o'clock. She didn't want him causing trouble so she had reluctantly agreed. She walked down the sweeping drive and into the street. Perhaps he was waiting for her there?

Something moved in the darkness a few metres down the road. Serena could just make out a long head of hair and a skirt that was very short. The woman paced the pavement in her high-heeled shoes. When she turned her back on Serena, it was evident that she had nothing on underneath the skirt.

A shadow slunk into existence opposite Serena, the red glare of a cigarette highlighting a large hand. It beckoned her. She peered at it, staying still. Then Ben moved under a streetlight, still beckoning, and she crossed the road. In nothing but her evening dress, she felt very exposed. If it were noticed, her behaviour would seem strange to her colleagues, and she wanted to get this over with as quickly as possible.

'Here, take this,' he said, handing her a cigarette.

'I don't smoke.'

'You do now. It looks like we're just having a smoko together. Here, just hold it.'

He lit it for her, inhaling, and then handed it to her.

'Why do you need to see me?'

'I leave tomorrow.'

'I know. And you wasted that journalist's time, so why should I give you any of mine?'

'I was checking her out – the journo, I mean. I wanted to be sure she was for real. I'm not giving her anything until I know I can trust her.'

'Or you're just yanking my chain and you haven't really got

anything worth saying.' Serena looked at the hotel entrance, keen to rejoin the party.

'I'd like to talk to her again.'

'No, Ben, she's not interested. If you have anything concrete, give it to me and I'll pass it on.'

'How do I know I can trust you?' he asked, blowing smoke.

'Ben, I don't have time for this. You wanted my help. You wanted to tell some big story to the world to get your revenge. Well, if you want my help, give me what you've got or find someone else.'

He inhaled and nodded slowly. She waited for him to say something.

'Well?' she asked, her voice brittle with frustration.

'I'll think about it,' he replied.

Serena threw up her arms and strode back across the road. She hurried into the hotel, drawn like a Bogong moth to the light inside. She had work to do: earlier that evening, she'd overheard Sue whispering to Ron that Bukowski was going to invite an exclusive few to his penthouse for an after-party. Sue intended to be one of them. And so did Serena. She might still get a chance to use the B0r3r tonight.

However, as Serena took the elevator to the top floor, she wondered if she were doing the right thing. A feeling of foreboding made her shiver. Bukowski was smart and she had to be careful.

Her instincts were telling her to leave, but her mind was telling her to stay. With other staff around, what harm could come to her?

Chapter 40

There was a small, ever-diminishing crowd around the top-floor bar. The roof had slid back and the whole area was open to the stars. Sue sat on a bar stool and sparkled as she moved. She kept flicking looks at Bukowski, who was in deep conversation with an Amazonian woman in a red dress. Serena had never seen her before. She scanned the group and was relieved not to see Colin. If her plan for tonight didn't work, she would find him in the morning and tackle the biometric mouse obstacle then.

Darko was lying back in an armchair, waving his hands around as he spoke to a man she recognised as the treasurer. Perched on the arm of Darko's chair was a petite and pretty woman, staring up adoringly at a man she was conversing with. Serena didn't recognise either of them.

Bukowski spotted Serena and gestured to her to join them at the bar.

'Amber, come and meet Gordana, Darko's wife.'

He said something quickly to the woman, who nodded. As Serena walked over to them, they each looked at her like they were studying a painting. Bukowski's face creased into his usual broad smile and he steered her towards the woman.

'Lovely to meet you,' said Gordana, extending a beautifully manicured hand. Her skin was flawless and honey-brown; her body muscular, like a dancer's. And she oozed sexual energy.

'Lovely to meet you too,' replied Serena.

'You worked in England, I hear.'

'That's right,' she replied. She must be careful to stick to her fake CV.

'I would love to visit England one day, but only in the summer. It is best then, yes?'

She turned to her husband before Serena could answer.

'Darling, we must go to England soon. And then to Paris and the Greek Islands. You have been promising me for so long.'

Darko grinned and came over to them. He took her hand between his.

'For you, my beautiful wife, anything,' he said with mock sincerity, winking at Bukowski.

She pulled her hand away in fake exasperation and leaned forward to Serena, whispering, 'I will get my way.'

'She always does,' he laughed.

Serena had never seen Darko so relaxed; he was a different man in the presence of his wife.

'Amber, a glass of champagne?'

She was about to refuse, having determined to stay on sparkling water for the rest of the night. But when she noticed the label, she changed her mind. It was a Krug Clos du Mesnil 1990. Very rare and very expensive.

'Yes, please. How could I say "No" to a 1990 Krug – especially that one?'

'Indeed, how could you?'

Bukowski poured, and she tasted it.

'Gorgeous, thank you. So, Gordana, how long have you been in Sydney? Or were you born here?' Serena asked.

'In Sydney; two years, I think. Before that, we were in New York.'

'Ah, so you've worked together before?' she replied, looking at both Bukowski and Darko.

'We certainly have. We're old friends. Dana and Cecile were inseparable. Dana is Jen's godmother,' replied Bukowski.

Serena noticed Bukowski fiddle with his left cufflink. It had some kind of cartoon character on it. Bukowski saw her looking.

'A present from Jen. It's the new Tingoon character. They're really big back home. She thinks her dad is far too serious, so she sent me these,' he laughed, showing Serena the strange little creature on his cufflink.

'So cute!' said Gordana, peering over Serena's shoulder.

'Let's have a look,' said Sue, who took his wrist and laughed a little too loudly at the cufflink. Did Serena catch a smirk on Bukowski's face?

For a while, Sue dominated the conversation, flirting quite openly with Bukowski. Sal eventually went home, as did the treasurer. The couple Serena hadn't recognised were introduced to her as Sasha and Craig.

'Craig heads up our China operations,' said Bukowski.

'And who might this lovely lady be?' Craig asked, taking Serena's hand and kissing it with mock gallantry.

'I work for Al,' she replied.

Craig's small eyes, set in a chubby face, looked at her approvingly.

'Do you, now? And what kind of work do you do?'

'I'm his PA. At least, while he's in Sydney. Then I work for the new local CEO.'

'Ever considered working in China?' asked Craig. 'My PA's a bloody dragon. Three kids, she's the size of a house and has a double chin bigger than mine! I've been meaning to get rid of her, but she's so frigging efficient I can't afford to let her go.'

'Isn't the issue that she's great at her job, not what she looks like?' asked Serena.

'Ooh. And feisty too! You've got a live one here, mate.'

'Craig, stop teasing poor Amber,' Bukowski said. He refilled her glass. 'Don't take any notice. By the way, I haven't thanked you yet for organising tonight's event. Well done.'

He raised his glass to her.

'Can I have some more?' asked Sue, frowning.

'Certainly, I'll get another bottle.'

Bukowski moved along the bar and ordered. With his back to them all, he poured Sue a fresh glass and then paused for a while. He fiddled with his pocket. Rejoining the group, he gave the glass to Sue.

Serena had discovered that Craig was VP Research and Development in China.

'So, have you any idea why Dr Munroe just disappeared like that?' she asked provocatively.

The smile froze on his pudgy face for a second before he responded.

'No idea. Probably stress. These scientists are under a lot of pressure, you know.'

'His family must be so worried.'

'As we all are,' said Bukowski. 'Now, tell me, Amber, have you ever been to New York?'

Sue slumped onto a bar stool, her eyes half shut. Serena took her glass and placed an arm around her waist.

'Sue, are you all right?'

'Just a bit sleepy,' she mumbled.

'Time to get you home, Sue,' said Bukowski, helping her to stand. Sue wrapped her arms around his neck like an octopus.

'I'll get her a cab,' said Darko, peeling her arms away from Bukowski and almost carrying her out of the bar.

'Come back to my suite after,' Bukowski called to Darko.

'Whoops! Looks like she's had a teensy-weensy bit too much to drink,' giggled Sasha.

'I'd like to invite you all to my penthouse; let's continue the party there. I just need to check some emails but you guys help yourself to the bar and order anything you want. Barman!' he called, 'another Krug to the Flannery suite.'

This was the opportunity she had been waiting for. Perhaps, as it was his temporary home, rather than his office, the mouse would not be biometric. Security was generally more lax at people's homes.

'You will come, won't you?' asked Bukowski.

'Darling, you have to join us. You are the special guest. We have you to thank for this lovely evening,' chipped in Gordana.

'Whoa, let's party!' whooped Sasha.

She surveyed the faces of the remaining guests: Gordana, Darko, Sasha, Craig, the CFO and someone she didn't recognise but thought was from the legal department. They were all up for a big night. Serena's plan was to encourage them to keep drinking so they wouldn't notice when she sneaked off into Bukowski's home office to use the B0r3r.

'Amber, come on,' said Bukowski. 'I have an awesome view from my deck. It's really worth a look. And I won't email for long, I promise.'

The Genesis Flaw

He had his head tilted to one side and his arms folded, daring her to say yes. She saw the challenge in his eyes. Her every instinct was telling her not to go, despite the opportunity it would afford. Something was wrong but she couldn't lay her finger on it.

'Please. I would really like your company,' pressed Bukowski.

There are times in everyone's life when one decision can change things forever. This was such a decision.

'Just for a little while.'

Chapter 41

The curvaceous body in red silk swayed to the hypnotic rhythm. Music beat softly. Taking Serena's hand, Gordana pulled her up from her chair to dance. Bukowski had disappeared into a room down the hallway to read his emails.

The moment Serena entered the enormous suite, she was plunged into a world of subdued light and shadows. Two table lamps provided low lighting, their force dampened by the midnight-blue lampshades. Candles flickered on every table, every bookshelf, in every nook and cranny, lining the floor next to sliding balcony doors. The lounge-room glass doors ran from floor to ceiling, ensuring an uninterrupted view of the city, which sparkled like jewels on a black velvet cloak. A butler came and went, dismissed for the night.

Gordana lifted her arm and twirled Serena around, laughing. The carpet was soft and luxurious and, as Serena danced, it stroked her toes through her strappy sandals. Then Gordana spun under Serena's arm, affording a view of her barely-there dress, which was backless and held up by spider-thread straps. In contrast, Serena's dress revealed less flesh, but still emphasised her curvy figure.

A man and woman laughed on the sofa. It was Darko and Sasha. The CFO and the man from Legal conversed in a corner. The champagne had been devoured and two bottles of Mount Mary sat in silver ice buckets. Out on the balcony, Craig stood alone, smoking. Serena wondered how much longer Bukowski would be. Blood was racing through her veins and she found it hard to sit still. She wanted to use the B0r3r and leave. But there was no sign of him – the home office door was still shut.

Serena left Gordana swaying sensually to the music, and made her way onto the balcony. Craig was her target. 'What a view!' she said.

He turned around so that he had his back to the rail and the view.

'I agree,' he replied, leering at her.

'Can I ask you something, Craig?'

'Shoot.'

'Do you think there might be a role for me in New York, working with Al?'

'Why don't you ask Al that question?'

'Well, I wanted to gauge if his PA, Monica, is a long-term thing.'

'It's a long-term thing. They have a special relationship, if you know what I mean,' Craig answered. His mouth was slightly open and his tongue kept playing with his lower front teeth. He made her feel sick. But she leaned forward conspiratorially and dropped her voice.

'Oh, I see. Thanks for telling me. Don't mention I asked, will you?'

He placed his heavy arm around her shoulders.

'You fancy Al. Strewth! What woman doesn't? Get over it. If you want my advice, you're better off working for me in China. I'd look after you.'

Serena pulled herself away from Craig's arm.

'No, I just find him interesting to work for.'

He laughed out loud.

'Yeah, right!'

'Craig, please don't tease me. Tell me about Al. How did he get to be so successful?'

'Brilliance, charm and ambition. That about sums it up.'

'I hear he can be terrifying when he loses it.'

Craig shook his head.

'He never really loses it. He's always in control. He never lets go.'

'So, it's true he doesn't delegate? That nothing important happens without his say-so?'

'You bet. Al hardly ever sleeps. He works all the time. He knows everything that goes on in Gene-Asis, and I mean everything. Never try to bullshit him. He'll know.'

'What, everything! Surely not all the R&D work as well?'

'Especially the R&D.'

'Wow! That's amazing.' Therefore, Bukowski had to know about the problems with Supercrop and T-Speed.

'You've really fallen for him! God help you.'

She did nothing to contradict his mistaken assumption, knowing that it meant she could get away with asking these personal questions.

'He's a lucky man,' continued Craig.

'Who's a lucky man?' asked a voice behind her.

Serena jumped. She smelled a spicy aroma of citrus, musk and sandalwood, and turned to see Bukowski illuminated in the doorway. His black hair glistened, his skin gleamed and his dimples seemed deeply etched into his smiling face. He'd changed out of his dinner jacket, and was dressed immaculately in a casual black shirt and black jeans.

'You, mate, we've been talking about you,' replied Craig, slapping Bukowski warmly on the back.

'Don't believe anything he says. It's all lies,' Bukowski joked, handing her a glass of wine.

'He's been very complimentary,' said Serena.

'I don't believe you,' he replied, still smiling, his head tilted to one side. 'Prove it. What did he say about me?'

He stood too close to her. Somehow, he seemed bigger tonight. As he looked into her eyes, he exuded a confidence that drained her of hers. This was the man she suspected of sanctioning intimidation and murder. This was the man involved in covering up the company's dirty secrets. This was the man who'd been checking her out, and she had no idea what he really knew about her. Serena heard her heart beating faster but held his gaze steadily.

'Only that you're brilliant and ambitious.'

'Now I know you're lying,' he laughed.

'Darling, this suite is divine!' said Sasha, squeezing Bukowski's arm. 'What are you all doing outside? We have something for you in the lounge.'

Craig stamped out his cigarette and followed Sasha inside. Serena went to follow.

'Wait.'

She stopped. They stood in semi-darkness, the only light coming from the weakening flickering candles within.

'If you want to come to New York, I can arrange it.'

'You heard!' she said, genuinely surprised. How long had he been standing there?

He raised his hand and stroked her cheek. The intimacy of his action startled her. Her pale skin flushed.

'And I am not having an affair with Monica,' he whispered, his hand cupping her cheek. Speechless, she stared at him.

'I never have relationships with my staff. That's why, if you come to New York, it will be as my guest.'

Dumbfounded, she still couldn't speak. Trying to regain her composure, she stepped back and his hand slipped away.

'And please don't believe what other people say about me. There's another side to me that most people don't see.'

He took a step towards her so that his face was barely a few centimetres from hers. 'Shall we join the others?' he said, gesturing inside.

She nodded. He placed his arm around her waist so softly she barely felt him steering her inside. As he walked, he leaned over and whispered:

'He's right about one thing. I am lucky.'

Serena asked to be directed to the bathroom. Bukowski was coming on strong and she needed some breathing space. Also, this might be her chance to slip into his home office unnoticed. She counted off sixty seconds and then silently opened the bathroom door. Laughter rang out from the lounge. The office was only one door down and nobody was about. She moved towards it and held out her hand to grip the door handle.

'There you are. The party's not the same without you.' Bukowski took her outstretched hand and led her back to the party. She swore silently.

Keen to create some distance between herself and Bukowski, she sat next to Sasha and Craig. She counted the guests and realised that the CFO and the legal guy had left, which made her nervous. It was time to cut her losses and leave. Craig offered her a glass of wine but she refused politely and stood up.

'I really must go,' she announced.

'No, you must not. Tomorrow's the weekend, so what's the rush?' said Bukowski.

'Really, Al, I want to go.'

'And I want to show you something. Come with me.'

He again took her hand. Short of pulling it away, she had no choice but to follow. She was stunned to find herself in his office. His smartphone was docked into a keyboard and the mouse looked different from the ones at work. It didn't have a pulsating red beam of light, which meant it probably didn't have biometric capabilities. If only she could get five minutes alone.

He picked up a digital photo frame.

'Jen at holiday camp. Doesn't she look fine?' The little girl was on a pony.

'She's a natural. And what's the rosette for?' asked Serena, pointing to a blue rosette on the horse's bridle.

'Jumping.' After ten seconds, the image changed to an extremely tall, white-haired, severe-looking man in a Stetson, leaning on a wooden fence post. 'That's my grandpop, the head of our family. He taught me the importance of family, of hard work and achievement. He built up an oil empire *and* ran a cattle ranch. Makes my life look like a walk in the park.'

'Al, why are you showing me this?' She didn't like being alone with him.

'To show you we aren't that different.'

The small office was only lit by a desk lamp, the head of which hung low, like a wilting tulip. The resulting semi-darkness and the close walls made Serena feel as if she were in a cell.

'Al, our lives are completely different.' Serena was partly in character and partly affronted at the idea she was like this ruthless man.

'I mean, my family is everything to me – my daughter, mom, dad, grandpop, my sis and brother. They drive me to do what I do. I want to make them proud, and they are proud; real proud. I want Jen to have a good life, a life even better than mine. It's a great tradition of ours in the States.'

Serena clocked why he was saying this. 'Yes, I see. I want a family of my own and you're saying that your family drives your ambition.'

He moved closer.

'So that's why I come down hard on anyone who gets in my way.' Bukowski said it with the smile of a man offering lollies but the words hit home. 'I will protect my own.'

Unsure if the remark were a veiled threat or an attempt to identify common ground, she betrayed none of the fear welling inside her. 'Of course you do,' she smiled back at him. 'Al, I really appreciate your candour and I've had a wonderful night, but I'm completely exhausted, so I think I'll make for home now.'

He dropped his chin forward. 'Ah, I've come on too strong and embarrassed you. I apologise.'

Before she could say anything, he left the room. This was too good to be true. She hesitated and glanced at the monitor. The Gene-Asis logo hovered on the screen: an indigo blue image of the planet, as if seen from space, with a tiny green seedling sprouting from the top of it. Behind the seedling shone an orange sunrise. She tapped the Enter key to see if Bukowski was logged in. He was. She couldn't believe he had been so careless. She touched the mouse and the cursor responded to her touch: it wasn't a biometric mouse. A sharp intake of breath betrayed her excitement. Her only obstacle was the ten-digit code on Bukowski's watch fob. Somehow, she needed to get him to touch the watch face. She'd then have two minutes to access the Highly Protected files. She would have to stay at the party a little longer.

The door bust open and Gordana swept in.

'Darling, what *are* you doing in here? Not work, I hope? Come join me.' Gordana took her hand and led her back to the lounge room, her long fingernails momentarily scratching Serena's palm. Serena felt as though her heart had almost burst through her chest.

'I just don't really know anybody here. Al left me alone to get some space.'

'My darling, you know *me*.' Gordana giggled, then nodded almost imperceptively at Bukowski.

Candles burned low. The view outside the penthouse had changed since her arrival, as the top floors slowly revolved clockwise. Darko emerged from the flickering darkness surrounding the group, holding a large joint. He lit it with a candle, sucking on it, inhaling deeply; then, head back, he released the smoke from his lungs.

He passed it to Gordana, who dragged on it slowly and seductively. She held it out to Serena, her lipstick leaving a red mark like a wax seal. Serena paused, wanting to refuse. Despite working in advertising agencies most of her working life, she'd only once succumbed to their drug culture, when she'd smoked a marijuana joint to help her relax after a particularly harrowing pitch. But relaxed was not how she wanted to be right now. She needed to keep her wits about her and remember her role as Amber Crosby, the PA. At the same time, she needed to hang around at the party for a little longer and blend in. If the group got off their faces, it would be easy for her to slip away and use Bukowski's system.

'No, thanks, I'm fine with the wine,' Serena said.

'Go on, try it,' said Gordana.

'I, er, won't, thanks.'

Gordana shrugged her shoulders and handed it to Craig, who dragged on it deeply, holding the smoke in his lungs for a long time before he exhaled. He smiled cheekily at Serena and offered the joint to her again, Gordana's lipstick print now a pale smudge. But Bukowski took it from Craig and walked over to her. He didn't smoke it, but kneeled next to her and spoke quietly.

'Try it. You're perfectly safe. I won't let anything happen to you.'

He peered up at her, the joint in his hand releasing a spiralling plume of smoke.

Everyone in the room was watching her, willing her to take it. Bukowski didn't move his outstretched arm. Serena didn't want to take it but knew that if she intended to stay, she'd have to go with the flow. This was too good an opportunity to find the professor's report. Serena knew that one puff wouldn't have much effect on her: she would still be in control of what she said and did. She placed her lips on the joint's dry paper and inhaled gingerly. Warmth tickled her throat, and she sucked a little harder, the hot smoke swirling into her lungs. It tasted bad, nothing like she remembered. She coughed as Bukowski took the joint and gently patted her back.

'Been a long time, has it?' he asked.

'A while. But I've never tasted anything like that before. What kind of grass is it?' she said, taking a gulp of wine to get rid of the taste.

'An atom bomb,' said Darko, leaning back into the sofa.

'What's an atom bomb?'

'Oh, a special mix. It's very good.'

Sasha and Gordana gave each other knowing looks.

'I'm going to get some water,' said Serena, standing.

'I'll get it for you,' replied Bukowski, passing the joint to Sasha. It hadn't touched his lips.

'Ah, a well-brought-up young lady!' said Craig.

'Not too well brought up, I hope,' murmured Darko, his eyes closed, and fingers moving to the music as if conducting an orchestra.

Serena registered his odd comment. But she flopped back into the armchair, trying to deal with the sensation that she was one step removed from the room and the people in it.

'Well, believe it or not,' Sasha said, exhaling, 'I didn't have my first joint till I moved to Sydney. I come from a strict Adelaide Catholic family.'

'Ah, nothing beats a good Catholic girl. They go off like a frog in a sock!' said Craig, patting Sasha's knee.

Serena continued to feel very strange. She had been slightly giggly from a joint before, but never like this. She needed water, and left the room to search for the kitchen. She felt along the hallway wall for the light switch but couldn't find one. She could see a subdued light coming from the room ahead, which she guessed might be the kitchen. But she couldn't be sure, as the door was almost closed. Serena heard Bukowski's voice, drowned out by a running tap. She couldn't hear his words clearly.

'No, not this time. I'm going to …' Bukowski said.

What did he say? 'No, I'm going to …' what? What was that?

'… enjoy this,' he said.

The tap stopped running and there he was in the hallway, clutching her glass of water.

Who were you talking to? she wondered. *Is there someone in the kitchen?*

'Here you are, Amber,' Bukowski said, handing her the water glass. She took a couple of big gulps.

'Better?'

'I think so.'

He took her arm and steered her back to the lounge room, past the office. She glanced at the door, trying to remain focused on her mission. Gordana was dancing alone. Bukowski took her place on the sofa next to Darko, who was dragging on the joint again. The conversation continued. It seemed they were still discussing Catholic girls.

'It has nothing to do with religion and everything to do with the woman,' said Darko.

'Last time I was in a Catholic church, I nearly did a runner. Should have, too! It would have saved me a bloody fortune. We divorced a year later,' laughed Craig.

'Religion is about control of the masses,' continued Darko, head leaning back, staring at the ceiling.

'Don't you read the Bible a fair bit, Al?' asked Sasha. 'I mean, you're religious, right?'

'A fair bit! He's a fucking saint! Every bloody morning he's reading a verse from his e-Bible. But that's all about control, isn't it, Al?' Craig said, winking at him.

Before Serena had registered that he was moving, Bukowski had stood up. He leaned over Craig and grabbed his face, squeezing the sides of his mouth together. Craig stared in shock, his face distorted, gawping like a startled fish trying to breathe. Bukowski was livid.

'Enough,' was all he said.

Not a word was spoken, the genial atmosphere chainsawed.

Then Sasha began to laugh, tentatively at first, as if seeking permission. Gordana joined her; a forced laughter, which didn't sound like her. Bukowski let go of Craig's face, his tight lips relaxing into a grin, then he, too, burst out laughing at Craig's shocked expression. Craig nodded with a nervous smile. Serena couldn't stop herself joining in, finding the comedy of the moment irresistibly funny. But she knew it wasn't funny. She had never seen such rage or such fear as she had seen on Craig's face. But everyone else's laugher was infectious. Tears streamed down her face. As the candles burned low, Serena watched the wax drip onto the glass tabletop. The room smelled of hot wax and the marijuana-mix.

Bukowski handed Serena the joint again, still laughing. She took it dreamily.

Chapter 42

Hands refill her glass and the room bubbles with conversation. Time passes. Serena feels totally at ease. Gordana is taking her hand, giggling, her pupils pinpricks. She is gently leading Serena away from the group.

'Let's dance,' she says, swaying to the beat.

Serena is moving dreamily to the music. She is watching Gordana, whose hands are following the contours of her silk dress, moving over her breasts, which swell as she presses them. A cloud of cigarette smoke snakes across the room as Darko watches, his sunken eyes gloating from afar. Gordana's arms are around Serena's waist and, moving in sync, they laugh like children in a playground as they swing each other around.

Serena is having fun. Stopping their circular motion, she sees herself over Gordana's shoulder, a large white candle highlighting the scene in a mirror on the wall. The candle is flickering, helplessly, nearly engulfed in its own melted wax. The fragile flame will not last the night.

Serena's hair is being drawn to one side and the mirror shows Bukowski's lips on her pale neck, eyes down, like a vampire sucking the life out of her. His body moulds into Serena's back as Gordana releases her hands. His body is warm and strong, and his scent intoxicating. She no longer fears him. She is light-headed, disconnected from the people around her. The candles in the room duck and flicker, as if a wind has blown over them. She feels his hands on her shoulders and, in the mirror, sees him slowly pulling her dress straps down. She pulls away, mouthing the word 'No', frowning. She is surprised that she is not more shocked by his presumption. She believes she is in control of the situation.

His face is half in shadow; his eyes, black as the starless sky, observing his prey.

Serena throws herself into a comfy sofa and sinks into the cushions, giggling. Darko languidly offers her another joint; a lit cigarette still in his other hand.

'No more,' she says, feeling a little nauseous.

'He likes you. Why don't you just go with it?' he whispers, his cigarette breath on her face.

She is feeling very sick suddenly and is not really listening.

'Where's the bathroom? I don't feel too good,' she says.

'Yeah, smack can do that when it's your first time,' replies Darko, gesturing loosely in the general direction of the hallway.

She is getting up and, not really feeling her feet, finds her way to the bathroom. Smack? The joint has heroin in it? No wonder she is feeling so weird. Serena is frightened: she doesn't know what heroin will do to her.

The vanity light is on and its comparative brightness is blinding. She registers an enormous sunken bath, big enough to fit everyone at the party. She only just makes it to the toilet before she vomits. Feeling better, she is standing up and washing her mouth out with water, her meticulously applied lipstick washed away. Serena is staring at her eyes: all she can see is the hazel and toffee colour of her irises, her pupils having shrunk to little black dots. Her self-preservation instinct is telling her to leave. Immediately. But she doesn't feel like rushing: it's too tiring. She's given up on the idea of accessing the file. Tomorrow will do. Dreamily rubbing her teeth with toothpaste, she again washes her mouth out, thinking how surreal everything is tonight.

Serena is making her way along the hallway towards the suite's main door, intending to slip away unseen, when Bukowski steps out into her path, blacker than the darkness around them.

Chapter 43

She feels Bukowski's body heat too close to hers and takes a step back, trying to escape his enveloping presence.

'Al, I must go. I'm not feeling well,' she blurts.

'Let me help you,' he says and, placing his arm around her waist, he leads her to another room, which, from the blinking of the electrical appliances, she recognises as the kitchen. The ceiling lights are off. A row of tea-light candles on the workbench gives barely enough light to find the sink. He runs the tap. With a sweeping motion, he moves the tiny candles aside where they remain cowering in a corner. He is lifting her up to the level of the kitchen bench, placing her on it, her feet dangling over the edge.

'Al, I really must go,' she says.

He is ignoring her, filling a glass of water and dropping something in it. Was it a little white pill? He is handing it to her. She is taking it. Her mouth is dry – she needs to drink.

'What's in it?' she is asking as she watches whatever it is dissolve at the bottom of the glass, producing tiny bubbles.

'It will soothe your stomach.'

She is hesitating. He is raising the glass to her mouth.

'Drink this and I'll call you a cab.'

'Whatever,' she says, unable to fight the drug already in her body.

He tips the glass at her lips and the water runs cold down her throat; when she has drunk half, she stops. The water is tasteless: there seems to be nothing medicinal in it.

'I'll call you a cab,' he is saying. She hears him give the cab company the address and hang up, but the call is not connected and Bukowski is not talking to anyone. She is trying to get down from the bench but he is standing in front of her, his hands on her waist, holding her there.

'Let's wait here,' he says and his hand is on her cheek, tracing her mouth with his thumb. Its surface is rough and something catches her lip. 'You are very beautiful.'

'Please, Al, I want to get down.'

'Drink a little bit more; it will help.'

She is too tired to argue so, picking up the glass, she finds herself drinking, spilling water down her chin. How is she missing her mouth like that? She is staring at the empty glass, trying to think clearly. Opening and shutting her eyes firmly, taking deep breaths, she is feeling sleepy. A hand is taking the glass from her and Bukowski is pressing his body close to hers, parting her legs.

'No, Al,' she is saying but her words are slurred. She places her hands on his chest to push him away but she has no strength. She is suddenly feeling very drunk, very weak, which tempers her agitation. His dark eyes are too close to her face and she cannot focus on them. He breathes the question 'Why?'

Serena is staring at him blankly, her head feeling very heavy. She slouches back into the kitchen wall cabinets, her spine weak. The walls are moving. Everything seems to be fluid.

Bukowski's mouth is at her ear and he is saying, 'Why are you spying on me?'

He is moving his head away and he is holding her chin in his hands, forcing it up so that she is looking straight at him. She hears the question, but is wondering if she is mistaken.

Serena tries to shake her head but its weight makes this impossible.

'I'm not,' she is saying, her tongue thick and awkward. Even opening her jaw is difficult.

Still holding her chin, he is shaking his head.

'Serena, Serena, do you take me for a fool?'

The Genesis Flaw

Fear, cold fear, spreads through her veins; her mind is racing. She hears him call her 'Serena', not Amber. Serena. He knows who she really is.

'How do you … ?'

She stares at him, trying to work out an escape. He knows she has been spying. And she realises now that he has drugged her, with heroin and then with … what? She hears his slow breathing, sees his dark, angry eyes, and knows she has to get out of there. She is trying to push him away but her arms are too heavy. Her wrists flop to her side. She is terrified he's used a date-rape drug.

He ignores her question. 'Who told you about Mutenda?'

Serena is thinking hard about the evening and what she has been saying. She is fairly certain she hasn't betrayed Tracey, or the professor, so how does Bukowski know about her interest in Mutenda?

'Don't make this hard. What is Tracey Pollack doing there?'

Bukowski has a knife in his hand and is running the flat side of the blade over her inner thigh. A whimper escapes her.

Serena sees a bony hand touch Bukowski's, pushing the blade away from her flesh.

'This isn't a good idea, Al. Let him deal with her,' says Darko.

She can barely lift her head but hears Bukowski's reply.

'Oh no! This is personal. Nobody makes a fool of Al R. Bukowski. Nobody.'

Darko's hand recedes, and Bukowski turns the blade and digs the tip into her flesh. She winces as a bulbous drop of blood trickles down her leg. And then another drop.

'Answer me.'

'Food aid, something … food aid. She writes … the er … *Post*,' she hears herself saying, her words slurred and clumsy.

'Why Mutenda?'

'I don't know.'

'Did Dr McPherson talk to you?'

She feels her eyes closing, her lids are heavy, her mouth dry as sand. He seems to know everything but she mustn't tell him anything. He will hurt them.

'Cops … the cops …'

Her eyes are closing. He shakes her, hard.

'Did he?'

'No … cops scared me.'

'Bullshit. What did he tell you, Serena?'

She is opening her mouth and trying to call for help. But her reactions are slow and his hand instantly covers her mouth and nose. She is trying to breathe and can't. Wide-eyed with terror, she is wriggling feebly, like a madman in a straitjacket. He is suffocating her. He is killing her.

'Tell me the truth and I'll let you live. Scream and I'll kill you.'

Serena blinks her tearful eyes. He takes his hand away and she breathes deeply, gasping in air, but even breathing is a clumsy process.

Barely able to hold herself up, she speaks.

'I did … n't … speak … to him,' is all she is capable of saying, her mind telling her to protect the professor.

'What do you know about the Gweru research?' says a voice she doesn't recognise. Where did it come from?

Another face is looking at her. A man. Pale blue eyes. Gaunt face. Darko. Cigarette smoke is swirling around him, as if he were an apparition. He is moving in and out of focus.

'Noth … ing. I didn't find … anything. I failed.'

'Of course you failed,' Bukowski laughs in her face, mouth wide, and she smells the wine on his warm breath. 'Did you really think you could outwit me? *Me?* You don't play *me*, use your sex to manipulate me. I play *you*. I control *you*.'

He is taking her face between his hands and his mouth is pressed on hers. It engulfs her, his tongue forcing her mouth open, his stubbled skin scratching hers. He demands her acquiescence. She wants to resist but her body is not responding. She cannot even control her jaw. He invades her mouth, and tears fill her eyes. The terrible realisation dawns that he has total control over her.

When he pulls away, Serena tries to speak. Barely opening her lips, she mouths in slow motion the tiny word, 'No'.

Serena is being lifted, her head flopping back; she's a dead weight. Her limbs are numb. Shadows are swirling around her.

'Well?' It is Darko.

'She doesn't know enough,' Bukowski is saying.

'And she won't remember?'

The Genesis Flaw

'Not a thing.'

'And the journalist? I don't like her sniffing around.'

'Arrange an accident,' Bukowski says.

She is glimpsing an upside-down image of the hallway and then the lounge room, her head bobbing. No one in the room looks up. They are busy. Craig's shirt is undone, flashing his tanned stomach, as Gordana runs her tongue over his chest, moving downwards, lapping like a cat at a bowl of cream. Sasha is masturbating as she watches them. A porno film is playing. Bodies writhe. Body parts merge, appear and disappear. Mouths open, tongues fill them.

The flickering light from the lounge room fades as Serena is carried around dark corners. She can see little, but she is feeling everything. She is touching crisp, cold sheets, but cannot move a finger. She cannot speak. Corpse-like, she is staring at the ceiling. Tears stream down her face. She is feeling her dress being removed; black eyes are staring down at her, his body towering over her.

Hands, lips, sweat dripping above her; whose lips are on her breasts? Whose mouth bites her lip and draws blood, leaving a taste of rust behind? Who rolls her over and places large cushions under her stomach, her head at an angle, lying heavily on the bedsheet?

Cigarette smoke is wafting over her and she smells Darko's rancid sweat as his arms manoeuvre her into position. He is receding, looking at her one more time before he leaves the room. She is trying to scream, to say no, but her mouth and tongue are lifeless. Through watery eyes, she watches the only candle in the room flicker and die. She can see nothing. She is feeling Bukowski's hands running down her back and cruelly gripping her hips. She is barely breathing, she is so terrified.

Darko returns and speaks.

'There's someone downstairs asking for her. He's coming up.'

Bukowski is still, but his grip on her tightens.

'Fuck it!'

He releases her and she lies there, like a discarded rag doll.

'Get a cab. Get rid of her,' Bukowski orders. 'Now!'

She thinks she is alone and then she sees his face.

'I own you, bitch,' Bukowski whispers. 'Never fuck with me again.'

Chapter 44

Throat dry, tongue stuck to the roof of her mouth. She tries to move it. It's like ripping Velcro.

Half awake, half asleep, she aches. Curled up like a foetus under a sheet, she floats in and out of consciousness. She wants to sleep some more but it's too bright. Why is it so bright? Her hair covers most of her face but sunlight peeps in underneath the strands. Her eyelids feel stuck together and she tries to open them. She can't. Eyelids closed, she watches pink bubbles float by. Her cheek is resting on her hand. She extends some fingers and it feels like moving them through liquid cement. She drifts into unconsciousness again and has no concept of the hours passing.

That light. Why won't it go away? She tries to open one eye and feels each eyelash tearing. Blurred shapes fill the room: white, yellow, black, brown. The room swims as if she is underwater. Prising open the other eye, she tries to focus, as if peering through binoculars that haven't been adjusted correctly. Her body feels so heavy. She tries moving her head and it is as if she is learning to do this for the very first time. Initially, it simply doesn't move. Then, as if in slow motion, it lifts, and a shooting pain stabs her behind the eyes, and she shuts her eyelids tight, gasping. She daren't move, hoping it will go away, and slowly it dulls to a throbbing ache. Why does she feel so terrible? Her eyes still shut, she tries to uncurl her legs and, as she does so, she registers a numbness in the one bearing the weight of the other. Slowly, they stretch out.

The Genesis Flaw

Why does her body feel so restricted? She moves her free arm down and feels the material of her dress wrapped around her legs. Her arm muscles retract in pain; an intense ache, as if she has been lifting weights that are too heavy for her. Why is she wearing a dress in bed? Still lying on her side, she pushes back the sheet and attempts to kick it further down the bed, but a pain in her left thigh stops her. She swallows.

Like a fragile old woman, she carefully moves her legs so that they dangle over the edge of the bed, and uses their weight to help her sit up. The room swirls around her and she grips the undersheet to prevent her from toppling over. She feels very sick and knows she needs to reach the bathroom. She wills the room to stop spinning, and stares at one spot until it's still enough for her to recognise her own chest of drawers, upon which are photos of friends and family. She knows now she is at home in Coogee. Serena looks down at the crumpled dress and notices a dark stain.

Where was I last night? And how much did I drink? Too much, far too much.
She has never experienced a hangover like this before.

Serena stays perched on the edge of her bed. As she becomes more aware of her body, so she becomes more aware of how much she aches. The nausea is more intense now, so she braces herself and, using her sore leg muscles she stands, falling forward into her chest of drawers, which saves her from collapsing. As she pants with the exertion, she notices her bedsheet. There is a small red patch on it. Blood.

Have I cut myself? Did I fall over in a drunken state? Why can't I remember?

Her body odour is sour. And alien. Her underarms are sticky with her sweat, sweetened by the fragrance of her deodorant. But she also smells aftershave and male sweat, raw and pungent. It makes her retch and she swallows, staggering to her bedroom door, which she urgently opens, and shuffles painfully to the bathroom, the brightness of the day forcing her to squint.

Closing the bathroom door, she leans over the toilet bowl, hands straight out in front, pushing against the wall to keep her vertical. The nausea comes and goes but she can't manage to be sick, so she sits on the toilet and groans, head in hands, hugging herself, grappling with her confusion.

The Gene-Asis dinner. Bukowski's hotel suite. Serena remembers going there. She can see Gordana in her red dress. She drank wine. She danced. But what then?

Oh God, what did I say? Did I betray myself?

Chapter 45

'You stupid, stupid cow,' she says weakly, too exhausted to fully express her self-disgust.

She keeps trying to remember. An image from last night materialises in her mind. She is in a dark room and she is smoking a cigarette. No, it's a joint. But she can't remember anything after smoking the joint. She can't remember when she left or how she got home. She groans.

With little steps, she reaches the kitchen and sips from a glass of water. She can feel it running down her throat and into her empty stomach. It feels so cold. Her mouth begins to unglue itself as she stares sleepily out of the window. She realises from the shadows outside that it is late in the afternoon.

'Hey,' she hears behind her, very quietly. She recognises John's voice. She knows she must look a mess, and is too ashamed to turn around.

'Hey,' is all she can say. Her voice is shaky.

'How are you feeling?' he asks, standing closer now.

'Terrible.'

She still doesn't look at him.

'Can I get you anything?'

'No, thank you. I need a shower.'

He says nothing in response and she guesses he has gone to another room. She takes some more sips of the water and then turns to find him standing there, concern on his face. He is clutching a newspaper he's been reading.

'I've been worried about you.'

'It's just a hangover.'

He starts to speak and then stops. He is clearly choosing his words carefully.

'I came to the hotel. It was late and I was worried. They said you'd left. I got home and you weren't here. Then, barely five minutes later, a taxi driver banged on the door. You were unconscious. I had to carry you inside. I almost called a doctor …'

'I'm sorry, John. I know I'm a mess. God, I need to sit down.'

She is feeling faint, and shuffles over to a stool and sits.

'I guess I had way too much to drink. I've no idea how I got home. I'm so embarrassed,' she says, as she lays her head in her folded arms.

'Did you go on somewhere after the dinner?' he asks, sitting on a stool opposite her. Still with her head on the table, she closes her eyes in shame. She knows that John will think her completely dumb when he hears what happened.

'Some of us went up to Bukowski's suite for drinks.'

She is expecting some kind of reprimand but receives none. Surprised, she moves her head and looks at him. There is a look of pity in his eyes; or is it sympathy? It confuses her.

'Bukowski was logged in, from his penthouse. I wanted to use the B0r3r. The B0r3r!' she says, suddenly wondering if she still has it. She lifts her tired arms to check her ears.

'I removed them. They haven't been used.'

'Oh.' She can't remember.

'Who was there?'

'Bukowski, of course, and Darko, his wife, and a couple I can't really remember. Oh yes, he was in charge of the China operations. Called Craig, I think.'

'Anyone else?'

'I don't think so, why?'

That look is still in his eyes, and he stretches across the table and takes both her hands in his.

'Serena, your dress was only half done up.' He stops, seemingly unsure how to continue.

'What?'

Then she thinks she understands his meaning. She lets her head hang and squeezes her eyes shut. She is mortified as she doesn't know if it is true. Over the last week, she'd allowed herself to wonder if she and John could become more than friends. The chemistry between them was magnetic. Now she knows John wouldn't want to touch her. And who could blame him? She goes to a party, perhaps fucks someone and can't even remember it.

'John, I already hate myself enough, so please don't ask me to explain. Because I can't. I can't remember anything, and I feel about as cheap as it's possible to feel.'

He looks away and takes a deep breath.

'What can you remember?'

'Oh, John, please. I've made a terrible mistake. I don't want to talk about it.'

She is about to stand but he grips her hands.

'This is important, Serena. What do you remember?'

'I remember going to Bukowski's suite. I tried to find the right moment to use the B0r3r. We drank. They offered me a joint. I smoked it. I remember feeling strange. Feeling sick.'

'What type of joint?'

'I don't know. Hang on, they called it something funny. A time bomb or something.'

'An atom bomb?'

'Yes, that was it.'

'Did you know you were smoking heroin?'

She is staring at him, shocked.

'I was? Oh God, John, I can't remember anything after that. What if I said something? What if I told them my real name, or mentioned you or Trace? Oh my God, what have I done?'

'Did they drop anything in your drink, or give you any pills?'

'I don't know. I can't remember.'

She is sobbing now, but is so dehydrated that the tears are salty and stinging. John moves and, kneeling next to her, puts an arm around her.

'Serena, you're covered in bruises, your leg has a stab wound, and you can't remember anything that's happened to you. You might have been date-raped,' he says, holding her tight, his voice shaky.

She is full of shame and wriggles free from his arms. She stands with difficulty, refusing to look him in the eye.

'I'm having a shower,' she mumbles.

'I don't think you should,' he says with difficulty. His face looks drawn and pale.

'Why?'

John is standing near her, gazing at her tenderly. She knows the answer but cannot face the possibility she was raped.

'You need to go to hospital as you are. You will wash away the evidence.'

His voice cracks as he says the last sentence.

Serena can't look at him and bows her head. He takes her gently in his arms and she leans into his chest, inhaling his fresh, soapy smell, and weeps, knowing she is safe now.

'I think I've been raped, but I don't know,' she sobs, her body convulsing. She knows he will hold her for as long as she needs him.

He whispers, 'I'm so sorry.' He waits for her weeping to subside and then wipes her eyes with a tissue.

'Would you like me to call the police or a doctor?'

She shakes her head.

'What's the point? I can't say who raped me, or even if I was raped. I think so, but what use is that?'

'You can tell them what you remember and who was there.'

'No, I can't do that. No.'

'But, Serena, how can they catch this man if you don't report it?'

'John, if I go to the police, I'll never find proof they killed Dad. I have to know what's in the professor's file. I'm so close to finding it. On Monday, I'll use the keylogger. Come hell or high water, I'll get proof.' She coughs and, as she lifts a glass to drink, her hands tremble.

'Serena! Forget the fucking file. It's you I'm concerned about. You need to see a doctor. And there's no way you can ever go back into the Gene-Asis building.'

'John, I am not going to let them beat me.'

'You could've told them everything last night. And if they know what you're up to, you're lucky to be alive. For Christ's sake, this is madness,' he says, his voice raised.

'John, please, my head.' She rubs her brow, trying to form clear thoughts. 'So, why am I? If they know, why am I alive?'

'I don't know, Seri, but it's time to stop. Seri?' he calls after her retreating figure.

'I must warn people – Keith, Tracey, McPherson,' she replies. He catches up with her in her bedroom and grabs her bruised arm. She winces in pain.

'I'm sorry.' He raises his hands in apology. 'Seri, just stop for a second. Let me do it. I'll make the calls. I'll make sure they're okay. But let me take you to hospital. They can run tests to see what drugs you took; find out … what happened.'

Serena ignores him, picks up the phone and sits shakily on the edge of her bed. She is trying to focus on the keypad of her phone but it is making her feel sick. It is swimming around in front of her eyes, but her strength of will drives her on. She sees him glance at the blood stain on the sheet. She pulls the top sheet over the stain, to hide it.

'Let me do it,' says John, and she hands it to him. In a faltering voice, she dictates a message, which he sends:

I was drugged by Bukowski and may have betrayed you. I am so
sorry. I can't remember a thing. They could be looking for you
right now. I will never forgive myself if something happens to you.
Go somewhere no one can find you.

'I think we should contact the British Embassy in Zimbabwe,' says John.

'Not yet. What if I'm wrong and I blow her investigations? No, let her decide. Now for Keith,' she says, taking back her handheld and blinking at the fuzzy keypad. She dials Swift Farm and gets voicemail. 'Keith, call me. It's really urgent.' Her head feels twice as heavy as it should as she lifts her eyeline to where John is standing. 'Where are they? Someone should be there,' she whispers. Serena dials Keith's mobile. Again, voicemail. She covers her mouth, unable to voice the nightmare vision in her head. She dials another number and reaches

Senior Sergeant Shane Weston. He hears the quiet terror in her voice and orders a car round to the farm.

'What's happened, Seri?' Shane asks.

'Just find my family. Please.'

'But you must tell …'

'I can't. Please just find them.'

She ends the call and slumps back onto the bed. Her head spins as she curls into a foetal position. 'McPherson,' she whispers, desperate for sleep, but refusing to succumb to the powerful concoction of drugs in her system.

'Does he have email or a phone number?' asks John.

'Nothing, he lives like a hermit. And his letters are read.'

'That makes it hard. I'll have to call in a favour.'

'How do you mean?'

'A mate of mine is a pilot up there. Seaplanes. I'll ask him to call in on McPherson. If needs be, he can fly the professor out of Shelleyman Bay. Are you able to give me the address?'

'Yes. At least I can remember that,' Serena replies, with a half smile. 'But why would your mate do that?'

'A few years back, we were surfing together and he got dumped by a really big wave. Didn't come up. I got him to the beach and did CPR.'

'You saved his life?'

'Pretty much. And now I'm calling in the favour. I'll ring on the way to the hospital.'

Serena pushes herself up to a sitting position.

'No hospital, no police. All I care about is my family. If they've touched a hair on their heads, so help me, God, I will destroy them.'

She clambered unsteadily to her feet.

'I need to scrub away the filth on me.'

John's phone rang. It was Shane, wanting to pump him for information. Kerry had gone into labour, and Keith and Katie were with her at the hospital. They were safe for now.

'Mate, do us a favour. Find them somewhere to stay near the hospital. Don't let them go home.'

The Genesis Flaw

'What's going on, John? Have they been threatened?'

'Yes, but I can't say any more.'

'You're putting me in a very difficult position.'

'I know, mate. But you know me, you know Serena. This is important, otherwise we wouldn't ask.'

'I'm on it.'

Chapter 46

Foggy-headed and disoriented, she dragged herself out of bed before her alarm rang and turned on the kettle. At least the nausea had subsided. Serena had hoped that this morning she might remember something, anything, of the rest of Friday night. A face; she wanted to see his face.

Waiting for the kettle to boil, she forced her mind back to that night but the part she wanted to visualise was a black hole. She could only recall smoking the heroin-laced joint. It was as if she had been watching a scene from a movie and part of it had been edited out and lay somewhere on the cutting-room floor. She wanted to pick up those pieces so she could view them, but they'd been swept away. She covered her face with her palms, weighed down by self-loathing and fear. She was disgusted by her own naïveté, which had potentially put her friends and family in danger. She was disgusted by the violation of her body. She found no semen but the wound to her thigh, her bruises, her partly done-up dress, the drugs and, most repugnant of all, the rancid stench of men's sweat all over her, led her to believe it must have happened. But, most of all, she was disgusted by the tiny, nagging doubt that she had perhaps encouraged the man. Had she, at least partly, brought it on herself?

Removing her hands from her face, Serena forced herself to select a mug from the cupboard and place a teabag in it. She added a second, needing an extra-strong brew. Today was an important day.

She felt an arm around her shoulder, and jumped with fright.

'It's just me,' said John.

She allowed herself to be enveloped in his arms, her head resting against his warm bare chest.

'You don't need to do this, Seri. Please don't go back there. We'll find another way to nail these bastards.'

A tear ran down her nose and then trickled down his chest. John's gentle hug was comforting and Serena could have stayed there forever. But she pulled back, mustering some inner strength, and he released her.

'Where's the B0r3r?'

'No,' he replied, 'I can't let you do this. It's too dangerous.'

'John, you've been amazing. Truly amazing. I don't know how to thank you enough for looking after me. But I will do this, with or without you. I can't stop now.'

'Serena, please. You're in shock. Bukowski may have raped you. Regardless, he hurt you. If nothing else, it was a warning. You can't just walk back into his office and pretend that nothing happened.'

'But that's exactly what I have to do. They'll think I won't remember anything, and they're right; I can't. I'm probably alive today because they know those drugs wiped my memory clean. So, yes, I'll go to work as normal. But don't think the very thought of this isn't terrifying me.'

He stroked her arm.

'How can you look at me like that when I've been such a fool?' she said, hanging her head.

'You're not a fool. You're the victim, Serena. Remember that. There is some low-life out there who drugged you and, and … I'd like to find him and smash his face in,' John said, with such vehemence she was jolted out of her self-pity.

She leaned forward and kissed him on the cheek.

'I'll be all right.'

'If you get scared, need help, anything, call me.'

'I'm worried about Trace. I've heard nothing.'

'Maybe she thinks your smartphone is compromised?'

'Maybe, but I'll call the British High Commission, anyway. I checked with some of her friends. Nothing. No contact. I even called her editor, pretending I didn't know she was on leave, and he has no idea where she is.'

'Let me. I can use my position at the bank to cut through some red tape. I'll report her missing, no contact for several days. I'll get them to send someone to Mutenda. With all the political upheaval, it's a dangerous place for a foreign woman by herself.'

The front door burst open and Baz's overnight bag was dropped in the hallway, followed by Baz himself. His motorbike helmet hung over his arm.

'Hey, guys, how's it going? The Blue Mountains were awesome,' he called from the hallway, as he headed straight into the kitchen. He found Serena and John standing face to face in the middle of the room, the lack of space between them suggesting a certain intimacy. He grinned, his blue eyes sparkling mischievously.

'So, looks like you two had a good weekend then.'

'Not really,' replied Serena, unable to look at him. Instead, she looked at John.

'You tell him, I can't.'

Baz's smile evaporated at the misery in her voice. He looked at his brother for an explanation.

'I'd better get ready for work,' Serena said, leaving the kitchen.

'What's up?' asked Baz.

'Mate, I'll tell you in a sec. Bear with me,' replied John, leaving the kitchen. He handed Serena an envelope with the B0r3r keylogger inside. She hooked one part through each ear. Then she checked her bag: two smartphones. One she was using, one she hadn't. Just in case.

Chapter 47

The executive-suite doors slid open to a silent office. Serena had intended to be the first one in but, staring down the length of the suite, she spied Bukowski in his office. His head was bent over and he was reading. His hair immaculate, his shirt perfectly pressed, his tie with its conservative angled stripes; he was every bit the fine, upstanding corporate leader.

Her legs felt weak and her hands shook but she'd be damned before she'd let Bukowski see her fear. This was her last chance. He, no doubt, felt triumphant. She would play that to her advantage. He wanted her under control. He wanted her weak. She could feign both.

Taking a deep breath, Serena walked slowly towards her desk. He still didn't look up, appearing to be engrossed in his work. She checked the other offices, all of which were empty. It would be another fifteen minutes or so before more staff arrived. Voices telling her to run were screaming in her head and it took all her willpower to stand firm.

Act as if nothing's happened. You have to.

She was at her desk, trying to move her tongue so that she could bid Bukowski a greeting, when he spoke.

'Good morning, Amber,' he said, without raising his head, 'How's the party girl?'

White-hot rage shot through her body. She wanted to scream at him. She wanted to accuse him, to scratch his face, to kick and punch him. But she forced herself to stand tall and fix on a smile.

She had to focus on the prize: the evidence and, with it, Bukowski's downfall. She forced a casual rhythm into her step as she entered his office. Breathing in his aftershave almost made her retch, its fragrance sickeningly familiar. Then there was a memory flash from Friday night: his face close to hers, offering her a joint.

'Good morning, Al, and thanks for a great party.' The words stuck in her throat.

He made her wait before he looked up, reinforcing his power. He smirked and folded his arms across his chest, as if he were examining a choice of whores in a brothel.

'From what I hear, you had a good time.' He winked, 'Quite a girl, aren't you, Amber!'

Serena wanted to reach across the desk and slap his face. She dug her fingernails into her clenched hands: she mustn't rise to the bait.

'I think I had a little too much to drink,' she responded, grimacing. 'I had *such* a hangover. To be honest, I can't remember very much of the evening.'

'Really? What about that guy you went home with?'

His coal-black eyes watched her face. Like an eagle hovering above its prey, ready to strike, he waited for her response. His words gave her a sudden jolt; Serena hadn't considered that possibility. She didn't believe him. The CFO and lawyer departed early, she was sure of that. That left six. And the only single man was Bukowski. He watched her face intently and appeared to relish her confusion.

'Who did I go home with?' she asked, sitting down, looking at the floor in fake embarrassment. She would play along.

'I've no idea. I didn't see you leave.'

'Someone must have?'

'Probably no one. The party was in full swing when you disappeared but I do remember you were very drunk.' He leaned forward, his chin in his hand. 'Amber, why all the questions? Don't you know the guy you went home with?' His tone mocked her. She didn't respond and he roared with laughter. She clung onto her composure, reminding herself that his smug certainty of her amnesia would be his downfall.

'Al, what drugs did we take?'

'Whoa, little lady! As far as I'm concerned, we didn't take anything. I don't do drugs.'

He was a liar. She remembered the heroin-laced joint clearly.

'Listen to me, Amber. And listen well. I did not take any drugs and nor did my guests. If you took something with this guy, then that's up to you. But do not go around spreading lies about me. I will not allow it.'

He played the moral outrage to perfection. He would have fooled a jury.

'I'm sorry, Al,' she said meekly, 'It's just that I can't remember much at all. I was kinda hoping you might be able to, well, fill me in.' Serena shifted uncomfortably in her seat. The discomfort was genuine but she was feeling far from meek. Her rage was beyond white hot; it ran like ice through her veins. It drove her on, keeping her ruthlessly on course. She would do anything to convince him she wasn't a threat.

'I can't. I must say that your behaviour is very disappointing. I expected better of you, Amber.' He tutted and pointed his finger at her. 'This is not how I expect my PA to behave. Who knows who this guy was or what you told him. Come to think of it, of the twenty, thirty, people there, there were some guys I didn't recognise. How do I know you can keep our company secrets?' He shook his head, as if he were at the gates of heaven, refusing entry to a sinner.

Serena could see where he was heading and she didn't like it. 'Al, I would never betray Gene-Asis.' She, too, could pretend outrage. She stood abruptly. 'My employment record is exemplary and my sex life is my own business.'

'True, but drugs are another matter. I'm sorry, Amber, but you are a security risk and however slight that potential risk is, I have to terminate your employment.'

Game, set and match to Bukowski. Or so he thought. She mentally swore at herself for mentioning the drugs – she'd handed him the winning move.

'But, Al, I love it here. Can't we just keep this between ourselves? Please.'

'I would like to, Amber. But it's out of my hands.' He shrugged, as if being CEO were a powerless position.

'But the Osaka paper? That's due today. You'll never find anyone at such short notice. Please give me another chance.' Serena clasped her hands together under her chin, as if in prayer. She was giving him exactly what he wanted – she was begging.

He clearly allowed himself a few glorious seconds to enjoy her grovelling and then turned his mind to the Osaka document.

'You'll do the English translation and then you'll be escorted from the building. Sue will look after everything else. You will not be able to access any other documents. I will downgrade your building access to this office and the lobby only. You will not be allowed anywhere else,' Bukowski said, deadpan. He then turned the charm back on and smiled congenially, as if they were the best of friends. 'I am in and out of meetings all day, so let me say thank you, Amber, for all your hard work, and I wish you all the best for the future.'

He graciously put out his right hand to shake hers and, as he leaned across the desk, she saw his left hand adjust the crotch of his pinstripe trousers. Bile shot into her mouth as she realised he had an erection. Disgusted, she held back, unwilling to touch him. But she had to play the game, so took his proffered hand. A static shock passed from him to her, and she pulled her hand back instantly. Bukowski appeared not to feel it and returned to his documents, ignoring her presence.

Serena walked slowly from his office and out of the executive suites, and then raced to the Ladies', where she threw up violently.

Chapter 48

She washed her mouth out with water and wiped her face dry with paper towels. She stared at her reflection in the mirror. Pale, with dark bags under her eyes, shoulders slumped, hands still shaking.

'Stay focused,' she said to her reflection.

She shook her head. Being in Bukowski's presence was like being violated again. Serena knew that to succeed she must stay close to him but that very closeness revolted her. She needed to get away from the building for a few minutes. She left the bathroom and jabbed her finger at the elevator call button. The lift arrived instantly and she took it to the ground floor and walked around the block, repeating to herself over and over the steps she had to take to find McPherson's file. Back on mission, she joined the tide of people entering the building and dived for the nearest elevator, the doors of which had just begun to close. Inside were two people: a woman she recognised from payroll, and Darko Petrinec. He was lounging against the elevator wall and, on seeing her, he grinned, revealing his crooked, nicotine-stained teeth. She instinctively moved to the opposite side of the elevator. His pale eyes studied her.

'Good morning, Amber.'

'Morning, Darko.' Her cheery reply sounded shrill to her but only she seemed to notice.

'You enjoy the party, yes?'

The payroll woman, overweight and in her fifties, eyed them both.

'Er, yes, thank you,' she replied politely. The elevator's cramped confines were making her feel hot and she didn't want to be having this conversation. She flashbacked to Friday night. 'Not too well brought up, I hope,' he'd said, referring to her, his tone lascivious. She shuddered.

'You are leaving us today?'

So Darko knew already. They had planned it.

'Yes, today.' *But not until I have what I came for*, she thought.

He took a few steps closer. She smelled his stale cigarette breath and, through his clean shirt, a hint of body odour. Panic engulfed her, her heart pumping, her mind telling her to get away from him. Suddenly, the black hole in her memory began to fill. Fractured images of the latter part of Friday night filled her head. She remembered his smoker's breath on her. She remembered his acidic body odour. She remembered him helping Bukowski position her lifeless body. She saw the dark figure moving, gripping her from behind. She heard the words 'I own you, bitch.' And she remembered then that Bukowski had toyed with her paralysed body. He'd been about to rape her when John's arrival interrupted him.

Darko was talking to her but she didn't hear a word. She froze, watching his mouth move, horrified at their brutality, at their arrogance, at the way they calmly acted as if nothing had happened. Darko was Bukowski's Beelzebub, doing his dirty deeds and assisting in his sadistic pleasures. Involuntarily, she asked, 'Why?' He looked at her curiously.

'Why, what?'

She stared at him, gathering her thoughts. 'I mean, you and Al are such great friends. I hadn't realised.'

'Oh yes, many years. It's about trust. He trusts me totally.'

The payroll woman watched her feet, recognising she was not a party to this conversation. Darko continued, 'We all have a friend we trust with our lives but sometimes we make the mistake of burdening them with too much, sharing too many secrets. It can be a dangerous road.'

Until that point, Serena had assumed he was talking about his friendship with Bukowski but then it dawned on her that he was saying this pointedly to her.

'Zimbabwe is a dangerous place,' Darko said and grinned a nicotine-stained smile.

It took every bit of her self-control not to display the shock on her face. He was studying her as he lounged against the elevator wall. Like Bukowski, he was tormenting her, safe in the belief she was powerless and defeated.

She was saved by the elevator doors opening at her floor and she stepped out hastily. Then the woman spoke. 'Excuse me for interrupting but if you're leaving today, can you come and see me later? I'm Julie in payroll.' She was preventing the doors from closing.

Serena stared at her blankly and Darko walked off, whistling to himself.

'Level forty-eight,' the woman persisted.

'I will,' said Serena, wishing to get rid of her. Alone, she leaned against the wall. She tried to recall more details of that terrible night. She remembered someone asking her questions, someone holding her still. She remembered the voice: it was Bukowski's. She felt the sting of the knife. Bukowski had grilled her about Tracey. Yes, he'd demanded to know about Mutenda. She'd tried to cover for Tracey – something about food aid. Regardless, they knew she was in Mutenda, which meant her life was in danger. Had Tracey heeded her warning to leave Zimbabwe?

Walking quickly back to her desk, she picked up her handbag. Bukowski was in a meeting, door closed.

She tapped rapidly at the keys of her Tbyte.

'GA knows about you. Alerted BHC to search for you. Don't use this email or number again.'

She pressed 'Send' and dropped it in her bag.

'I need your handheld.'

A security guard stood in front of her.

'I'm sorry?'

'The techos need to check it over. It's company-security procedure. You can have it back when they've finished.'

He put out his hand.

'No, I don't have to hand over my personal possessions.'

'I'm afraid you do. You either hand it to me or it'll be taken from you.'

'Then you'll need to take it from me.'

The man picked up her bag. 'You are going nowhere until I have it.'

If she made a fuss over the phone, it was possible they'd make her leave immediately.

'Okay, but can I have my bag, please?' He handed it to her and she gave him a smartphone – the unused one. The one she'd used to text Tracey was still in her bag.

'And your password?'

'That's private.'

'They'll work it out. I'll be checking your bag when you leave.' He walked away.

'Sorry to hear you're leaving us,' Sue said with mock sincerity, clearly pissed off about Friday night. She pointedly looked towards the departing security guard. 'Must be *very* embarrassing for you.'

Serena ignored the jibe. She needed to get Sue out of her face so she could focus on using the B0r3r.

'Al wants me to finish the Osaka document before I leave. I'd better get on with it.'

'I know,' she responded, flicking her hair back. 'He said you must show it to me when you've finished and then Security will escort you out.' Sue sauntered over to her own desk.

Serena needed to keep Sue well away from her computer if she were to succeed in using the B0r3r. Fortunately, no one could see the content of her screen unless they stood directly behind her. Adrenaline was pumping through Serena's veins and she was thinking clearly for the first time since Friday night. The first thing she needed to do was ensure she wasn't being shadowed. If she were being watched remotely by the service desk, they would see the keylogger working. She turned on her computer. Her toolbar was red: she was being shadowed. She wasn't surprised.

Bringing up her initial draft of the Osaka document, she worked on it for the next half-hour, hoping the shadowing would be turned off. It wasn't. She had to find a way to get it switched off. Minimising the document, she told Sue she was popping down to payroll. Sue clearly didn't know about her restricted access to other floors.

Serena took the elevator to the IT and security departments. She had to get in there without using the retina scanner. The spy-eyes would be watching her but, hopefully, the person controlling them wouldn't see anything suspicious about her behaviour. It was after nine-thirty in the morning but many of the systems penetration testers were still strolling in. A lanky guy in combat trousers and a grey T-shirt placed his face in the retina scanner and the security doors slid open. He lumbered through them, Serena colliding with him from behind as she raced to get through.

'Hey, lady, what's the rush?'

'Sorry, got an emergency.'

Serena walked away, flashing her Gene-Asis ID at him.

'Oh, yeah, okay ... I guess.'

She raced into the IT department before he could say another word. She just hoped he was too lazy to report her.

The place hummed with conversation. Row upon row of computer screens were alive with colour and movement. People buzzed around. Serena spotted Kylie, talking to another woman.

'G'day, Amber, how can I help you?'

Kylie didn't ask Serena what she was doing inside the IT department so, clearly, Bukowski had failed to adequately communicate her restricted access to the building. He must assume she was no longer a threat.

'I wondered if I could have a quiet word,' Serena said in hushed tones. Kylie stepped forward and looked up at the taller Amber, exposing some dark hairs on the tip of her chin.

'Go on,' she said.

Serena looked around her, making a big show of the fact she didn't want to be overheard.

'It's a bit embarrassing, really.'

Kylie was lapping it up.

'Go on.'

'Well, Mr Bukowski wants me to shop on the Net for a gift for his new girlfriend.'

'A new one, huh? Do you know her name?'

'I can't tell you, because she works here.'

Kylie's thick eyebrows shot up.

'Are you serious?

'Sure am.'

'Well, I'll be. Go on,' said Kylie, huddling closer.

'He wants me to buy her some underwear, but not just any underwear. The kind you get from a sex shop.'

'Bloody hell! The dirty bugger. And he's getting you to buy it!'

'So, my problem is that he wants it ordered and delivered today, and I need to go on to these sex shop websites to buy it, and I'm being shadowed by your service desk.'

'I see the problem. So, when do you want to do your, um, shopping?'

'I can't say precisely when, as I have an urgent document to finish, so would you be able to turn it off now, and I'll call you later today and let you know when I've placed Mr Bukowski's order?'

Kylie looked furtively around the enormous IT department and then whispered in her ear.

'I'll tell you what, mate. I'll turn it off straight away if you do something for me.'

'What's that?'

'You tell me exactly what you ordered for him,' Kylie said, laughing and slapping Serena a bit too hard on her back.

'With pleasure, Kylie. And thanks.'

'Oh, no worries, Amber. Believe me, you've just made my day.'

Serena looked fleetingly across the floor at Colin, considering whether she should work on him now to gain access to Bukowski's mouse. No, it was too early. Colin would place a time restriction on her use of the mouse and she didn't even have the B0r3r in place yet.

By the time she was back at her desk, her toolbar had switched from red to blue. As Serena was no longer being monitored, she was free to use the B0r3r. She had removed the two parts from her earlobes and held them tightly in her hand. Unnoticed, she slipped the red-tipped part of the B0r3r into its slot in her computer's dock. That was easy. Her big problem now was getting the transmitter into Bukowski's computer dock without him noticing. She felt sick at the thought of stepping foot in his office again, but this was the only way to nail the son of a bitch.

Chapter 49

Serena worked slowly on the Osaka document, biding her time, keeping an eye on Bukowski and hoping he would leave his office. His meeting with Amanda ended and she waited until he had walked past her desk, heading for the suite's entrance, before she spoke.

'Al, can I ask you a question when you get back?' She wanted to find out how long he'd be away.

'I'll be back in a few minutes,' he said and walked out, turning left down the corridor. She guessed he was going to the Mens', which meant she had to be very quick. She checked out the location of the other executives. Amanda was back in her office. Darko and Henry were somewhere else. Next, Serena considered the PAs. Liz was off sick, and Sal had left the suite. Sue and Ron were at their desks, which meant they would see her enter Bukowski's office. But she had no choice. It was now or never.

Taking the B0r3r from her handbag pocket, she held it tightly. Picking up the day's mail, she walked into Bukowski's office. As she did, she had her back to the suite entrance, so she couldn't see if he'd returned. She walked behind Bukowski's desk, which faced the door, and, lifting her eyes quickly, she glanced through the glass wall. No Bukowski. But Sue was looking directly at her. Serena smiled at her and then placed the letters in his in-tray, while lifting his smartphone from its dock with the other hand. Serena hoped his monitor was blocking Sue's view of her movements.

Another quick glance. Still no Bukowski. Sue was talking to Ron. Serena's hands felt like jelly as she clumsily felt around for the port. She couldn't find it. What if John were wrong and there was no port? Leaning down to look for it, she caught sight of Sue walking towards Bukowski's office. *Shit, where's the damn port?* Then she saw it: a nearly circular point, within which was a metallic device. Between this metallic device and the circumference of the outer circle was a millimetre-wide gap. Serena slipped the B0r3r into that gap, and it became invisible. She placed the smartphone back in the dock. Nobody would know that the B0r3r was there.

'What are you doing in here, Amber?'

'Leaving Al his mail.'

'You're not meant to be in here and I deal with his mail now.'

'Sorry, Sue.'

Seizing the letters from the in-tray, Serena handed them to Sue and walked out of Bukowski's office. As Serena arrived at her desk, he walked back into the executive suite.

'So, what did you want to ask, Amber?' said Bukowski, in his normal cheery tone.

'Oh, it was nothing. I've worked it out.'

Serena watched Bukowski. He was now on the phone. He hadn't used his keyboard yet. Once she had his password and watch-fob code, she would need to persuade Colin to link her fingerprint to Bukowski's name in the biometrics database. She'd then be able to use Bukowski's computer, which was one of the few in the company with a USB port. Of course, sitting at his computer and copying data without raising suspicion was a challenge; which, as yet, Serena had no idea how to overcome. But there had to be a way. She had an hour or two before she would be escorted from the building, and she was determined to leave with a copy of McPherson's Zimbabwean research.

Bukowski touched his keyboard and the B0r3r keylogger activated, sending each of his strokes to her screen. She held her breath. On one of her monitor screens, she had the Osaka document displayed. On the other, she watched as letters she hadn't typed began creeping across the screen, until they formed his user name, 'ARBukowski'.

He pressed 'Enter'. His password would be next. The alphabet soup serpent paused on screen for only a second but it felt like a lifetime to Serena. 'AM8ER'. 'Enter'. She nearly jumped out of her skin. He was using her name as his updated password. She shot him a look. He was focused on his computer monitor. Her heart was racing as she looked around to check no one was able to see her second screen. She watched as his ten-digit watch-fob code appeared before her eyes: 2847200946. She nearly whooped with elation. But she remembered that this watch-fob code was only valid if he didn't log out. If he did, it could only be used for a set time before it became obsolete. For how many minutes it would remain valid, she still didn't know.

Bukowski appeared to be emailing. She saw 'Reply'. It took a while for her to decipher the message but, when she did, she found it related to the status of some impending patent applications. His next email was to the company lawyer in New York, enquiring about the progress of a court case. It seemed that one of Gene-Asis' largest competitors had headhunted Gene-Asis' security director in New York, and Gene-Asis was taking them to court. Next, he typed an email to someone called Wilson Chirunga. It read:

> 496 million Zimbabwe dollars agreed. Destroy her
> evidence. Do whatever is necessary to keep her quiet.
> Remove anyone who cooperated with her. When you
> open this email its contents will be wiped clean in thirty
> seconds. It cannot be forwarded or copied.

Serena nearly gasped out loud. Bukowski sent the email and logged out. He picked up his smartphone and left his office. Serena shut down the keylogger immediately.

'I'll be back in ten,' he said to Sue.

He left the executive suite. Because he had logged off, she only had a few minutes. But in those few minutes, she would nail the man who was paying a mercenary to murder Tracey.

Chapter 50

Finally, she'd seen proof Bukowski was the killer she'd believed him to be and it fired her up like rocket fuel. She went to the Ladies', retrieved her Tbyte from her bag and texted John about Wilson Chirunga. He responded immediately: he'd get on to the British High Commission again and also contact Tracey's editor. It was time for the mighty media to use its influence.

Next, Serena raced to the IT floor. The retina scanners were empty and the solid doors were shut. The spy-eye, suspended from the ceiling, sensed her presence and moved around to get a better view of her. A young woman, immaculately dressed in a linen suit, arrived, placed her face in the retina scanner and the doors opened. Serena dived for the opening, following hot on her heels.

'What are you doing?' she asked Serena, once they were through the doors.

'I'm in a rush, that's all. Here's my ID.'

'That is not right. You *have* to go through the retina scanner. Please do it now,' she said in a strong French accent.

'I'm sorry but I don't have time for this. Mr Bukowski needs me to see the service desk right away.'

'I don't care. You *have* to use the retina scanner.'

The Frenchwoman stood in her way. Serena was cornered.

'Amber, good to see you,' said Colin, poking his head over the woman's shoulder and waving.

'You know this woman?'

'Yes, Amber is Mr Bukowski's PA. Why?'

'Mon Dieu. I am late,' she said, throwing up her arms in exasperation.

Serena took Colin's arm, truly overjoyed at his timely arrival.

'Colin, you're just the man I need,' she said, steering him back into the IT department. 'Mr Bukowski has been growling at me like a wounded bear all morning and he's given me a terrible headache.'

Colin allowed himself to be led, obviously enjoying the feeling of Serena's arm through his.

'What have you done, Amber? You always in trouble. Why you always in trouble?' he said, patting her hand. Colin hadn't asked her about her departure today, so she assumed that he didn't know yet. The bureaucratic wheels were, fortunately, moving slowly this morning.

'Oh, Colin. It's not my fault that Mr Bukowski's mouse isn't working.'

They were back at Colin's desk and she had manoeuvred him into his seat while she was sitting on the edge of his desk.

'What? Not working?'

Putting on his thick-lensed reading glasses, he deftly brought up the biometrics database. Little beads of perspiration formed on his upper lip, trickling between the few black hairs of his morning shadow. He checked that Bukowski's fingerprint was still under his name where it should be, and that everything appeared to be functioning normally. He shook his head.

'I don't understand. It should be working perfectly. What did he say was wrong?'

'Well, he's gone out now but he said sometimes the mouse responds to his touch and sometimes it doesn't. Look, Colin, here's how it is. He had an important email up on his screen when his mouse died, and he's asked me to respond to it for him as a matter of urgency. So, I simply need to be able to activate his mouse to see it.'

'You sure he wants you to see a Highly Protected email? This is very unusual,' Colin asked, wide-eyed.

'Colin, don't you believe me?'

'Of course, but it's better I fix his mouse so it recognises his fingerprint. If it doesn't work for him, then it won't work for you.'

'How do you know? Why don't we try it?'

He shook his head again.

'I don't know. I must ask Mr Bukowski.'

'But, Colin, he's asked me to sort this out as he's in a meeting, and he'll be mad if I miss the response deadline for this email. It's from the chairman of the board. It's very important.'

'Oh no. I don't know what to do,' said Colin, swaying backwards and forwards in agitation.

'Just place a duplicate of my fingerprint under Mr Bukowski's name and link them for ten minutes. I'll call you when I've responded to the email and then you can sever the link.'

'But he's logged out. You can't respond to the email.'

'He told me his password and fob code. I can log back in.'

'Really? He did that? Wow, he must trust you.' Colin rubbed his hairless chin. 'Okay, okay, I do it, but just ten minutes.'

'Better make it fifteen … just in case,' she said, smiling at him.

He copied her fingerprint so that it not only sat in the biometrics database under the name of Amber Crosby but also under Al R. Bukowski.

'Thanks, Colin,' she said, giving him a big kiss on the cheek. 'I'll call you in fifteen, I promise.'

'Call me if mouse is still not working.'

'I will.'

'When fifteen minutes are up, I'll delete your second fingerprint. Okay?'

'Okay.'

In the empty lift, she took a few deep breaths, trying to focus on her plan. Timing would be everything. Serena checked her watch: it was 11.40 am and she had until 11.55 am to use Bukowski's mouse. A minute would be lost just getting back to her desk. On top of this, METRO would switch back on at precisely 12.30 pm and the B0r3r would instantly be discovered.

Serena tried to sneak back to her desk unnoticed but Sue was on her back immediately. She stomped over to Serena in her stilettos.

'Amber, where've you been? You're running out of time. It has to be emailed by two.'

'No problem, Sue, nearly there. I'll put it on the server and you can check spelling, grammar, etc. while I keep working on it,' Serena replied calmly. That would keep Sue occupied for a while.

Ron sidled up to her. 'Amber, sorry to hear you're going. I'd organised a bit of a lunch to say goodbye but Sue says you have to keep working on something, so maybe we can do it another time?'

'That's lovely of you, Ron, but you guys go. Really. I'm almost finished and I should be able to join you, once security has frog-marched me from the building,' she said with a wry smile. With the PAs gone, her task would be much easier.

'Why don't we wait? I can move the booking.'

'No, no, you go, really.'

'Well, if you don't mind … I have to be back by one. It'll just be me and Sal – Sue's getting a sandwich.'

At that moment, Bukowski walked back into his office, and Serena reactivated the B0r3r keylogger, willing him to log back in. He stood with his back to her, staring out of the window, deep in contemplation.

Come on, I don't have time for this. Log on now.

Bukowski sat at his desk, replacing his phone, and pressed his keyboard. Glancing around, she found Ron filing some documents behind her. *Shit!* He was meant to be going to lunch. She minimised the keylogging on her screen and waited until he had gone. She heard the filing cabinet lock with an electronic click, and then Ron and Sal left, followed by Sue, who gave Serena a superior nod.

'Won't be long,' she said.

Serena maximised the keylogging image and read it carefully. 'ARBukowski', then 'AM8ER', then '1729465109', being the new watch-fob code. He was logged in. Yes!

Henry, the CFO, with a balding, bearded man beside him, appeared at Bukowski's door. Bukowski beckoned them in and Serena watched in despair as they sat down. He didn't log out. Precious seconds ticked by.

Come on; get out of there, you two.

Bukowski was laughing and clapping his hands. The balding man was grinning and showing him something on his handheld. Another precious minute was lost. Then Serena noticed the keylogger record Bukowski logging out, which he hadn't physically done. He hadn't touched his keyboard again. The only explanation was that his watch-fob code had a two-minute life cycle: if his computer sensed no activity after precisely two minutes, it automatically logged out to keep security tight. This meant that from the time Serena viewed the new watch-fob code, she had less than two minutes to get into Bukowski's office. How was she going to get him out of his office at precisely the moment she needed him to? Then she had an idea. Everybody has an Achilles heel, and Bukowski's was his vanity.

She checked the time: nine minutes to go before Colin removed her fingerprint from Bukowski's biometric mouse. At last Henry and his guest left Bukowski's office, and Serena closed her eyes for a second with sheer relief. Bukowski logged back in, with a new ten-digit code, '3362917002'. Serena picked up the phone and dialled the florist in the building's atrium.

'Hi. I'd like an immediate delivery of the biggest bunch of flowers you have to be hand-delivered to Al Bukowski at Gene-Asis, signed, "From an admirer". Oh, and can you make sure that he collects it personally from reception, on the second floor? Please don't leave it with the receptionist or allow anyone else to collect it for him. It's a special surprise, you see. But it has to be delivered right now.' She gave her credit card details and hung up.

She waited and watched. Bukowski had clicked his way into a high security research and development folder. Inside it, he searched for a folder called 'EKoch'. Serena recognised the name: Edelgard Koch was one of the four key scientists credited with genetically engineering Supercrop Ultra. Inside this folder, Bukowski did a search for 'BlockerX202'. He scrolled down through the report, but she, unfortunately, couldn't view its contents. What was 'BlockerX202'?

He stopped clicking. She looked up to see him talking on the phone. He'd had a call on his direct line. Serena saw him grin. He nodded and ended the call. Logging out, he left his office, a smug smile on his face. The flowers must have arrived and he was going to collect them.

She checked her watch: it was 11.50 am, which left her five minutes before Colin stopped her using Bukowski's mouse, and just under two minutes before Bukowski's computer shut down. The only person around was Henry and he was deep in conversation. From her bag, she pulled out the tissue on which she had scrawled the file name she believed to be the professor's research: '~^1~^G/569/:P`12/6/2011'. On the same tissue, she jotted down the current watch-fob code, '3362917002', and ran into Bukowski's office. Throwing herself into his chair, her shaking hand took hold of his mouse. The cursor moved: it was responding to her touch.

Not daring to look up, she tapped in 'ARBukowski', then 'AM8ER' and then '3362917002'. The screen lit up like the Harbour Bridge on New Year's Eve. She had no idea where to find McPherson's file, so she used the search facility and tapped in '~^1~^G/569/:P`12/6/2011'. The tiny magnifying glass icon found no file by that name. She then tried looking for any file containing the word McPherson and then Mutenda. No files. This didn't make sense – it had to be there. She ignored the tightening in her chest and her plunging stomach. She tried to think logically and went to the R&D file, where she found a hundred or so folders, ordered alphabetically under the scientists' names. As her eyes skimmed the list, she noted 'EKoch', making a mental note to copy the 'BlockerX202' file if she had time. But there was no file for FMcPherson and nothing even resembling file '~^1~^G/569/:P`12/6/2011'. Serena shot a look out into the executive suite: Henry hadn't noticed her. Perspiration ran down the back of her neck. She stumbled across a folder entitled 'Food Trials'. She clicked to open it and an icon popped up, demanding a password. Another password? What password? She couldn't believe it. In desperation, she tried 'AM8ER'. 'Invalid password' flashed on the screen, beeping loudly. Then '3362917002'. Invalid.

Think, Serena, think. What did Liz say about Bukowski's computer security? Did Bukowski say anything?

She was at a dead end and she couldn't see any way out. It was almost impossible to guess a password. Four minutes to go.

Think, for God's sake. What do I know about Bukowski? He likes football, he loves Jen, he's got a wanky numberplate, and he's religious …

Then, like a dam bursting, she remembered Craig taunting Bukowski at the party about his Bible reading. His reaction had been unbelievably aggressive. What had Craig said? That he read his electronic Bible every morning. Now it all made sense. The professor's letter had been more than a clue to help her locate Mutenda in

Zimbabwe. He had been insistent that she read the Bible every day and then she would discover 'the Truth'. The truth. The password.

Bukowski had his Bible minimised in a corner of his screen, so she maximised it. It was bookmarked at 1 Samuel, Chapter 17. She noticed that on the bookmarked page, every line had been given an electronic tick, up until the first line of verse 45. Serena recognised the story of David and Goliath. Racking her brains, she wondered if the ticks monitored more than the progress of Bukowski's morning reading. Was this how he updated his password? The first line simply said, 'David answered'.

Three minutes to go. Her perspiring hand slipped on the mouse as she tapped in 'David answered'. The computer beeped loudly flashing 'Invalid password'. She nervously deleted 'answered' and entered only the word 'David'. The file instantly opened. She blinked with disbelief. She had done it.

Inside were about twenty files, all with encrypted names. Third down was file '~^1~^G/569/:P`12/6/2011'. Holding her breath, Serena opened it. She heard a door open and, jerking her head up, saw Henry showing his guest out. He was facing the other way but on his return would inevitably see her in Bukowski's office.

Panicking, Serena scanned the file. Bukowski could arrive any second. She saw the words 'Dr Fergus McPherson' and 'Gweru district', and the date 'December 6th 2011'. Hallelujah! She had hit the jackpot. Now to copy it. She retrieved a USB key from the folds of her sleeve but it didn't fit the port. Gene-Asis must use uniquely designed keys. Her elation faded. She yanked open his drawers, searching for one, and found a mini DVD. That would do. She tore off the plastic film protection and pushed it into the side of the dock. One minute to go.

She pressed 'Save as DVD'. The computer hummed for a few seconds and it was done. Closing that folder, she opened 'EKoch' and copied the 'BlockerX202' file onto the same DVD. Barely breathing, she ejected the disc, closing down all the windows. With DVD in hand, Serena ran from Bukowski's office.

Chapter 51

Serena grabbed her handbag on the run, and placed the disc inside. She slowed as she spotted Henry at the elevators, bidding his guest farewell.

'Thank you so much for coming in,' he said, shaking the man's hand.

Henry's visitor and Serena stepped into the lift together, and she urgently pressed the ground-floor button. At that exact moment, Bukowski stepped out of another elevator, clutching a huge bouquet of roses and lilies. He didn't notice Serena.

How long before Bukowski realises someone's used his computer? How long before he wonders where I am?

Then she remembered she hadn't ejected the B0r3r. She'd left it in his computer dock. If he found it, he would know she had information worth killing for. And he might trace it back to John. Her pounding heart quickened.

'Warm day,' commented the man, making polite conversation.

'Yes, very,' she replied, as she watched the spy-eye on the elevator's ceiling move to gain a better view of her. Her mouth was dry with fear, but she needed to befriend this man.

'I'm Mr Bukowski's PA, by the way.'

'Good to meet you.'

'Your meeting went well?' she asked.

'Yes, went very well, I think.'

The doors opened and she walked out alongside him, chatting animatedly. As he placed his temporary pass in the slot of one of the security exit doors, Serena stayed close. The pass was swallowed and the massive doors slid open. She walked through with him, so that her exit from the building would not be registered. Hopefully, they'd think she was still inside.

Outside the atrium, cars flashed by, the sun reflecting off their windscreens. Serena spotted a passenger leaving a taxi on the other side of the road. Traffic flew by with an incessant whine but, without hesitating, she ran into the road. A delivery van narrowly missed her, the driver slamming on its brakes with an ear-piercing screech.

'Hey! What the fuck ya doin'?' he yelled through the open window.

She waved her arms at the taxi and its driver waited for her.

'Where to?'

'Emergency. Just drive,' she shouted, throwing herself onto the back seat.

Two armed security guards in black and white uniforms raced from the building, heads moving rapidly from side to side, searching. One pointed at the taxi and they sped after her, dodging oncoming cars.

The taxi driver pulled away, frowning at her in the rear-view mirror.

'Where to?'

'Darling Harbour car park, and please hurry,' she said, watching the two guards weaving between the traffic. 'I'll pay double,' she added.

'You want fast, love, I'll give you fast,' and he drove up onto the kerb to illegally overtake a slow driver, then zoomed off.

Staring behind her, she saw the security guards had stopped running. One was talking into his earpiece, crimson-faced, leaning forward. She clutched her handbag as if it were the last life vest on a sinking ship and allowed the taxi's air conditioning to cool her burning body.

'Oh my God. What have I done?' she whispered.

She had just committed a criminal offence and, what was more, Gene-Asis knew. Bukowski wouldn't hesitate; not this time. If she had the right documents, she could destroy Gene-Asis, and Bukowski would do anything to stop her. The taxi driver pulled up outside the car park entrance and ran into the car park's shady vaults. Serena checked if she had been followed. She couldn't see anyone. This was too easy. But would they be waiting for her at her car? She ran down the concrete path, past the boom gates and row upon row of parked cars. She spotted the payment booth. Her car was parked nearby.

A Vietnamese man in the booth was focusing on a transaction for a customer. A large man with an army-style haircut waited in the queue, talking on his mobile, eyes focused on a footbridge leading to the car park.

Serena slowed down, not wanting to draw attention to herself. The Vietnamese man looked up and saw Serena. Eyes widening, he raised his hand and pointed at her energetically, mouthing words that couldn't be heard through the glass booth. The man with the crew cut charged in her direction.

She ran, opening her bag, searching its messy interior for her car keys. She always placed them in the same pocket, so why couldn't she find them? She shoved her hand in deeper, but they weren't there.

'Hey, lady, hang on.'

Serena looked over her shoulder. The man was running towards her, knocking people out of the way.

'Amber, I just want to talk,' he called. His voice was coarse, like sandpaper on wood.

Her hand touched something round and metal: it was the key ring. Her hands trembled as she pressed her remote locking system until she heard a click.

'Stop!'

She threw open the door, hurling her bag on the floor and locked her doors again.

Bang. A large splayed hand slapped onto her window.

'You gotta come with me, Amber. It's no use running,' he shouted, banging on her window, his face peering down at her like some hideous giant.

Starting the engine, she rammed the gears into first, speeding off. The wheels squealed, leaving a stink of burnt rubber. He ran alongside her, pulling at the door handle, using his elbow to try to smash the glass.

'Amber, the cops are coming.' She doubted that.

She accelerated violently around a corner, losing the man, who stumbled to the floor.

Round and down she sped, concrete pillars passing by her in a blur. The exit gate was three floors down. She had to get there before her pursuer did; she guessed he would use the stairs. She could see the red and white exit boom gates ahead. He wasn't there: she had beaten him to it. She accelerated up to the gates and then slammed on her brakes. She half-opened the window to insert her plastic pass into the machine.

An arm shot through the gap and grabbed her throat, forcing her head back into the headrest with a thud. The speed of the attack stunned her. She gasped for air, clawing at his hand. Her throat was being crushed.

Chapter 52

The car park boom gate rose but the car remained stationary. The man's hand gripped Serena's throat, her eyes bulging, her mouth gaping. Her lungs were about to burst, as she stretched her left arm towards the gearstick and, with her outstretched fingers, just managed to push it into first. Her foot went flat on the accelerator and the car lurched forward, his arm knocked away from her throat. He roared with pain as the car wrenched his arm and dislocated his shoulder.

Hardly breathing, her throat tight and painful, she drove like a maniac. In the mirror, she saw him nursing his damaged arm.

Serena sped down one road after another. The traffic lights ahead flicked to amber and she accelerated across as they turned red. Her throat throbbed and she tried swallowing, but it was too painful. Even breathing hurt. She ducked and weaved through traffic, checking her rear-view mirror every few seconds. Serena needed to email the disc's contents to the media as soon as possible. She didn't trust the police and once the news was public, Gene-Asis would find it difficult to cover up. She pulled over and, removing her Tbyte from her bag, tried inserting the DVD. The Tbyte rejected the disc, spitting it out. It had some kind of special content protection and only John would know how to bypass it.

Frustrated, Serena drove off and took a sharp left down a narrow side street. After a minute or two, signs in Mandarin and Cantonese started to appear over food stores. She passed a hair salon and a couple of run-down-looking importing and exporting businesses.

Shiny orange-skinned ducks hung cooked and helpless from hooks in restaurant windows. The windows dripped with condensation. She was in Chinatown. Perfect.

She spotted a gap between a Juicy Fresh van and a beaten-up beige Datsun. The road sign said, 'No standing'. She ignored it, parked, and headed out into the throng of people on George Street. Every person who walked towards her scared her. Every person who walked behind her might be following her. She took the next bus heading north, and got out at Wynyard. Crossing George Street, she took the next left and found what she was looking for – the entrance to John's bank. She took the elevator to reception.

'Can I see John Flynn, please? It's Serena Swift.'

Her voice sounded raspy. It hurt to speak. The receptionist eyed Serena suspiciously, her eyes flicking onto the reddened skin of her neck and to her dishevelled clothes.

'Is he expecting you?'

'No, but he'll see me.'

'Will you take a seat, please?'

Serena was too agitated to sit and paced the reception area. A woman in a navy blue suit looked her up and down, and when Serena caught her eye, she returned her gaze to the *Financial Review*.

'Serena, are you all right?' John asked as he strode towards her.

'John, I need to talk in private,' she whispered, aware the receptionist was eavesdropping.

'Of course. Come through.'

He took her into the elevator and pressed the button for level four. As the doors closed, he stepped forward and gently held her shoulders.

'Serena, what's happened? Oh my God, your neck!'

His blue eyes were angry.

'Did Bukowski do this?'

'No, a security guy. John, I've got it. The file. It's in my bag,' she said excitedly, ignoring her painful throat. 'But I can't read it.'

'Wait a sec. You did it? You used the B0r3r?'

'Yes, but I couldn't use my memory key. I had to use a Gene-Asis DVD and I can't read it. I need you to find a way to open it.'

The elevator doors parted. He ushered her quickly past a number of luxurious meeting rooms and into a room with a computer.

'We can look at it here,' said John.

'Can you lock the door?'

'No. Were you followed?'

'I don't know. A man tried to strangle me in the car park. I don't know if he followed me. I left my car in Chinatown.'

He shook his head.

'Strangle you?'

'Yes, they were trying to stop me getting away.' Her voice was hoarse. 'John, I remember everything. Bukowski knows who I am. He knows about Tracey.'

'Then it won't take long to work out where you've gone. They probably know you live with me.'

Serena started to cough. Her throat was burning up.

'Please, can I have some water?'

John poured some still spring water into a glass. Serena took a few sips: it felt like swallowing cricket balls.

'Bukowski was going to rape me. He abused me. Darko helped. But something stopped him going further. It was your arrival at the hotel. I remember him saying to Darko that I didn't know anything, so that's probably why I'm still alive.'

John took her hands in his and spoke quietly.

'Seri, we must call the police. Otherwise, Gene-Asis will hunt you down.'

'No, John, we can't. I have to be sure this disc will see the light of day.'

'Serena, do you understand what you've got? You may have the key to destroying the company. They'll kill you.'

'No, they won't. Not if I nail them first.'

'Seri, I'll do anything to protect you but I'm no match for these people. Only the police can do that. I know there are some bad cops out there, but most of them are straight and do a good job. If there's anything on that DVD that's criminal, the police will prosecute the people responsible.'

He picked up the phone and dialled Emergency 000.

'This has to stop.'

Chapter 53

She leapt up and cut the line dead.

'No, John, I can't risk this DVD disappearing. I'll go to the police when it's public.'

'No, now.'

She continued. 'Please listen to me. I heard the Minister of Agriculture jump when Bukowski said jump. He's in Bukowski's pocket. I've been threatened by cops in Shelleyman Bay who are Gene-Asis' spies. You have no idea how powerful they are. Please, John, I've risked my life for this disc. Just look at it first.'

She handed him the DVD.

'Hmm. Looks normal. Ah, I think I know what they've done.' He dropped it into the disc drive. It popped back out immediately.

'Nice one,' he said, fascinated. He held it under a desk lamp. 'I thought so,' he said, as his fingernail picked at the surface of the disc.

'What is it?'

'Some kind of protective film,' he replied as he removed it.

'It was already in a protective film envelope.'

John looked up, frowning. 'That could be bad.'

She was about to ask why when the disc's contents appeared on the monitor. John clicked open the first of the two files, '~^1~^G/569/:P`12/6/2011'. A digital clock appeared on the screen. It said '05:00:00'.

The Genesis Flaw

'Just as I thought,' John said, checking the clock on the wall. It was 12.45 pm. 'It's counting down time. Five hours. That's how long we have before the disc is wiped clean.'

'You're not serious?'

'I am; it's data leak protected. When the disc is exposed to oxygen, it triggers the clock. It's a way of minimising the likelihood of confidential data falling into the wrong hands.'

'Can we copy the files somewhere, so we don't lose them?'

'No. That's the whole point.'

'So, if this is the evidence I need, I only have five hours – well, four hours and fifty-eight minutes – to show it to anyone?'

'Let's check what you have first. I may be able to do something.'

The file contained a research paper entitled *Food Trials to assess the impact on human health of the Koch Bottlebrush Virus (KBv) conducted on behalf of Gene-Asis Biotech, by Dr F. McPherson.*

So, Edelgard Koch had created the viral promoter used in all Supercrop plants. She recalled he was also one of the four scientists credited with developing the soon-to-be launched Supercrop Ultra range.

Serena hurriedly scanned the index for the conclusion, bypassing all the pages of scientific data and diagrams. The digital clock now said '04:55:01'. John pulled up a chair behind her.

'Why "bottlebrush" virus?' he asked.

'Looks like one,' she said, pointing to its image in the report. They read on in silence.

'Holy shit. Is this for real?' said John.

'Yes, it's for real,' said Serena.

'This is unbelievable. How can they sleep at night?' he asked as he read. 'The birth defects he's describing here are terrible. But I don't get it: most of the developed world eats genetically modified food. So why them and not us?'

'Because, look here,' she said, pointing at the monitor screen. 'It says that of the 1400 people involved in the food trials, 700 ate nothing but GM plants containing the Koch Bottlebrush Virus for five years.

'But for us, only some of our daily fruit and vegetable intake contains KBv; perhaps around half? These poor people in Zimbabwe ate nothing but food with the Koch Bottlebrush Virus for five years.'

'So, if companies like Gene-Asis have their way, in the next few years all our food will be GM. What this report's saying is this *could* happen to us.'

'I get it,' said John. 'Look here. He says that the 700 people in the control group, who didn't eat any GM foods, were fine. But if Gene-Asis knew KBv was harmful, why didn't they just stop using it?'

'They can't,' replied Serena. 'They have to use some kind of viral promoter and they've patented KBv. To develop a new one would cost the company millions. Millions they'd rather not spend.'

'But why do they need to use this KBv at all?'

'Well, take this example here,' Serena said, pointing at the screen. 'These people ate carrots, grown from Gene-Asis seeds. Gene-Asis had engineered faster-growing carrots by placing a human growth hormone into the carrot's DNA.'

'Human growth hormone! That's sick.'

'The carrot's cells automatically protect its DNA from foreign invaders, such as this growth hormone. But, if you use an aggressive virus such as KBv, the carrot's DNA is forced to switch on the human growth hormone. The cell's defences are by-passed completely.'

'But Dr McPherson proved that KBv is highly unstable and its behaviour can't be controlled. Gene-Asis has always claimed horizontal gene transfer – from a food product into a human cell – can't happen. Well, it does. The professor proved it. The virus is passing through people's intestine lining, and causing horrible damage and birth defects.'

'So a whole new generation could be born like this?'

'Exactly.'

They stared at the screen.

Eventually, John spoke. 'Jesus! No wonder they want this kept under wraps. But why hasn't anyone questioned the health impact of GM foods? Aren't these things supposed to be tested for safety?'

'John, Gene-Asis donates millions to political parties around the world – in the US, Europe, here … Think of the influence that buys; how they can shape legislation favourable to them and keep the lid on embarrassing issues.

'And they're also one of the world's single biggest contributors to scientific and medical research. If they don't like a result, they threaten to withdraw funding. When scientists with integrity stand up to Gene-Asis, they lose their jobs or, worse, disappear. There is no truly independent testing of GM foods.'

'But surely they can't get away with telling us it's safe?'

'Course they can. We were told Thalidomide and smoking cigarettes were safe.'

'Point taken.'

'John, look here. Dr McPherson talks about the hepatitis virus.' She scrolled down and read aloud.

'"KBv is reactivating ancient sleeping viruses, embedded in our DNA." It says our ancestors had immunity to these viruses but we no longer do.' She continued reading. '"The KBv is moving from the food into the human stomach, and then attaching itself to the DNA of dormant, deadly viruses. It is then switching on these viruses."'

'Look at this,' said John, also quoting from the report, '"KBv belongs to a group of viruses closely related to the human hepatitis virus." He's saying this KBv could trigger any dormant hepatitis in our DNA and that hep S could be a sleeping virus that's been reactivated.'

'And here,' Serena pointed, 'he says that once the virus has been reactivated in a few people, it could then be transmitted via blood, saliva or semen, depending on the strain of the virus. Well, that explains the hep S pandemic.'

John paused, as the implications finally sunk in. 'This is what killed Kat.'

'I'm sorry, John, this must be very hard for you.'

'But why her and not me? Why?'

'God, I don't know. Maybe you have some kind of immunity?'

'Evil bastards! How long have they known about this?'

'The date's here,' she said, pointing.

'But that's years ago!' He stood up, toppling the chair backwards. 'How can they do that? They know about hep S. They know they've caused it and they don't do a damned thing.'

'No, as McPherson said, what they're doing is trying to cover up their mistake. Bukowski would have his top people working on a solution and, in the meantime, he goes on selling the stuff and raking in massive profits. I would bet any money his new range is an attempt to prevent horizontal gene transfer.'

'But how do they do that?'

'I don't know, but I'm hoping this next file will tell us.'

Serena opened the 'BlockerX202' file and John leaned closer to the screen.

It appeared Dr Koch had developed BlockerX202, which stopped the virus from passing through the human gut into the bloodstream, therefore preventing the KBv from wreaking havoc with human DNA.

It did this by coating the inside wall of the small and large intestines with a protective barrier, which allowed some of the goodness from the food to be absorbed but stopped the Koch Bottlebrush Virus from passing through. But the side effects of BlockerX202 also appeared to be alarming, even if Koch had played them down. They included malnutrition, stomach cramping and nausea.

John paced the room, deep in concentration. His face was pale.

'What do you want to do with this, Serena?'

'We need to make this as public as possible, as fast as possible. Emailing these files to the major newspapers and TV channels around the world is the fastest way but can we do that?'

John sat hastily. 'Unlikely. But I'll have a go.' His fingers moved over the keyboard in a blur of activity.

'John, I left your B0r3r inside Bukowski's computer. I just bolted. I'm sorry. They'll trace it back to you.'

He didn't react. 'You'll need to get away from here,' she urged.

His frenetic attempts to attach the files to an email continued as he spoke. 'No, Serena. I'm with you all the way. I've already lost one exceptional woman and I don't intend to lose another.' He glanced at her face to gauge her reaction.

'John, I ...'

'... need to hurry. I know.'

Chapter 54

The on-screen clock displayed '04:37:18'.

'I think I might have done it,' said John. 'We'll use one of my personal email addresses. It's as safe as you can get. What do you want to say?' He turned to look at her expectantly.

> Our lives are in danger, so this is in haste. Please read the
> two attached files carefully. What they reveal is the truth
> about Gene-Asis GM food products: they caused the hep
> S outbreak and birth deformities. Gene-Asis have known
> about this for years but so far have kept it secret.
>
> These documents have been stolen from Gene-Asis'
> highest security files – they are genuine. This is not a
> prank.
>
> Please act quickly and make this public. In just over
> four-and-a-half hours, the attached evidence will be
> erased.

'Done. Now, who to?'

She reeled off a couple of news editors' addresses she'd memorised.

John then pressed 'Send'. The on-screen clock displayed '04:32:55'. A message appeared in John's inbox: 'The attached files could not be sent. Permission denied.'

'Shit,' they said in unison.

Serena stood. 'I'm going to take it to David Tuckett at Channel One. They're the largest TV station and they're only in North Rocks. Shame all the other stations have moved out of town.'

'I'm coming with you.'

At that moment, an email arrived. It was titled 'I warned you not to fuck with me.'

'It's him,' she whispered, feeling her strength begin to drain away. Bukowski's choice of words had been deliberate and effective. Haunting images of her assault filled her head. She could hear his voice in her ear: 'Never fuck with me again.'

'Let's see what the scumbag wants,' said John, opening the email.

You have something of mine. Return it to me and all will be forgiven. Fail, and you will both discover the true meaning of pain. Show its contents to anyone and they will not last the night. In four hours and thirty minutes the contents of the DVD will be erased. If I don't have my disc back before then, so will you.

Serena swallowed hard, refusing to let his threat weaken her resolve.

'He's running scared if he's emailing us directly,' she commented with a bravado she didn't feel.

They watched the black lettering begin to fade until Bukowski's email disappeared.

'How? How did he do that?' she asked. The phone rang. They both jumped. John hesitated, and then answered it on speakerphone, so Serena could hear.

'There's a gentleman in reception, who insists on seeing you. He won't say where he's from.'

'I'll be right down.' John hung up.

'No, you can't. He'll be from Gene-Asis.'

'Serena, take the disc to Channel One. Leave by the fire exit and I'll deal with this man.'

'John, he'll kill you if he thinks you've seen the disc. Come with me to Channel One.'

He ejected the disc. The countdown clock read '04:27:22'.

'No, I'll buy you time,' he said, handing her the disc and showing her the fire escape stairs. 'At the ground-floor fire door, press 5990 on the keypad and it'll open without the alarm going off.'

'Come with me,' she pleaded.

He shook his head. She kissed him on the lips, and ran into the concrete confines of the stairwell.

Chapter 55

Bursting out of the fire exit into a narrow alleyway crammed with garbage bins, she took a back route to her car. Once inside the sweltering vehicle, she locked her doors. Serena set off for Channel One, ducking into one of the many cross-city tunnels that would take her under the Harbour. Her Sat-Nav gave her directions. The traffic slowed in front of her as they neared the toll booths; it was being funnelled from four to two lanes. This was slow-going and she didn't speed up again until she'd been through them.

Serena accelerated, weaving in and out of lanes. Ahead was another tunnel; this time, cut into a steep hill. She checked her dashboard clock: it was 1.45 pm, which meant she had four hours before the disc went blank. As she entered the tunnel, she noticed massive fans suspended from the roof, like aeroplane engines, moving air through the tunnel. Its walls were dank and moisture dripped down the exposed rock. It must have been constructed many years ago. To pass through the tunnel, the traffic was being forced into one lane in each direction.

A piercing light bounced off her rear-view mirror. Squinting, she could make out the massive headlights of a semitrailer, with its huge steel grille and bullbars. It was twenty metres behind her and closing in. She moved her head, trying to catch a glimpse of the driver, but could see nothing other than the outline of a man. As it closed in on her little car, the truck moved out of its lane to overtake her. Relieved, she gently pressed the brakes, keen to let it go by. The lanes were clear up ahead, so he had plenty of room.

The massive hulk of the truck dwarfed her car as it moved parallel to her. Even with her windows shut, she could hear the drone of its powerful engines. She looked up at the driver's windows but they were tinted: all she could see was his outline. Then the weight of the truck hit her, the thud so powerful that she thought there had been an explosion. Sparks flew and the side of her car began to cave in with a hideous creak.

Serena pressed her foot on the accelerator, trying to release her vehicle from the truck's weight, but the crumbling car was locked tight. Her steering wheel useless, she watched, as if in slow motion, the jagged tunnel walls looming closer. She was being forced into the rock. With a *thwack*, her car hit the rough wall and sparks flew, her passenger window shattering into a kaleidoscope of fragmented glass. Her windscreen cracked. Airbags burst out, metal screeched on rock, as the truck continued to grind her car against the unyielding tunnel walls. Serena let go of the steering wheel and covered her face. Her passenger door caved in. She was trapped, like a sardine in a tin.

In the surreal world of near-death, she was calm. She waited for the end. She didn't hear the frantic car horn or the truck speeding off as her car ground to a halt with a neck-breaking bang. Hands still over her face, she didn't see the steam hissing from her car bonnet or the fluids leaking onto the tarmac. She didn't move a muscle.

A creak of twisted metal intruded on her stillness.

'Can you hear me? My name's Jim.'

'Don't move her, mate. She might have a broken neck,' commented another.

Whose are these voices?

'Call an ambo, and the police.'

The police? No, I don't want the police.

She opened her eyes and blinked into the back of her hands. Something white and round lay beneath them. The airbag. She had survived. Carefully, she pulled her body backwards and lifted her head. Her neck ached badly.

'Love, I don't think you should move. You had a bad accident.'

She looked into an unshaved tanned face.

'I'm Jim. What's your name, love?'

'Serena.'

'Serena, just stay as you are until the ambos arrive. Best not to move.'

'No police, no ambulance. I'm fine,' she mumbled, using her hands to feel her body. Nothing felt broken but her legs were constricted. 'Please, help me to get out of here.'

Jim leaned forward through the battered doorframe.

'Aw, I don't think that's a good idea. Just wait a few more minutes. They'll be here soon.'

Serena started to try to wriggle her legs free, but the steering wheel column had dropped on impact and she was trapped. She reached out and tugged at the man's T-shirt, distorting the lettering 'Jim's building supplies' printed on it.

'Can you move my seat back? My legs are trapped. I have to get out of here,' she said, her voice high-pitched with panic. She banged her hand on the steering wheel in desperation.

'Hold on, hold on one sec. I'll help you, but just stop a moment or you'll hurt yourself some more.'

Jim called over his shoulder, 'Tony, over here. Help me move her seat.'

Tony, a dark man with a small build, put his face in the car.

'You sure, mate?'

'Yeah, she's panicking, we better get her out,' he whispered.

Together, they yanked the seat lever up and tried pushing the seat back. It was jammed.

'What if we lay the back of her seat flat and then she can slide out that way?' suggested Tony.

'Good one, mate. Serena, we're going to flatten your seat so we can slide you out.'

'Please hurry.'

The seat back moved flat, and then Jim put his muscular arms around her waist and pulled. Her already bruised knees hit the steering column and she cried out.

'Shit! What if we're doing the wrong thing?' exclaimed Tony, shaking his head.

'I'm fine, really. I'm nearly out.'

His strong arms still around her, she was dragged out of the car and onto the tarmac at the front of the car. Tony had cordoned off the area with two hazard cones and was directing traffic around the accident site. Jim kneeled in front of her.

'How're you feeling?'

'Not bad. Just a bit shaken up.'

'You're lucky to be alive. I couldn't believe it when I saw the truck ram you. I reckon the truckie must've fallen asleep, 'cause when I honked on me horn he pulled away.' He tutted. 'Wish I'd got his rego.'

'Jim, thank you for being so wonderful. You saved my life. But I'm not hurt and I desperately need to get to Channel One. Can you drive me there? It's really important.'

'You can't just leave your car here, love; it might cause another accident. And anyways, the police and ambos are on their way. Best wait for them.'

Serena was wasting precious time. And she needed her handbag. The DVD! She struggled to stand up and, as she did, she noticed a tear at the knee of her black pants.

'Here, let me help you.'

'My handbag,' she replied, walking unsteadily towards her smashed car.

'I'll get it. Where was it?'

'On the passenger seat. But it's probably on the floor somewhere.'

She sat back on the road.

The car bonnet had stopped hissing. Jim kneeled on the driver's seat and felt around on the floor on the passenger side. Thrown right forward with the impact, her bag was hidden in the darkness under the dashboard. Feeling his way, he found a strap and pulled it: it was her bag. He also found her Tbyte – the face was smashed. Handing the bag and phone to her, he went to join Tony, who was directing the crawling traffic through the tunnel. Serena eagerly checked for the DVD and breathed a sigh of relief when she held it in her hand. It wasn't damaged. But her smartphone was useless. That was all she needed. The interior of the tunnel was lit up by rotating red and white lights, hypnotically reflecting off the roof, as an ambulance wove its way through the queue of cars. A man and a woman stepped out.

'Hi. I'm Cath and this is Max,' said the freckle-faced woman kneeling before her. 'What's your name?'

'Serena. Serena Swift.'

'Are you hurt?' she asked.

'No, I'm fine. Just a bit shocked. I'm so sorry Jim called you. There's no need.'

'Are you in pain anywhere? Does your neck hurt?'

She hesitated.

'Best we put a collar around your neck and take you to the hospital to get checked out. Looks like a pretty bad accident,' said Cath, glancing at Serena's car.

'I don't need to go to hospital. I'm not hurt.'

Cath glanced up at Max, who kneeled down to Serena's level.

'Is there anyone else hurt?'

'No, the truck driver bolted.'

'Look, we're here now, so we might as well take you to the hospital, just to be sure you're okay. It's just up the road.'

'How far?'

'Five minutes.'

If Serena went to the hospital, she could take a taxi from there to Channel One.

'Let's go.'

'Hey, mate!' Max called to Jim.

Jim jogged over.

'You happy to wait for the police? We're taking Serena to the hospital.'

'No worries,' he said, winking at Serena and breaking out into a craggy smile.

'Thanks, Jim,' Serena replied, as Cath placed a rigid white collar around her neck.

'Can you walk?'

'Yes,' she said, as Max helped her stand.

Cath helped her into the ambulance, where Serena lay down, her bag in her hand. The ambulance pulled away, sirens blaring, and she closed her eyes. Her thoughts turned to John. Was he all right? Where was he? The ambulance swayed marginally as it turned off the freeway, followed closely by a Toyota Corolla, its windows tinted, its driver unidentifiable.

'Nearly there,' said Cath. 'How are you feeling?'

'No different.'

Serena lifted her arm and stared at her father's watch. It was 2.15 pm. Too much time was slipping away.

The ambulance stopped. The doors opened and Serena tried to sit up.

'Serena, just lie down now. We'll wheel you in.'

She lay still and watched, as the white interior of the ambulance became clear blue sky and then cream corridor ceilings. There was an unmistakable smell of disinfectant. Serena heard Cath talking to a doctor before she came back over to her.

'Dr Wong will be with you soon. We're off now,' said Cath.

Alone in a curtained cubicle, Serena sat up and removed the restrictive collar. It was time to get moving.

She peered through the cubicle's white curtains and found the corridor was empty, except for a nurse with a bedpan. Serena waited for her to enter another cubicle. Unsure of the location of the exit, she took a punt and turned right, following one of the many coloured lines painted on the shiny floor. A doctor in a white coat, stethoscope round her neck, rushed by; a nurse behind a reception desk glanced at her and then returned to her paperwork.

'Excuse me, where's the taxi rank?' Serena asked the receptionist.

'You'll need to call one. Number is over the phone in the corner.'

'How long do they take to get here?'

'Depends. Ten, fifteen minutes.'

At the public phone, she tapped in her Tbyte user ID so the call would be charged to her account, and dialled the number. They told her the taxi would be fifteen or twenty minutes. 'How far from the hospital to North Rocks?' Serena asked. 'About ten kilometres,' the woman answered.

Serena ordered a taxi, knowing she couldn't afford to wait that long: it would be a last resort.

She needed to know John was safe. She dialled his mobile. It rang and rang, and then there was a click. She could hear breathing.

'John?'

She heard a voice but it wasn't John's. It hissed at her like a cobra: 'Who else did you tell, Serena?'

Chapter 56

A sharp intake of breath and all the colour drained from Serena's face.

'Where's John?' she mouthed, barely audibly.

'We want the DVD. John's life for the DVD.'

She knew that her response would dictate whether John survived or not. 'How do I know he's alive? Put him on.'

'Cocky bitch, aren't you? He ain't going to be alive much longer if you don't hand over the disc.'

She heard a thud, like a punching bag being hit, and a low moan.

'You listening?' asked the voice.

Down the phone, Serena heard a low cry like that of an animal in pain and it chilled her soul. The man's voice was distorted by his agony but she knew it was John's.

'Stop hurting him …'

'Deal or no deal? But make it quick.'

'Deal. It's a deal.'

'Meet us at Garigal National Park at …'

'No. In the city, at the crossroads of York and George Streets.'

She wanted lots of people around her. In a busy city street, it would be harder to kill her.

'Be there at four, alone. Call the cops and he's dead.'

The line was cut and the phone hummed its dial tone. She had to save John, no matter what. And she needed help. She dialled Baz.

'Yup?' he answered. She could hear laughter in the background.

'Baz, it's me. I need your help.'

'Serena, what's wrong?' His tone had changed instantly.

'It's John. He's ... in trouble.'

'Wait up. What? Johno's what?'

'Baz, please listen. There's not much time. John told you about my ... what happened to me Friday night?'

'Yes.'

'The same person who ... assaulted me is trying to kill me. Al Bukowski. I stole some documents from him, and John helped me, and now they have him and they're hurting him ...'

'Wait, Serena, slow down. John hacked Gene-Asis?'

'No, I did. He gave me the keylogger, so I could steal the file. He's been helping me. Baz, they have him and I heard them beating him. They'll kill him if I don't give them back their DVD. Please, I need your help.' Her words exploded from her mouth like steam from a geyser.

'Is this a joke? Cause I'm not laughing,' said Baz, clearly rattled.

'No, it's no joke. Please, Baz, John needs you.'

'Serena, Johno is fine. I saw him leave for work this morning ...'

'Baz, Gene-Asis is going to kill him unless I get this disc to them by four.'

'Why? None of this makes sense. What disc?'

'I'm sorry; I don't have time to explain. The disc has information that'll destroy them. It proves their foods are killing people. It proves they caused the hep S outbreak, which killed Kat.'

'Jesus fucking Christ, and I encouraged him to help you! God, what did I do?'

'I'm sorry, Baz. Hate me if you want, but please help me get John back. I'm meeting his kidnappers at the junction of York and George Streets.'

'Where are you?'

'Baulkham Hills Hospital.'

'Shit. What are you doing ... You'll barely make it into the city by four.'

'I'll get there. Baz, will you help me?'

'Of course. He's my brother. I'll meet you outside the Gloria Jean's on the corner. And I'm phoning the police.'

'No police. Not one. If they see a cop, John will die.'

Baz was silent.

'Baz, promise me, no police,' she begged.

'No cops, and I'll be there.'

Chapter 57

Dropping the phone, Serena nearly collided with a male nurse as she ran towards the entrance and out into the car park. Now for transport – she'd steal a car if she had to. The taxi rank was empty. Shielding her eyes from the glaring sunshine, she surveyed the car park, searching for someone who'd just arrived or was about to leave.

'Amber? Is that you?'

She recognised the deep and raspy voice. Looking round, she saw Ben Hartstone, wearing a wide-brimmed battered hat, reflective sunglasses, baggy shirt and shorts, and workman's boots. His face was almost completely obscured except for his ski-slope of a nose.

'I thought it was you. What are you doing here?' he said cheerily.

'I … was in a car accident,' she replied. 'And you? I thought you were leaving on Saturday?'

'My mum got sick, so I stayed a few more days. I was just about to visit her,' he said.

'Ben, I need to get to the city really urgently. Someone's life's in danger and I have to be there by four. I need your car.'

'Strewth! What's happened?'

'I've no time to explain. I'm sorry but I have to take your car. I'll bring it back in an hour or so. I need your keys.' She held out her hand.

'Nah, I'll drive you. I can see Mum another time. This sounds important.'

He strode off across the car park and Serena kept pace. Spots of tarmac melted under the intense sun, creating an unnerving sensation that the ground was collapsing beneath her.

'Has this anything to do with Gene-Asis?' he asked, approaching an old black utility.

'Everything.'

'No surprises there,' replied Ben.

He dived into the ute's cabin and, turning on the ignition, revved up the air conditioning to cool the suffocating interior. The back of the ute was open and a number of white sacks lay there, together with a shovel and a red can of petrol. She saw the Gene-Asis logo on the sacks. Serena's step faltered. She glanced at the writing on them and saw the words 'fertiliser' and 'ammonium nitrate'. Why would an IT guy be driving a ute full of Gene-Asis fertiliser? And, come to think of it, why was he dressed like a gardener? Uneasy, Serena leaned into the cabin. She didn't get in.

'Ben, what are you doing with Gene-Asis' fertiliser?'

'It's not mine. It's my brother's. He's a landscaper and I've been helping him out. Come on, get in.'

Serena could always tell if people were lying by looking at their eyes. But Ben was still wearing his shades, so she couldn't see them. Desperate, she got in.

'So, where we going?' Ben asked.

'The city. Can you drop me near the corner of York and George?'

'Sure. But what's going on, Amber? Whose life's in danger?'

Serena hesitated.

'Amber, you can trust me. I know Gene-Asis do bad shit, remember,' he said, giving her a sideways glance over the top of his shades. He took a slip road onto the freeway and she saw a sign for Sydney. Reluctantly, she took the plunge.

'It's my flatmate, John. I've copied some confidential Gene-Asis files. I made the mistake of showing them to him and now they're going to kill him unless I hand over the disc.'

'Fucking oath! I knew you were up to something. Your mate's in deep shit.'

'I know. We're doing a swap: John for the disc. I may need you to watch me and call the police if it goes wrong. Will you do that?'

'Of course. Have you called the police yet?'

'No. They said if I called the police, John was a dead man. I'm meeting his brother there.'

'Very wise. And you've picked a good place to meet them. Nice and public. Leave the police to me. I'll call them if they're needed.'

Had she said that she'd picked the rendezvous location? Serena frowned. He must have assumed she suggested it. They were approaching the junction with Highway 3 and she checked out the signs. They said Pymble and St Ives.

'Ben, we're going the wrong way. The city's the other exit.'

'I know a quicker way.'

He sped up and moved into the fast lane. An icy tingle ran up her spine. Something was wrong, very wrong. Outside her window, parched trees, their bark peeling from their trunks, barely moved in the blistering breeze. The carcass of a cat, its guts strewn at the side of the road, rotted in the heat.

'Ben, I have to be there by four.'

It was nearly 3.00 pm.

'We'll be there.'

Serena rubbed her temples, trying to grapple with her increasing feeling of disquiet.

'So, what's wrong with your mum?' she asked, as casually as possible.

'Er ... appendix.'

The same hospital. It can't have been a coincidence, can it?

'How did the accident happen?' Ben asked.

'I was rammed off the road,' replied Serena, not keen to discuss it.

'That's terrible. Did you see the guy?'

'No, tinted windows.'

'I was hit by a truck once. Sent me ploughing into a ditch. Couldn't believe I walked out alive. Those semitrailers can be lethal.'

Serena's stomach plunged. She stared straight ahead, frozen, as her mind raced, adrenaline pumping through her veins. She hadn't said that a semitrailer had hit her. There was only one way he could know that: he was working for Bukowski. He must have been all along. Ben had been spying on the spy, reporting back to Bukowski.

This time they wouldn't hesitate. Ben was going to kill her.

Chapter 58

Ben cast a sideways glance at her, moving his sunglasses down his nose to get a better look.

'What's up, Amber?'

She stared out through the windscreen, trying not to betray her terrifying realisation. She had to let him think she trusted him.

Either side of Highway 3, the bush was charred and black from a recent fire. Only the very tops of the tallest trees clung, desperately, to a few green leaves, the undergrowth still smoking. The sun was low and shining straight at them, which made it hard to see, but in the distance she spotted a service station. Looking at Ben, she forced a weak smile.

'I'm not feeling too good. Must be the shock. Can we stop at a service station?'

'I'd rather we keep going.'

'I think I'm going to be sick. Look, there's one now. Please, I have to stop.'

'Righteo,' he sighed and pulled in. 'Let's make it quick, okay?'

The service station consisted of ethanol and petrol pumps, a diner and a shop. It was clearly popular with truck drivers: semitrailers dominated the expansive parking area. Behind the service station was thick green bush that had escaped the blaze. He pulled into an empty spot right in front of the diner. She registered disappointedly that he could see through the windows of the diner to the door of the Ladies'.

268

She hopped out, clutching her bag, and ran into the diner, breathing in the sickening smell of animal fat. The Ladies' was cramped and the windows too tiny to crawl through. What was she going to do now? If she ran for it, he would catch her. Opening her bag, she used her lipliner to write a message on a torn-off piece of paper towel:

Help me. Call police. Don't say a word, he's watching.

At least with the police, she stood a chance. They might take the DVD, but she would survive. With Ben, she had no chance.

She left the bathroom and, weighing up which was the shortest queue, she stood in line. She itched to barge to the front and hand over her desperate plea for help, but Ben would realise she was up to something. There was one person in front of her: a woman ordering a long list of food for her husband and three boisterous boys. Serena clutched the piece of paper towel in her trembling hand, hidden underneath a fifty-dollar note.

'What are you doing?' said Ben, his shades still on, hat tipped over his face. Serena noticed the surveillance camera facing them and guessed why he wanted to keep his features hidden.

'I need something to calm my stomach. Something to eat.'

'We're running out of time. We have to go.'

At that moment, the woman ahead of her moved off.

'Fries and a water, please, to take away,' she said to a teenage girl with braces on her teeth. Serena looked at Ben. 'I won't be a second. There's no need to babysit me.'

'I'll wait.'

The teenager returned with a brown paper bag. Serena handed her the fifty-dollar note, the piece of paper towel hidden underneath it.

With one hand, Ben grabbed her wrist; with the other, he tore away the money and scrawled note. He placed both in his pocket.

'I'll get this.'

Ben had seen the note. It was over for her. Serena stepped back and yelled as loudly as she could, 'Police! Call the police. This man's kidnapped me. Help me!'

The diner went silent, the girl behind the counter staring at Serena in stunned silence, her hands hovering over the till. The family devouring their burgers stopped chewing and gawped.

A couple of truck drivers with tattooed arms looked over. Ben grabbed her arm, snapping at her 'Stop it!' as she tried to pull away from his grip.

'Someone help me!'

The girl behind the counter ran into the kitchen and one of the truck drivers with a drooping moustache shouted:

'Hey, mate. Let go of the lady.'

A man with a name badge saying 'Gary' scuttled towards them from the kitchen.

'What seems to be the problem?'

'There's no problem,' said Ben, releasing her arm.

'Please call the police and don't let him touch me. He's going to hurt me.'

'I'm sorry, folks. My wife is very ill and I'm taking her back to hospital.'

'He's lying. I'm perfectly well. Just call the police.' Her eyes pleaded with the diners.

'If she's your wife, mate, why's she so afraid of ya?' said the big truck driver with the moustache as he lumbered up to them.

Ben was calm. 'She's not well, mate. Schizo. One minute she's fine and the next, she thinks everyone is trying to kill her, including me. She's been in and out of hospitals for years. She hasn't taken her pills and so she's gone off. I'm trying to get her to her doctor.'

'That's not true. I know what I'm doing and this man is going to kill me because he wants to keep me quiet. Now, just call the police, will you?' She was angry at their inaction. She moved towards the kitchen to increase the distance between her and Ben, and could feel the heat on her back from the deep fryers.

The manager looked at Serena's grubby blouse and torn pants, and hesitated. His face said it all.

The truck driver looked sympathetically at Serena. 'Mate, call the cops. Where's the harm? Then you've done the right thing.'

'Will both of you sit down quietly over there if I call the cops?' asked the manager, indicating a quiet corner of the diner.

'This is fucking ridiculous! Can't you see she's ill?' shouted Ben, losing his cool.

'I'll sit. But please hurry,' said Serena.

She sat on the squeaky plastic seat, her eyes fixed on Gary as he used the phone, refusing to make eye contact with Ben. She must not let him intimidate her. But he leaned on the table between them and, keeping his voice low, said, 'If you want to see John alive again, you'll tell the manager not to call the cops.'

'It's too late. We'll miss the deadline and John will die because of you,' she spat back.

'Not yet. One call from me and he's a free man. But if the cops arrive here, your pretty boy is dead. Which is it going to be?'

Conflicting emotions fought for control: joy that John was still alive and fear for her own life.

'Why are you here? I was going to hand over the disc. What more do you want?'

'Never trust your enemy is my golden rule. It's my job to make sure nothing goes wrong, and we get the disc back nice and quiet. Now, if you want to see lover boy again, stand up and hold my hand. I want you to tell them not to call the cops. Do you understand?'

She nodded again and stood up. He took her hand and crushed it in his, so tightly she winced. The low hum in the diner subsided again. They walked to the counter, Ben saying loudly, 'It's all right, my love. Everything'll be fine.'

'Please don't call the police. I'm sorry to have caused trouble,' she called to Gary, who stopped mid sentence.

'You sure?' Gary asked.

Serena nodded.

'Sorry about this, mate. We're going now,' said Ben.

Gary continued with his phone conversation. 'Sorry, cancel that. The situation's under control. No, really, we don't need you anymore.'

Ben silently led her out. She knew too much and she was going to die. But there was a chance she could save her life-long friend, the man she had come to realise she loved.

Chapter 59

Ben unhurriedly reversed out of the parking spot, aware the diner's guests were watching, and then drove off to the freeway. With a click, he centrally locked her door so there was no escape.

'You fucking bitch!' he yelled.

'Ben ... you've got me. Just let John go.'

His hand swung out from the steering wheel so fast she barely had time to blink. He hit her across the right side of her face and she yelped in shock.

'You'll do what I fucking say. Now, hand me the disc, nice and slow.'

She gave it to him and then rubbed her burning cheek. He placed the prize in the tray between them and then dialled his hands-free, putting it on speaker.

'I've got the girl and the disc. Make it look like a kidnapping gone wrong.'

'No,' she screamed, grabbing the steering wheel as the man on the other end of the line replied. The ute swerved across the road and rammed into the central barrier. But Ben was strong. He forced the steering wheel back towards him and the car moved away from the median strip. He elbowed her hard in the upper chest, digging deeply into the soft tissue between the shoulder socket and the collar bone. The force pushed her away, which gave him time to draw his gun.

'Try that again and I'll blow your brains out!' he shouted.

'Hey, boss, everything okay?' said the man on the line.

'Just get on with it,' roared Ben, ending the call.

'John doesn't know anything. Please let him go,' she begged.

'He knows too much.'

Ben turned on the radio and blasted Triple M through the speakers, drowning out her protests. He steered with one hand, the other keeping the gun pointed at her. Serena looked at Ben's finger on the trigger and then glanced at the lock on the passenger door. She was trapped. He turned onto Highway 3, heading towards St Ives and Garigal National Park. He was going to kill her and bury her there; and she realised, with numbing clarity, that if John wasn't already dead, he would be soon. Her only chance was to talk Ben out of it.

'Ben, let us go. We'll disappear. Everyone will think we're dead. I can pay you,' she shouted above the loud music.

'Shut up,' he snapped. Then, as an afterthought, he turned down the volume. 'You think you're so clever, don't you? But you're nothing but a dumb bitch. You thought you could spy on Gene-Asis, right under Mr Bukwoski's nose, and he wouldn't notice! That's fucking dumb. But me, on the other hand, I got brains. I know never to cross Mr B.'

'He's not infallible. He can be fooled. *I* fooled him and *we* can fool him again. I can pay you lots of money to disappear. We have a large farm ...'

'Yeah, nice property. Worth a few mill.'

Serena winced. 'You've been there?' she breathed.

The car jolted as it ran over some roadkill. Probably a possum. Ben kept the gun barrel pointed firmly at her.

'Not me.'

'You leave my family out of it,' she demanded, aware she was in no position to demand anything.

He looked over the top of his sunnies. 'With you and John gone, they'll be left alone.'

Relieved, she persevered with her bribe. 'We can sell the farm; it's worth two, three million. It's yours, Ben, if you leave us alone and free John.'

Ben was getting irritated. 'Shut it. Mr B's been good to me and I won't ever forget it.'

With a jerk of the steering wheel, Ben turned down a rough track. The ute and its contents bounced from side to side but the gun still resolutely stayed pointing at her. Stones flew up and clanked against the metal bodywork. She broke out in a cold sweat. This, literally, was the end of the road.

'How long have you known about me?'

'We've been watching you from when you tried the Gibson file. I think you saw me once, in the car.' Serena remembered the silhouetted man parked outside the Coogee apartment. 'Mr B took a real shine to you but on Friday, when he worked out who you really were, and that you were playing him for a fool, he was mad. Fucking furious. He always gets his way with women, see. And there he was finding himself drawn to you and you not only rejected him, you betrayed him.' Ben waved the gun at her, like a wagging finger. 'Come to think of it, never seen him let his emotions overrule his mind. But that night at the party, he wanted revenge on you. I offered to beat it out of ya. I called him that night, when you were already drugged up to your eyeballs. He said he had his own way of finding out the truth, and he was going to enjoy it. I bet he did too.'

'Go to hell!'

'No, bitch, that's where you're going.'

In desperation, Serena yanked at the door handle. It was a futile exercise and Ben laughed.

'You brought this on yourself. Mr Bukowski was going to let you off the hook. And that's unusual. He musta liked ya. But you had to keep digging, didn't ya? You had to go and steal his fucking property.'

He glanced at her. 'Stealing that disc made me and him look like dicks, and I'm gonna enjoy killing you. I like the look in people's eyes when they realise they're going to die. There's nothing like that look.'

Serena turned away. She didn't want to betray her fear.

'In my line of work, you get to see some weird shit. Not every day you see a CEO hang himself.'

Her head jerked round in surprise. 'You watched Tony Mancini hang himself?'

'Yeah, saved me the trouble. That Munroe was stirring things up, getting Mancini all upset. Mancini even tried to tell Mr B it had to stop. How fucking dare he? Seems the man had a conscience after all, but, as Mr B says, there's no room for a conscience in business. Mr B couldn't risk them talking to the wrong people.'

'And Munroe?'

'He'll never be found. Swallowing sand in the desert.'

Serena couldn't prevent a moan escaping her lips. He shot her a satisfied grin. 'Yeah, and Mancini's suicide note was a real doozy. Could have placed Mr B in a difficult position. He was happy I took the letter. Yeah, real happy.'

Serena didn't want to hear anymore. As they rolled into a pothole, there was a loud thud. Something in the back had fallen over. On either side of the track, thick dry bush formed an impenetrable wall. Dust flew up behind them. Ben slowed right down, peering into a tributary track even narrower than the one they were on, and drove down it, branches scratching the sides and roof of the vehicle. At a clearing, he stopped.

A desperate desire to survive had her tugging at the door handle again. She screamed, knowing in her heart that no one would hear her. Then she felt the cold steel against her head. She could smell the gun metal and clenched her jaw tight.

'Keep very still,' he breathed.

She shut her eyes. He moved the barrel of the gun from her temple and ran it along her lower lip. It felt ice cold.

'Stay exactly where you are.'

She didn't move, hearing his door open and then slam shut. Then her door creaked open and she opened her eyes. The gun was pointing straight at her.

'Get out and walk ahead of me.'

'Huh?' she cried, looking over his shoulder. It only took a few seconds but he looked behind him. She took the disc and hid it in her bag.

'Get out.'

Clutching her bag, she did as he instructed and stood trembling in front of him. All around her, bark cracked and popped from the heat of the day as the cicadas screamed deafeningly. But there was no human voice, no sound of a car, not even a dog. She was totally isolated.

Ben's mobile rang in his pocket. 'Yup. Good.' The call ended.

'I guess you'll be digging two graves. Go round the back and take the shovel.'

'No, please God, not John.' The words died in her throat. She felt tears welling in her eyes.

'Move!'

Shakily, blindly, she moved to the back, and stopped by the exhaust pipe.

'You won't be needing that,' he said, yanking her bag away and dropping it at his feet. The bag burst open, spewing some of its contents into the dirt. The disc remained hidden.

'Get the shovel.'

She blinked away the tears, seething with rage. The shovel was furthest away, lying across a fertiliser bag near the cabin. She smelled petrol. The red canister had fallen over and its stopper was half off. Petrol was leaking, spreading out in a puddle towards the fertiliser bags. Serena knew she had one last chance of survival.

'No,' she said.

He thumped the small of her back so hard that her knees cracked into the car bumper. Bent double, her head hit the tailgate. 'Get it,' he yelled.

'Get it yourself,' she breathed through clenched teeth as she dragged herself back to a standing position and turned to face him. 'You're going to kill me anyway, so get it over with. I'm not going to help you.'

Did she say that? Did she feel the cold barrel of the gun forced into her mouth cutting her lip and hitting her teeth? She shut her eyes tightly, but the gun was just as quickly pulled out of her mouth. Forcing her to her knees, he was livid with anger.

'Move an inch and you'll die so painfully, you'll beg me to get it over with.'

Unlocking the tailgate, he swore, finally noticing the overturned petrol canister. He righted it, then got into the ute and leaned down to pick up the shovel. Serena reached for her handbag, clawing at its contents, frantically searching for the matches John had given her. She found them and lit one. In a single fluid motion, she stood and, taking three steps forward, dropped the flame in the petrol pool. Igniting instantly, flames shot into the sky.

The Genesis Flaw

'What the …' she heard Ben say as she ran. She heard a gunshot and then a boom, which threw her onto the track, face down. Then another boom, like a cannon going off. It felt like her skin was being blowtorched. An arm's length away, she saw the DVD winking in the firelight. She scooped it up, coughing at the toxic fumes. She ran into the trees, not daring to look behind her. Her childhood on a farm had saved her life; many times she'd watched her father blow up tree stumps using an ammonium nitrate and petrol mix.

But had it been enough to kill Ben?

Chapter 60

Boom, and then another boom, the second one even louder. The fertiliser bags were exploding. Even at ten metres away, it was as if a hand had shoved her forward, the force nearly toppling her over. But, righting herself, she ran on through the thick bush, dodging trees and their branches, the dry undergrowth snapping beneath her feet.

Was he dead or was he following her? She daren't look back. She had to keep running. Every branch cracking in the thick bush made her shudder. Every shriek of an animal made her sob aloud. Someone from the road must have seen the flames or heard the bang. Perhaps a park ranger? Surely someone would come to her aid?

There was a rustling behind her. She ran faster. Above the deafening hum of the cicadas, she detected a low traffic roar. She stumbled on, following the sound, and burst from the undergrowth onto a six-lane freeway. Behind her, black smoke billowed above the treetops. Serena ran alongside the busy freeway, cars speeding by, and, when she saw a gap, crossed to the central reservation. She needed to go back in the direction she had come. A car honked its horn at her as she waited in the centre. Another gap in the traffic and she crossed to the other side. Serena saw a Holden Statesman driving towards her in the slowest lane. She raised her arms and waved them, shouting, 'Help!' The car drove by, and, in a second, was gone. Another car, this time a four-wheel drive. She threw herself out into the freeway and waved at it desperately. The driver swerved around her and sped off.

The Genesis Flaw

An ancient station wagon appeared in the slow lane. She could just make out a female driver; the car was packed to the ceiling with boxes. Serena stepped out in front of it, yelling for help. The car slowed to a halt a few metres ahead. A shaggy mop of hair popped out of the driver's window.

'Need a ride?' called the woman.

'Yes. I've got to get out of here.'

'Get in,' she said without hesitation and her head disappeared inside the car. The passenger door swung open.

Serena got in, and faced a darkly tanned woman in her forties, wearing many wooden beads. Her eyes widened very slightly as she took in Serena's dirty state.

'Please drive. I have to get away from him.'

The woman accelerated hard, the old car spluttering with the effort. Serena craned her neck to check for Ben but couldn't see him. Perhaps he was dead.

'Can you go any quicker?'

'I'll go as fast as I can.'

But they were already doing one hundred kilometres an hour and the car was groaning under the strain. They sat silently for a few seconds, Serena staring straight ahead at the lowering sun, willing the car to go faster. The woman glanced at her.

'Where're you going?' she asked, flicking back her thick mop of curls.

'Channel One.'

'Channel One?'

'They're in North Rocks.'

'I know where they are, but you sure you're okay? You look pretty shook up to me.'

'Can you take me there? Please?' Serena grasped the woman's arm, sheer desperation on her face. 'It really is a matter of life or death ... Mine.'

'It's kinda out of my way but I guess I could.'

'Thank you. Thank you.'

'I'm Danielle, by the way.'

'Serena.'

'Who you running from?' Danielle asked, looking at the road ahead.

She didn't answer.

'You hurt?'

'No, I'm just a bit dusty. Danielle, do you have a phone I can use?'

'Sure, darl. Use away.' Danielle picked up a very scratched mobile phone. 'It works fine. Just doesn't do all the fancy stuff.'

Serena dialled Baz's mobile. He answered immediately.

'Baz. It's Serena.'

'Where've you been? What happened? I'm at Gloria Jean's but I haven't seen Johno.'

'John isn't going to come.' She said nothing for a few long seconds, then said, 'I'm so sorry, Baz.'

'What do you mean? Where is he? Why didn't you meet me?'

'He … won't be coming. He's dead,' she whispered, fighting hard to hold back her tears.

'No, not Johno. No way.'

'I'm so sorry,' she said faintly, her eyes blurred with gritty tears.

'Tell me this isn't true,' he pleaded. His voice had a shrill edge to it. 'Tell me he's alive.'

'I …'

Serena could hear in the background the clank of coffee cups and people talking, but Baz was silent.

'Baz?' she said.

'Where … is he?'

'I don't know, I'm sorry. I can't say much now, I'm with someone. But they may come after you too. Don't go home. Go to the police and tell them everything you know.'

'I want to know where he is,' Baz yelled. She could hear that he was panicking.

'Go to the nearest police station, please, Baz. They'll find John. Please, Baz. You need to do this.'

'What I need is my brother back.'

And the line went dead.

'I'm sorry, Danielle. I guess this all sounds very bad. Someone I loved very much was killed today,' was all she could say, smudging away her tears with her dirty hands.

'Sounds to me like you're in a whole heap of shit and you need some help.'

'It's best we pretend you never heard that conversation.'

'What conversation?'

Silence.

'You wanna go to the cops? I can take you there.'

'No, please. I have to get to Channel One. When I'm there and I've done what I need to do, then I'll call the cops.'

'You got something on these guys who are after you, don't you? You're going to get it on the news,' said Danielle, nodding at her in awe.

'Something like that.'

'You're a brave woman,' she said, smiling at Serena.

'Or stupid.'

'Nah. You gotta stand up to the bullies. It's taken me seven years to do it myself. Seven bad years of marriage to a bully. So now I'm on my way to start a new life, alone, someplace where he can't find me.'

'You're the brave one.'

'We'll see. So, Channel One?'

'Yes,' said Serena, looking at her watch, brushing the dust off its face. It was 4.10 pm. She had one hour and thirty-five minutes before the DVD went blank.

'Okay, darl. I'll get you there, but you can't go walking into Channel One looking like that. You gotta clean yourself up a bit. Take a look,' Danielle said, pulling down the sun visor in front of Serena and revealing a small mirror.

She had a cut along her cheekbone that was caked in dried blood. Dust clung to her face, except where tears had left streaks. Her bottom lip was swollen, bruised by the gun. Her clothes were grimy and torn. Serena touched her cut cheek and winced at the pain.

'I want you to climb into the back seat and open the striped laundry bag. It's got clean clothes in it. Take what you need from there and get changed.'

Serena clambered into the back seat, squeezing through a narrow gap between some sealed boxes, a suitcase and a lamp.

'And take a towel from that same bag and clean up your face. Here's some water, darl.'

'Thanks.'

Wetting the towel, Serena dabbed her face carefully, the cut stinging as she wiped away the dried blood. Next, she washed her hands and arms.

'That's better. You look almost human,' joked Danielle, smiling at Serena through the rear-view mirror.

She squeezed Danielle's shoulder in response, grateful for her warmth and generosity. Unzipping the striped bag, she found a white T-shirt and some faded blue jeans, slightly frayed. She and Danielle were a similar build, and the clothes were a pretty good fit. She climbed back into the front seat.

'How can I ever thank you?'

'No need.'

Chapter 61

It was almost 4.50 pm. Serena could only hope she'd find David Tuckett before 5.45 pm, when the DVD would become useless. Danielle drove accelerator to the floor, but time was slipping away.

'Nearly there.'

They turned off the freeway and found themselves in an industrial park dominated by two buildings, like glass tornadoes ten storeys high, linked by walkways: Channel One. Danielle pulled up outside the main entrance.

Serena jumped out and peered in the open window to say goodbye. Danielle held out a one-hundred-dollar note.

'You'll need money. Take it. It's a gift.'

Danielle sped off, dropping the money, before Serena could refuse. She picked it up.

The glass doors slid back to reveal a reception desk manned by two beautiful women and one robot. Serena had heard about these robots but never seen them in action before. Channel One had bought one as a gimmick and given it a lot of media coverage. Not too dissimilar from clothed crash dummies, their faces were made of malleable rubber so they could smile, and their mouths moved as they spoke. Their eyes, however, did not blink, so they stared through unnervingly lifelike eyeballs. Both women were busy, so Dan, the robot, addressed her.

'Welcome to Channel One. How may I be of assistance?'

Behind the reception desk were thirty-one TV screens, covering each of Channel One's thirty-one sister channels, all owned by the same conglomerate, Global News Matters Inc.

'I need to see David Tuckett right away. I have a story for him that can't wait.'

'Do you have an appointment with David Tuckett?'

'No, I don't but he'll want to see me. I have an exclusive for him.'

'I am sorry but you cannot see David Tuckett without an appointment.'

'Listen, do you want to be responsible for denying this station the biggest news coup of the century?'

'No, I do not want to be responsible for denying this station the biggest news coup of the century,' the robot meticulously repeated. 'But without an appointment, you cannot see David Tuckett.'

She took a deep breath.

'Can I please speak to a person?'

'Yes, of course.'

One of the beauties came to her assistance.

'How can I help?' she asked.

'I must see David Tuckett urgently. I don't have an appointment but please tell him I have evidence that Gene-Asis' GM foods have caused the hepatitis S outbreak. Millions of people will die if a cure isn't found and I know the source of the outbreak. I have to see him now. Time is running out.' She eyed a clock on the wall: it was 5.04 pm. 'And please hurry.'

'I'll call his assistant, Paula Day. What's your name, please?'

'Serena Swift.'

'Paula, I have a Serena Swift in reception. She wants to see David right away … yes, I know, but she says she's got evidence that Gene-Asis have caused the hepatitis S outbreak … certainly I will. Thanks, Paula.'

The receptionist looked at Serena.

'Paula Day will see you at 6.30 pm, after the news has gone to air. David Tuckett is not available. You can visit our café, if you wish.'

'No, 6.30 pm is too late,' she yelled in exasperation. 'I have to see him now.'

'I'm sorry, Ms Swift, but that just isn't possible.'

Calming herself, Serena tried again.

'The evidence is on a disc. It erases itself after five hours. Those five hours are nearly up. It's my only proof. Gene-Asis has committed terrible crimes. Please call David Tuckett and let me speak to him.'

The receptionist eyed one of the security guards.

'I'm sorry, I cannot …'

Serena pretended to make her way to some seating and then dashed for the elevators. She had to find him. Before she could get there, her arm was grabbed. A second security guard barred her way.

'You're leaving right now, young lady.'

They almost lifted her above the ground as they swept her towards the exit.

'Heather speaking … certainly,' Serena heard. Then the receptionist called, 'Stop! There has been a mistake. Please let Ms Swift go.'

The guards released her and she ran over.

'He'll see me?' she asked.

'Yes. Here's your visitor's pass. Take the elevator to the sixth floor, where you'll be met by Paula,' beamed the beauty. Next to her stood the robot. His rubber face creased into a corpse-like, toothless grin.

Chapter 62

Serena was led into the untidiest office she'd ever seen. Every surface was strewn with papers, newspapers and manuscripts. Books were messily piled onto bookshelves. On the walls were framed awards for excellence in TV journalism. The air conditioning was on full blast. The room was freezing. A tall man with a crooked jaw and pockmarked skin stood up and shook her hand.

'David Tuckett,' he said, his lopsided mouth barely opening and his expression intensely serious. His shoulder was slightly lower on one side than the other, and he therefore appeared to be leaning slightly to the left at all times. She shook his hand, which was very cool and dry, his long fingers wrapping round hers. On a huge screen behind him ran Channel One's current program. He gestured for her to take a seat at a round meeting table. Some double doors in the opposite wall were slightly ajar, the room on the other side in darkness. But she could just make out a boardroom table and chairs.

'So, the world's leading biotech company is behind the hep S outbreak, is it?' he mocked. 'You've got five minutes to convince me.'

He tapped his fingers on the polished desk's surface.

'Three billion people around the world eat GM foods primarily produced by Gene-Asis. Gene-Asis uses a specific virus, the Koch Bottlebrush Virus, in their genetic engineering process, which is passing through our stomach lining into our bloodstream. We all carry ancient viruses, which lie dormant. But, in some people, KBv is reactivating these ancient viruses; in this case, hepatitis S. Once activated, it becomes contagious and spreads like wildfire. I have proof Gene-Asis has known about this for years. Instead of stopping production, they've engineered new products which they hope will stop the reactivation. But their so-called cure has nasty side effects.'

He nodded, expressionless.

'And how do you know all this?'

She held up the tiny DVD.

'On here are two files. One is a scientific report on Gene-Asis' Zimbabwean food trials. It proves the hep S link. It also proves that their GM food can cause severe birth defects. The other is the report on their solution – a new product line called Supercrop Ultra. This contains a blocker designed to prevent horizontal gene transfer. But it can cause malnutrition, as it reduces our ability to absorb the food's goodness. They're launching this in just two days' time. They have to be stopped.'

He raised a greying eyebrow.

'Really, Ms Swift, this sounds fantastical. I don't believe a word.'

'But I have proof.'

'And I doubt it's genuine. I've never heard anything so ridiculous.'

'Mr Tuckett, we don't have much time. This DVD will erase itself in forty minutes. Just look at it.'

'Do you have hard copies or any other disc copies?'

'No, this is the only evidence. Please hurry.'

'Give it to me,' he said, stretching out his skinny arm.

'I'll take that.' A hand snatched it from her, the perpetrator moving with confident ease. The double doors to the dark boardroom were now wide open. He perched on the front of David Tuckett's desk, waving the DVD in his hand like Chairman Mao waving his little red book: Bukowski.

She could hardly breathe. He had toyed with her, assaulted her, killed John, and wanted her dead. He now had the only weapon she had against him. Bukowski smiled smugly as he addressed David.

'Thank you, David, for your cooperation. You will be receiving a number of highly prized news exclusives from us.'

'Glad to be of assistance, Mr Bukowski. We look forward to getting them.'

David rose. Open-mouthed with disbelief, Serena managed to speak. 'You're surely not going to let him stop you breaking the biggest news story of all time?'

'We don't use fabrication,' said David, frowning at her.

'It's all true. Look at the disc. Just read it …'

'Calm yourself, Serena,' Bukowski said. 'Dave's a happy man. The GNM empire, of which Channel One is the key player, will now receive the lion's share of our global twenty-billion-dollar advertising spend, as well as some editorial coups thrown in for good measure.'

'How can you walk out of here never knowing the truth?' she screamed at David. 'What if I'm right? Do you understand what this means? Hep S could kill millions. A whole generation of deformed babies will be born. All because *you* did nothing to stop it.'

David hesitated and looked at Bukowski, who shook his head very pointedly.

'She's a lying greenie militant, David. Gene-Asis is constantly under attack from people like her, with no understanding of the real science, of the rigorous testing we do. There is nothing but libellous material on this disc, I assure you.'

David nodded. 'I have things to do,' he said, leaving.

'No, you can't leave,' she pleaded. 'He tried to kill me. I'll die if you leave me here.'

She had got hold of David's shirtsleeve. He looked at Bukowski, a dark cloud crossing his face, his bushy eyebrows crinkled in a deep frown.

'Has she been threatened? She has the right to free speech.'

Bukowski stepped forward. Serena, terrified of him, let go of David's sleeve and moved away. Bukowski stood face to face with the editor. Shorter than David, he was still an intimidating presence.

'You have my word that she will come to no harm.'

'Of course,' said David, slapping Bukowski on the arm in camaraderie. Without another look at Serena, he left her to her fate, shutting the door behind him.

She backed away from Bukowski. 'Get away from me or I'll scream.'

'No, you won't. If you scream, you'll just make it worse.'

Unsure what to do, she halted her retreat and he began to circle her.

'You weren't very nice to Ben, were you?' He clicked his tongue, tutting at her. 'He's very angry. I can only imagine what he'd do to you if I let him near you but, fortunately for you, he's getting medical attention.'

He must have warned Bukowski I was coming here.

'So, is another killer waiting for me outside? Or are you man enough to do it yourself?' she challenged.

He stopped circling Serena and placed his face so close to hers that their noses almost touched. Despite trembling from head to toe, she defiantly stared back at him, refusing to blink. She would not give this man the satisfaction of seeing her fear.

'Serena, it's been fun, real fun,' he breathed, 'but I need to get back to the office. I have more important issues to attend to.'

'You won't get away with it. If not me, someone else will show you up for the lying, murderous bastard you are.'

He turned and folded his arms, shaking his head as if she were a naughty child he'd caught bunking off school.

'Did you really think a failed ad exec like you could succeed in causing the world's third-largest company even the remotest embarrassment? You, Serena, have been nothing but a minor – but very attractive – irritation.'

'And you're a sad fuck who can only get laid by drugging women!'

His eyes narrowed and jaw clenched. She expected him to strike her. Instead, he waved the DVD under her nose and whispered in her ear, so closely she could feel his hot breath on her neck.

'John suffered. Oh yes, he suffered. He died slowly and painfully. For what? This. His death is your fault.'

Serena swallowed a sob as his words stabbed her deeply.

Bukowski sauntered to the door.

'I'm telling the police everything,' she called after him.

'Go right ahead, Serena – you can't prove a thing. Not about Gene-Asis or myself. However,' he paused deliberately, his eyes disappearing in a sickening grin, 'within the next hour, the cops will have something they'll be keen to talk to you and Barry Flynn about.'

'What?' she barely managed to whisper.

He was about to open the door to leave.

'I no longer need to sully my hands with your death. You see, my good friends in the police will have you both locked up for the murder of John Flynn. No matter what you say about me, nobody will listen. How will you like prison, Serena?'

Chapter 63

Her legs threatened to buckle beneath her. All she could hear were the words 'John suffered. Oh yes, he suffered,' reverberating in her head like a screaming phantom. Bukowski had relished saying them, like a jealous lover lashing out. Bile rose in her throat as she realised that John's death had given him particular delight. The silence of Tuckett's office reinforced the emptiness she felt: she would never see John again, never tell him she loved him. It was too late. Her grief would overwhelm her if she allowed it free reign. She could feel it paralysing her limbs and mind. So, she concentrated on her anger: come what may, she was going to nail Bukowski for John's murder. She didn't have time to grieve – not now. And that bastard wasn't going to send her or Baz to jail either. No way.

Coming out of her introspection, she became aware of the noisy news-room buzz outside Tuckett's office and the security guard watching her. How long the man had been standing there, she didn't know.

'Miss, you have to leave now,' he said.

'It's okay, I'm leaving. No problem.'

She suspected Bukowski had already made his call to the police. She strode ahead of the guard, eager to get out of there as soon as possible.

In the foyer, the security guard called a cab for her.

'You wait here till it comes. Don't move.'

She gazed out to the car park, expecting to see police cars any minute. She toyed with the idea of bolting through the door and running for it but, just as she did so, a taxi pulled up. The passenger was paying the driver.

'I'll put you in that one but just wait a tick,' said the guard.

But Serena was now distracted by a Channel One newsbreak on the massive foyer monitor. Filling the whole screen was a photograph of John's smiling face, relaxed and happy. Each seat in the foyer had an accompanying headphone and she raced to use one.

'Police are concerned about the whereabouts of John Flynn, Chief Information Security Officer for one of Australia's leading banks. There are fears he has been kidnapped. He was last seen leaving the bank with an unidentified man. Surveillance cameras show him being forced into a car at gunpoint. Mr Flynn has access to highly confidential information regarding the bank's security systems. The police would like to question his brother, Barry Flynn, and Serena Swift.'

Photos of Baz and Serena appeared on screen. It was the one of her with red hair, from her fake driver's licence.

'Shit!'

She ran to the taxi. The security guard clocked her movement but not her face on screen. However, Dan the robot was programmed for facial recognition.

'Stop!' said Dan. 'Call 000.'

'Shut it, metal brain!' she snapped.

Before the guard could work out what was going on, she had dived into the cab's back seat, just as the passenger scrambled from the front.

'Coogee and fast,' she requested, keeping her face angled away from the Channel One building. She noticed the driver's smartphone mounted on the dashboard.

'Can I use your phone for a local call? I'm happy to pay.'

The driver gave her a surprised look but agreed.

'Baz?' she said.

She heard his laboured breathing. He was running.

'I went to the police and told them what you'd said. They said they'd look into it and I left. Then, a few minutes ago, they call me. Ask me weird questions, like I'm suspect or something.'

'Baz, we're being ...' She didn't want to spook the cabbie, so she hesitated.

'Framed? I know.' Baz completed her sentence in a heavy voice.

'Where are you?'

'I'm still in the city. I'm keeping moving. I know they can trace my location through this mobile.' He paused, his breathing heavy. 'Is he really dead?'

'Bukowski said so and ...' Serena glanced at the driver. She had to choose her words carefully. 'Baz, I'm using the taxi driver's phone.'

'I see.'

'Baz, I'm so sorry. I loved him, you know?'

'Don't use past tense. He could still be alive – he's a tough'un. We Flynns don't give up without a fight.'

He was asking her to give him hope but, in her heart, she doubted there was any. Serena looked at the driver, who appeared to be listening to an interview on ABC Radio. She lowered her voice. 'They're not on our side. Bukowski's got them in his pocket,' she said, meaning the police.

'So, we gotta hide. But where's safe?'

'Where would John go?'

'You think he may be hiding?' Baz's blind optimism was devastating.

'If he escaped, he could be. And he'd want us to find him.'

Baz had stopped panting, apparently standing still for a moment. 'I've tried Mum and Dad's, Uncle Dave, and Ric, his surfing buddy.'

'Where else?'

'Um, the beach, I guess. Lots of people.'

'You sure? It's so public.'

'No, I'm not sure but he loves the beach. There are caves in the cliffs. Maybe he's in one.'

'Right. I'll see you there and if you don't have a hat, get one to hide your face, and avoid security cameras. I'll see you at the southern end.'

The beach might not have surveillance cameras but the surrounding streets did.

Chapter 64

Baz was waiting in a shady spot on the beach, his suit jacket and shoes placed on a large boulder. He'd done his best to blend in. He nodded in her direction but didn't wave. Serena's large-brimmed hat sat low on her brow. It had cost her the last of the one hundred dollars Danielle had given her but it hid all her hair and most of her face. She'd been careful to look down, avoiding surveillance cameras. She gave Baz a big hug, like two friends enjoying the beach.

'Any sign of John?' asked Serena. She didn't expect a positive answer but felt her stomach twinge with anticipation.

Baz shook his head. 'Not yet. I've checked out the caves. No luck.'

They perched on a boulder, side by side, watching the hundreds of people enjoying an evening swim.

'Any news on the radio?' asked Serena. Baz had been listening to various bulletins on his Tbyte. They just repeated what they already knew: that the police wanted to question them.

'No.' He looked at her anxiously.

Then his Tbyte beeped with a message. It simply said, 'Look up'.

Both their heads shot up. On the boardwalk, leaning on the railings, was John. He lifted a finger to his lips. Serena's face glowed; John was alive! But neither said a word or hurried their stride as they casually strolled across the sand and up the steps. Serena was about to fling her arms around him when he held up his hands to keep them away.

'Act casual,' he said quietly. 'Let's walk.'

He turned in the direction of their unit and walked away. They followed. Baz couldn't resist giving him a pat on the back. 'We thought you were dead.'

John bent forward slightly, his face screwed up in pain.

'Go easy, Baz,' he replied. 'I think I've got a couple of broken ribs. They gave me a beating.' Serena noticed his normally strong stride was a little hesitant and that he held one arm across his chest. His mouth bore a livid cut and, although it was partially hidden by his sunnies, his right eye was bruised.

'Do you need a doctor?' she asked.

'No, I've had worse. Look, we don't have much time. There were cops watching the unit. I've sent them on a wild goose chase but it won't take long for them to work it out and come back. We've gotta take what we need and get out of here.'

Serena stretched out her hand to touch him, to know he was really there. She took his hand for a moment. 'You have no idea how good it is to see you.' She squeezed his fingers gently. 'Bukowski told me you were dead. I heard Ben order your execution. He said to make it look like an accident. So how did you …'

'Get away?' he anticipated. They were climbing the hill. John was finding it hard to get enough breath. 'Shit, it hurts to breathe.' But he continued walking. 'Why did we choose to live somewhere so hilly?' he joked.

'How *did* you get away?' asked Baz.

The hill was getting steeper and John was walking more slowly.

'Everyone has a price,' he replied. 'They beat me almost unconscious and then dragged me back to the flat. Going to drown me, head in the bath. Wanted to make it look like I'd been tortured for information about the bank. But I offered them money for my life. Enough that they could live like kings for the rest of theirs.'

'But Bukowski will have them killed.'

'Yeah, well; with a hundred million each, they were happy to disappear.'

Baz and Serena stopped in their tracks.

'How much? said Serena.

They were about to turn into their street. John peered around the corner. The police car hadn't returned.

'We'll take the back lane, to be safe.'

They followed him and Serena persisted, 'But a hundred million each? How?'

'I hacked my bank.'

'What?'

'It was that, or die.'

He opened the back gate and entered the small yard at the rear of their block. A neighbour's freshly washed clothes hung on the line, flapping in the breeze. They peered past it, to check for anyone lurking around the back door. Nothing. They entered the cool, dark interior of the Art Deco building and surveyed the stairwell. They pressed the timed light switch and climbed the stairs, entering their home. Everything looked perfectly normal except that the shoe stand at the door had been knocked over.

'How long have we got before the police come back?' Serena asked, removing her hat and sunnies.

John leaned against the wall, his loose shirt soaked with perspiration, breathing in short, painful gasps. 'Not long. I tapped into the police radio frequency, sending them to a home shooting that never happened.' He noticed the small cut under her eye. 'Who did this?'

'Ben Hartstone. Turns out he's Bukowski's hired gun.'

John shook his head. 'I knew he wasn't to be trusted.'

She removed his hand. 'If the police are coming back, we better get a move on. John, sit down for a second.' She led him to the lounge, where she drew the blinds so they couldn't be seen. Baz stood next to his brother.

'As I see it, Bukowski and the cops believe you're dead.' She looked at John. 'For now, let's keep it that way. The police are looking for Baz and me, so …'

At that moment, she noticed the answering machine was flashing. She looked at John and Baz questioningly, then nervously played it.

'Seri, how are you? We're all fine.' She smiled with relief at the sound of Keith's voice. Her family was safe. 'Can you call me?'

She dialled him straight away. 'Are you okay?' she asked.

'We're fine. Been a few guys hovering around the farm having a stickybeak but I shooed 'em off with me rifle.'

'And how's the baby? And Kerry?'

'Both good. They're still in the hospital.'

'Have you seen the news?'

'Yeah, saying John's been kidnapped or something. That true?'

'No, Keith, but I'm going to disappear for a while. I can't say any more but don't believe what they say about me on the news.'

Keith was the most level-headed person she knew; it took an awful lot to ruffle his feathers. 'Righteo,' he said. 'Before you go, I gotta read you this weird message from that London friend of yours. I won't say her name, you know, just in case. Anyway, where's the note?' Serena imagined Keith trying to find his glasses. 'Ah, here it is. So, she said and I quote, "All the evidence you need is on its way to my roses heaven. Check out the footage of you and me at your leaving party. Use it to nail them. Turns out I can't even trust my own rag. They won't print the story! So it's up to you. Love, Crazy Bird." I hope that makes sense to you?'

'Keith, you've just made my day.'

Serena knew exactly who Tracey's 'roses heaven' was: Joe Hosp, creative director of a London commercials production house called Devil Joe Productions. Tracey had met him through Serena. He and Tracey had had a very tumultuous relationship that lasted a year and they'd remained good friends.

Tracey had sent her documentary to Joe. It was in the guise of party footage taken at Serena's London leaving do. She must have beamed the documentary from her smartphone, via satellite, and placed it in the Rooneys' file, on the clients' server.

Ending the call, she yelled, 'Wahoooooo!'

'Good news?' asked John.

'Tracey has video footage. It's hidden on a production house's server. In London. Which means two things – Tracey is alive and we have evidence!'

'So we're back in the game.'

'Oh yes, we're back in the game, as long as my password hasn't expired.' Serena wondered if her Rooneys client server login still worked. Companies often forgot to change passwords when people left.

'Let's check,' said John, rising awkwardly and moving to his office.

Serena joined him, checking the street for anything unusual. She closed the blinds. 'We better make this quick.'

'So, we get this doco to the media and Gene-Asis is toast,' said Baz as he joined them.

'That's easier than it sounds,' she replied. 'Trace tells me she couldn't even get *The Post* to print the story.'

John grinned. She knew that look. He had an idea.

'We're going to New York.'

'But why?'

'First, we need to get out of Sydney. The police will hunt us down. In fact, I think we should get out of Australia altogether. Then we're out of jurisdiction. Second, the head office where this launch thing is happening, it's in New York, right?'

'Yes,' she responded, unsure where this was leading.

'If you can get me near the Gene-Asis head office, I can wreak havoc on their launch day.'

'How?'

'I'll tell you later, but let's get out of here.'

'Do we need to leave the country? Can't you hack Gene-Asis' HQ from here?' she asked.

'I could but it would take weeks. The launch is in two days, right?'

'Yes, on Wednesday.'

'Then the only sure-fire way to do it is if I am right next to the building where the launch shindig is happening.'

'But what if we're on the airport watch list?'

'Doesn't matter. We're travelling as Sarah and Ray Bradley.' He pulled two Australian passports from his desk drawer and two eTicket printouts. Serena studied her passport. A blonde Serena stared back at her from the pages, under the name of Sarah Bradley.

'Dare I ask who Sarah Bradley is?'

'Best not.'

'But how did you get these?'

'I had a friend prepare them, just in case. He's the best forger I know. Sarah's real, by the way; we've just changed the photo.' He took them back. 'I always like a plan B.'

'But you told me forging a passport is really hard.'

'It is and it takes time, much longer than the driver's licence we got you. I commissioned these weeks ago.'

'Won't using your credit card tip them off? For the tickets, I mean.'

John smiled crookedly. 'One of the gentlemen I told you about earlier was so thrilled with his newfound wealth, he decided to buy us two tickets to New York. Somehow, I don't think he's going to report an unauthorised transaction on his card, do you?'

Serena laughed.

'But wait, there's more,' John was now laughing too. 'It's the Dreamliner. So it's non-stop to New York. And business class, too.'

'You know, you are a genius, after all!' said Serena.

'I'm coming with you,' said Baz, interjecting.

John looked at his younger brother. 'Baz, it's better you don't. I'm looking at life in prison if I'm caught and Seri won't fare much better. I want to keep you out of this.'

'But I'm already an accessory. I helped Seri get the job.'

John shook his head. 'True, but we'll both say you had no idea what that was all about. With a good lawyer, your sentence would be minimal. So, go up the coast, hire a car and find a holiday house somewhere remote. Use cash. Just keep a low profile till this all blows over.'

Baz opened his mouth to protest again. John used his ace card. 'Mum and Dad would never forgive me if I dragged you into this. I'm the black sheep, remember?'

Baz nodded reluctantly and left.

John got Serena into the Devil Joe Productions' website. 'Tap in your login.'

She did as he asked and was straight into the client server. Her old password still worked. 'We're in business,' she said, 'Bukowski will be completely blindsided. He won't know what's hit him.'

Chapter 65

Their flight was at midday the following day, which meant they would arrive in New York late afternoon on Tuesday. The New Dawn launch was on Wednesday. They booked into a small airport motel under their false names and John set up his workstation. He wanted to be sure that Sarah and Ray Bradley's passports weren't on any watch lists. The owners of the identities had sold their passports for cash, never intending to use them. But there was a remote chance they might panic and call the authorities.

While he did that, Serena keyed in her Rooneys password. On the server was a near-final cut of a Rimmel commercial, a series of Sainsbury's commercials and, in the 'Social' file, a video file called 'Serena's leaving do'. She saw herself and Tracey, arm-in-arm, bleary-eyed and very drunk, at her leaving party in London a few months ago. She stopped the footage.

'This is it,' she said. 'I just need to find the doco hidden behind it.'

John paused what he was doing and looked across at her. 'How do you know about steganography?'

'One of the creatives in London was really into that sort of thing. He showed me how it worked. At least we know Tracey is alive,' she added, nodding at the image frozen on screen.

'At least she was when she satellite-beamed it to the server,' John said, looking concerned. Serena downloaded the file to her hard drive, and then, using decoding software, extracted the hidden documentary.

The Genesis Flaw

Behind the party footage lay a thirty-four-minute unedited documentary that Tracey had titled *The Genesis Flaw*. Eager to view it, Serena speedily reloaded the party footage onto the server, having removed all evidence of the documentary. She didn't want a casual observer to notice anything odd about the file, nor did she want to raise suspicions by deleting it.

'I'm impressed,' commented John. 'I'll make a hacker of you yet.' He nodded at her laptop screen as his smile faded. 'I want to see this.' He drew the curtains.

With heart racing, Serena pressed 'Play.' Tracey's documentary started.

Images of Zimbabweans came and went in rapid succession, like bullets to the brain. Still, wax-like faces stared dully at the camera. Neither Serena nor John spoke. Both sat with necks craned forwards, listening intently. Serena had imagined she knew what to expect. She had read Dr McPherson's descriptions of the deformities and sicknesses but they had just been words and statistics. Now she saw people crying in distress. Now she saw people screaming in agony. Now she saw the death and despair. She was horrified to her core.

John once or twice ran both hands over his face and then removed them, returning his stunned gaze to the screen. Serena's mouth opened to speak and then closed again, her eyes were wide with shock. As the unfinished documentary suddenly ended, they both stared at the blank screen, speechless. Finally, John slumped forwards, resting his face in his hands.

'How could they?' he muttered.

'Those poor, poor people.'

They sat in the darkened room, the curtains drawn, trying to cope with the distressing images they'd seen.

'What kind of evil are we up against, Serena?'

'A powerful one,' she replied.

'Yeah. That's the bit I'm worried about. If they can keep this quiet, they can do anything.'

'Don't give up. We can do it, John. We can outwit them. Everything we need to bring them down is right here. And you can hack into anything; you're the best there is.'

'I can't believe they went ahead anyway, selling that shit. Jeez, we've probably eaten it ourselves.'

'I don't want to think about it.'

John prowled the room like a caged animal. 'How do they sleep at night? Don't they feel guilt, feel anything? All those people with hep S. The fuckers killed Kat.' He kicked the wardrobe door, cracking it. It caused him pain and he hugged his ribcage. She reached out to touch him. 'Oh, John, don't do this. We have to stay focused.'

He calmed himself. 'You're right. If I can transfer 200 million from a bank and hide it so it'll take them days to realise it's gone, I can screw up the Gene-Asis launch.' John's eyes were cold and hard. 'It's time someone knocked the halo off their fucking heads.'

Chapter 66

That night, they slept fitfully, in each other's arms. In the morning, Serena had woken first, and lay there watching him, wondering if this was the right time to tell him how she felt. Then she'd woken him with a cup of coffee, ready at last to express her feelings. But John had leapt out of bed to again check that their borrowed identities hadn't appeared on any watch lists. Now was clearly not the time. She went to the bathroom and changed her hair colour from red to the strawberry blonde of her passport photo. The result wasn't bad, for a bottle of hair colourant. At the airport, they endured the rigours of full body X-rays, as well as those of their carry-on baggage, but were never challenged.

The flight to Kennedy Airport was uneventful and they slept most of the way. The clank of the breakfast trolley woke Serena. Her neck ached. John's head rested on a small pillow wedged against the window. He was fast asleep. She watched him for a moment: the dark eyelashes, the greying at his temples and the line of his lips. She remembered the night he'd kissed her. It had been at her leaving party, the night before she moved to London. Friends and neighbours had filled the house. Multicoloured lights were strung up around the verandah, the dining table was laden with food and the punch had been a big hit. Dad had made a speech about how proud he was of his successful daughter and how much he would miss her. Alcohol flowed and she'd drunk her fill. The party was in full swing when John had taken her hand, and led her away from the house and down to the creek. She'd been stunned when he'd kissed her and even more stunned by her eager response. She'd kissed him back, pushing her body into his. He'd held her tighter. His desire had been too intense for her and she'd pulled away.

'Why now, John? When I'm leaving?' She'd taken a step back.

'I've been wanting to for a long time but I ...' he began and then saw her rub the back of her hand across her mouth. He must have mistaken the gesture for one of disgust, as if she'd been wiping away his kiss. To this day, she didn't know why she'd done it but it hadn't been in disgust. That kiss had been the best one she'd ever had.

'I'm just not good enough for you, is that it?' he'd said, furious.

'No, John, I'm confused. We've been friends for so long and I'm going away tomorrow. I ...'

'Forget it. Forget it ever happened.'

He'd stormed off. By the time she'd returned to the party, John had his tongue down Sharon Glessop's throat. It was well known that Sharon wanted to get her hands on John and that she hated Serena because of her close friendship with him. Serena's guests stared at her, watching her reaction, and she couldn't bear the humiliation. She'd started dancing and put on a good show of indifference, but she'd felt totally humiliated and hurt. Shortly after, John had left the party with Sharon in tow, who was smirking triumphantly.

Serena stretched out her hand and, without thinking, ran her finger along his lower lip. She barely touched it but he woke.

'Hey,' he said groggily.

'Breakfast,' she said, softly.

After some food, coffee and a bottle of water, she was wide awake. John ate silently, deep in thought.

'John?'

'Uh-huh.'

'I'm sorry I never read your emails or took your calls.'

He opened his eyes wide and his lips parted slightly in astonishment. He shuffled into a more upright position.

'I'm sorry I hurt you.' He spoke quietly and carefully. Serena had never wanted to speak about that night before and he clearly didn't want to muck it up.

Serena leaned closer. 'The kiss was lovely, too lovely. It scared me. I was shocked by my own feelings. And then you went off with Sharon. I felt so humiliated.'

The flight attendant leaned over them, offering tea. Serena shook her head. They waited till she'd moved further down the aisle. John undid his seatbelt, and turned his body towards her and took her hand.

'I was a prick, I know. I took Sharon home to hurt you and, God, I regretted it. It's just, well, it had taken me years to build up enough courage for that kiss.'

'Years?'

'Yes. We'd been best mates for so long, I didn't know how to change it.' He paused and then tilted his head to one side. 'You never read any of my emails, did you?'

She shook her head. 'I was too angry. I deleted every one.'

'Shit.' He half-smiled. 'I spent hours composing them, trying to explain. And you know what? The very thing I'd been afraid of – that if I kissed you, our friendship would never be the same – well, that's exactly what happened. That night, I lost my best mate.'

Serena undid her seatbelt and turned to him. Their faces were barely a few centimetres apart.

'More coffee?' asked another flight attendant.

'No,' they said in unison.

'You haven't lost your best mate,' said Serena. 'No way. And who knows? When this is all over, maybe we can try that kiss again?'

He smiled mischievously. 'Why not now?'

'I don't want to get it wrong this time,' she replied, smiling.

He laughed loudly. 'I can wait,' he said, settling back into his seat.

Serena retrieved her bag from the overhead locker and made her way to the bathroom, where she changed into smart black trousers, black boots and a pale pink polo-necked jumper. The smarter they looked at passport control, the less likely it was they'd be stopped and questioned. Inspecting her face in the mirror, she realised the cut on her cheek had bruised badly, so she applied a thick layer of foundation to conceal it.

She returned to her seat and handed him her foundation. 'Try covering up the bruise. A black eye kinda draws attention.'

'I can't believe I'm doing this,' he said, staring at the tube of make-up. But on his return from the toilet, his black eye was well hidden. John leaned over to speak and grimaced.

'How're the ribs?' she asked.

'Maybe they're not broken, just bruised.' He lowered his voice. 'I've been thinking about our plan.'

'Yeah?'

'I've worked out how to stop their media presentation and run Tracey's footage instead. That's no problem. I'll need to do some shopping when we land 'cause I need to build something. That's easy enough, but my main problem will be cracking the encryptions in time.'

'Well, we've got a Plan B but I'd do anything to avoid it,' said Serena.

'If it comes to Plan B, I'll do it, not you,' said John.

'Let's just hope there's no need.'

They lapsed into silence, Serena staring out at the dark sky outside. Their problems would begin once they landed. If Bukowski had planted convincing evidence, the Australian Police might call on the NYPD. With their photos in circulation, they stood no chance.

'Bukowski will be landing about now,' she said, touching John's arm. 'I know because I booked his pilot. I guess I got something out of my time as his PA. His private jet lands half an hour before we do. There's a risk he'll see us.'

John shut his laptop and ran his hand over the top of its smooth surface. His second laptop was in the seat pocket in front of him.

'Don't worry. He'll be whisked through passport control way ahead of us. He'll be in his limo, on his way to a hotel, before we even get on the ground.'

They were scheduled to land at 5 pm and it was pitch-black outside, apart from the snow, which blew at a low angle. Having expected to see the bright lights of New York City below, Serena could see nothing through the white flecks. The plane circled the airport for twenty minutes. Then she saw the runway lights, looking like a smudged painting. The engines roared as the pilot struggled to slow the enormous plane on the icy runway. Specks of snow now flew horizontally by her window as they taxied to the gate.

'I'm going to freeze. My winter gear isn't warm enough,' said John, looking out of the window.

The plane stopped, but the seatbelt sign remained on and the flight attendants stayed seated. Several passengers stood up and were told to remain in their seats. But, like a Mexican wave, passengers standing at the front of the plane prompted others further back to stand. Once again, the purser asked everyone to remain seated. The captain had not given the order to open the doors. Why? What were they waiting for? Serena glanced at John.

'What's going on?' she whispered.

'I've no idea. Maybe there's a problem with the door.'

He squeezed her hand reassuringly. From where Serena sat, she could only glimpse the purser when she stood in the aisle. Otherwise, passengers' heads obscured her view. Now two flight attendants opened the massive doors at the front of the plane and two New York cops in dark-blue uniforms stepped inside. They consulted with the purser, and began walking down the aisle towards Serena and John.

Her stomach did a somersault and she held John's hand tighter. Had the Australian police tipped off the New York police about their flight? The cops strode towards them, a buzz of whispers following like a swarm of bees, as intrigued passengers speculated. The first cop looked at the number above Serena's seat. She dared not look at him. John turned his head and smiled at the man. A second's pause and both cops continued walking towards the tail section. They'd simply been checking the seat numbers.

Craning her neck, Serena saw them leaning over a man in an aisle seat. She could hear voices, and then shouting: 'I've done nothing. Get your hands off me, pigs!' The man was yanked from his seat and handcuffed, while he swore repeatedly. The cops then steered him back down the aisle and out of the plane. 'Thank God,' was all Serena could say as she released John's crushed hand. The instant the police left, the seatbelt sign went off and everyone stood up.

John and Serena followed the flow of passengers down the escalators, into passport control. The enormous space was filled with people and the heating was on overdrive. On one side were ten meandering lanes of people queuing as non-US citizens. On the other side one lane of US citizens walked quickly through passport control. Serena nervously looked for Bukowski but he wasn't in the queue.

'Want one?' asked John, offering her a mint.

'Thanks,' she said, taking one, her eyes darting back to the US citizens line.

'He won't recognise you even if he does see you. You look so completely different as a blonde. Don't worry.'

They filled in their green visa waiver cards as they shuffled along at a snail's pace. A beagle was led up and down the queues, sniffing the carry-on luggage. Serena watched it bark and sit in front of a girl's daypack. Embarrassed, the girl shook her head and then, finally, nodding in recognition, opened her pack to produce a banana, which the security officer confiscated, patting the dog and rewarding him with a treat.

They were now just three people away from the line of twenty booths, which resembled sentry posts. Each booth was surrounded by glass, except for the space where the visitor stood to hand over their passport. There was a narrow desk counter, upon which rested what appeared to be a mini lightbox. Serena watched as a man placed his left hand on the lightbox. It lit up with a red glow. He then did the same with his right hand. The officer checked the fingerprint scans against those on his computer and then nodded the visitor through.

'Have you seen what they're doing?'

'Yup, pretty spooky. It's like they have your soul on file.'

'Yes, but my prints won't match Sarah Bradley's,' she whispered.

'Oh yes they will,' John replied. 'Why do you think forging passport identities takes so long?' She nodded.

It was their turn. Serena went first, walking up to booth six. She handed over her passport and visa waiver card.

'Where're you staying?' the officer asked, as he checked the photograph in her passport. He swiped the passport through a reader.

'Hotel DeVere in Greenwich Village.'

'Business or pleasure?' he said, not looking up as he checked her visa waiver card.

'Pleasure.'

'Ma'am, can you place your left hand on the box and wait until I ask you to remove it.'

Serena hoped he didn't see her swallow the lump in her throat. He scanned her left and then her right hand. The box felt warm and her hand left a sweaty nervous residue on the smooth, glassy surface. Serena focused on trying to look relaxed and confident but the heat and tension were getting to her. The customs officer paused. He turned on his swivel chair and looked hard at her.

'You need to update your passport, ma'am.'

'I do?' she stammered. Without thinking, she touched her hair. It was blonde, so what was the problem?

'Any defining marks, such as the scar on your face, must be noted in your passport.'

'Oh, thank you. I'll get it updated.'

He returned her passport. She was through, closely followed by John. They had arrived safely on American soil.

John bought a thick coat, paying in cash. As they walked out of the building into the freezing cold, Serena pulled her coat collar tight and her hat down over her ears. Snow fell in gusts, forming dirty, mushy heaps on the ground. There was a constant flurry of activity as snow ploughs worked to keep the roads clear. Cars, double-parked, honked at each other as airport staff shouted at them to drive on. The pavement was like slippery glass in patches, despite efforts to keep it ice-free with sand and grit. Serena stepped carefully in the direction of a taxi rank, blinking rapidly as her eyes watered in the intense cold.

The rank was to their right. There were only eight people waiting and yellow cabs arrived pretty regularly, directed by a man in an airport uniform, blowing a whistle every few seconds. They joined the queue.

To their left was a mini-van, illegally parked, with two wheels up on the kerb. As they shuffled forward, the driver pulled away. A black limo with darkly tinted windows was parked on the other side of the road, and a chauffeur was holding the door open for a man in a long tailored black woollen coat, buttoned to his neck, with a cream cashmere scarf tucked in his collar. He nodded at the chauffeur and got inside the limo.

'Oh no,' Serena breathed. 'Bukowski.'

John hadn't heard her. She grabbed at his arm and pulled him out of the queue.

'What are you doing?' he asked.

'That was Bukowski. I'd rather wait till he's gone.'

She was trying to keep her panic under control.

They walked away arm in arm, heads bowed against the chill, back into the arrivals section.

'Did he see us?' Serena asked, once they were inside.

'No, no way. Rugged up like this, he couldn't possibly recognise us.'

'It's just … when I see him, I remember that night,' she said, her voice trailing off.

'I can't even begin to imagine what this must be like for you,' he said, 'but if we get this right, that'll be the last time you ever have to be near that bastard.'

She smiled. 'You're right. I mustn't let him rattle me.'

They rejoined the taxi queue and, within a few minutes, were inside the damp interior of a yellow cab. The plastic flooring was wet and the warm air smelled like wet dog fur. The driver's head never moved as he asked them, 'Where to?'

'Hotel DeVere, Greenwich Village, please,' said Serena.

The driver nodded and drove off.

John spoke softly so that only she could hear. 'Seri, I said we had to be in a hotel no more than a kilometre away from their building, with uninterrupted views. Greenwich Village is no good.'

'Trust me,' she said. 'There's a reason.'

They spent the rest of the ride gazing out of the steamed-up windows at the houses and parked cars covered in snow, at the Williamsburg Bridge, and at the skyscrapers, which towered above them like enormous tombstones. Both were aware that valuable time was ticking by.

Getting out at the DeVere Hotel, they waited for the driver to leave. Whistling loudly, Serena hailed another cab, asking for the Times Tower Hotel, Times Square.

'Clever,' commented John, nodding. 'We'll be harder to follow. But why the Times Tower?'

'Because it's the tallest hotel in New York and the top twenty floors will give us an uninterrupted view of the Gene-Asis building. How does that suit you?' she said, smiling.

'It suits me very well. As soon as we're there, I'll get to work. Which reminds me, I need a few things.'

The Genesis Flaw

For the rest of the journey, John was on the phone ordering a strange assortment of gadgets. He then pulled from his laptop bag a mini telescope.

'What do you need a telescope for?' she asked, as he placed it in front of his eye.

'I'm gonna spy me a CEO.'

Chapter 67

They pulled up outside the Times Tower as it stopped snowing. A red carpet, slightly soggy from snowy footprints, tumbled down the stone steps, just short of the icy pavement. The cab door was opened by a bellboy in a thick, gold-embroidered bottle-green cape, heavy black boots and a peaked gold-embroidered cap.

'Good evening,' he almost sang. Then he danced to the back of the cab to grab their bags.

'Now, this I like! I love guests who travel light!' he said, as he picked up their hand luggage and led them into the stunning foyer with cream marble floors, backlit onyx ceiling and a central water feature resembling a waterfall encircled with glass.

'Have a great day!' he said, returning to the bitterly cold outside steps. He began singing along in perfect harmony to 'Moon River', which was playing on the speakers at the front of the hotel.

John requested a room on one of the top twenty floors, facing Broadway. 'No problem. May I have your credit card, please?'

'We're paying cash.'

The receptionist, whose nose was red and sore due to a cold, looked at him as if he were from another planet.

'I'm sorry, sir, but we have to take your credit card details, for additional expenses like the minibar.'

'Well, can we pay for two nights in advance and give you a passport as security?' he asked, checking his watch.

The Genesis Flaw

'Certainly. Thank you, Mr and Mrs Bradley, you're in room 70201.'

The room was a small box, with twin beds and an en suite bathroom, and a computer dock, keyboard and screen. Serena threw herself onto one of the duck-down, quilted bedspreads.

Holding back one of the thick curtains, John stared out of the floor-to-ceiling windows.

'Is that it?' he asked.

Serena dragged herself off the bed and stood next to him. Before her stretched New York City: glittering lights glinting in the dark. To her right, she could see the dazzling illuminated billboards of One Times Square and the curved NASDAQ building, like a castle turret, brightly lit with blue and green advertising messages. Traffic crawled along Broadway and Seventh Avenue, like lines of ants forming a chain. Looking diagonally across Duffy Square, she saw Two Times Square, with its electronic billboards, piled one on top of the other, flashing and gyrating advertisements for Coca-Cola, HSBC, Samsung and Chrysler. It was like the Tower of Babel, clambering up to the heavens, offering God a Diet Coke and a bank account.

But the most imposing building of all was the one on the corner of West 46th and Seventh, where the Times Square Visitors Center used to be. Serena had instantly recognised the Gene-Asis global head office. It spiralled upwards, like a giant double helix, twisting its way into the sky, the rungs in the middle forming the floors. All 120 floors were of black glass, which reflected, like a giant mirror, the flashing multicoloured lights of Times Square. Its exterior only revealed the building's secrets on those floors where the lights were switched on. She had never seen a structure like it.

'Holy shit! That's something else,' John said.

'You're telling me. I can't believe they managed to build a twisting structure like that. And so high,' said Serena, shuddering at the sinister way the building dominated Times Square and, indeed, Manhattan itself; its predominantly black exterior in harsh contrast to the bright, colourful playfulness of Times Square and the theatre district.

'I'll get set up,' said John.

'What can I do?' asked Serena.

'Order strong black coffee and a burger for me. It's going to be a long night.'

'Whatever you want, maestro.' She placed the order, times two.

As John set up both his laptops, Serena considered her role in their back-up plan if he failed to hack the system. It was nothing short of suicidal. To distract herself, she turned on the TV and channel-surfed. Tomorrow's Gene-Asis launch was on every news bulletin.

John took the telescope and looked out of the window.

'Good, it's cleared,' he said, nodding at the sky. 'So, which is Bukowski's office?'

'Very top floor. It'll be a corner office,' she said, moving to join him.

John placed the mini telescope to his eye and scanned the top floor. 'Some white-haired guy; nah, that's not him. Okay, hold on. No, that can't be him, unless he's had a sex change. Here we go … Yes, there's the piece of shit. Perfect, just where I want you, Bukowski.' John looked at Serena. 'He's practising the presentation. Take a look.'

He handed her the telescope. In the clear night sky, Bukowski's luxurious corner office shone like a beacon. She was amazed she could see into the building so clearly. She saw a laptop on the desk and Bukowski pacing the room, speaking to a projected image on the wall. She could even discern the words: 'Supercrop Ultra', 'Bruise-free Fruit' and 'Long-life Meat'.

'Yes, that's the launch presentation. So, how are you going to do this without being detected?'

'They won't know what's hit them till it's too late,' he replied. 'The first thing I need to do is own the computer that'll run the presentation, which we now know to be Bukowski's.'

'What do you mean by "own?"' Serena asked.

'Sorry, Seri … I have to compromise his computer so I've got full control of it. Then I "own" it.'

'I get it. And you need some equipment to do that?'

'Yes, the stuff I've ordered is to build a Wi-Fi sniper rifle.'

'What do you mean by "rifle"?' said Serena, alarmed.

There was a knock at the door – the waiter with the coffee and burgers. John poured himself a steaming cup, no milk, and took a sip. Serena loaded up sugar in hers.

'Damn. They make coffee hot here,' he said, touching his burnt upper lip.

The Genesis Flaw

Serena crossed her arms. 'John, I want to broadcast this documentary and expose Gene-Asis but I don't want to kill anyone. No rifles, okay?'

'Relax. This rifle allows me to pinpoint and control Bukowski's laptop and the projector. It uses radio waves, working up to a kilometre away, but I need to point it directly at the target – hence, the location of this room is perfect. We're, what, only half a k away from their building?' He took a big bite of his burger.

'So, tell me what you're going to do,' she asked, ploughing into her own burger. She was famished.

'I have to knock Bukowski off the network. I'll get onto their wireless network and then I'll launch a DOS attack against his laptop.' He noticed Serena raise her eyebrows, as her cheeks bulged with food. 'You look like a startled hamster,' he said, smiling.

Serena's mouth was too full to protest.

'Okay,' he continued, 'a DOS is a denial-of-service attack. I'm gonna use an exploit framework tool I have. In it will be numerous DOS attacks. It's a case of firing one off, seeing if it works, if not, trying the next one, and so on. Different attacks work on different computers, you see. I'll know when one's worked because I'll see his laptop drop off the network.'

Serena swallowed. 'But won't access to the Gene-Asis network have some kind of password?'

'I'll crack the crypto key … the password needed to connect to the wireless access point. Then I'm on their network and I win.'

Serena grinned. 'Of course you will.'

A piercing ringtone made them both jump. John answered the room's phone and asked for the delivery to be brought up. A number of boxes arrived on a trolley pushed by a teenage bellboy, who eyed them inquisitively.

'Metal sculptures. We just had to buy them.'

'Yes, sir,' he said, beating a hasty retreat.

John laid out the contents of the unmarked boxes on the carpet: various pieces of scrap metal, a number of cable ties and gaffer tape, a Yagi antenna, a pigtail connector, wiring, batteries, a radioshack adapter plug, something that looked like an electrical circuit board inside two pieces of plastic, and a tripod, similar to those used by photographers.

'If I had a welder and a drill, I could make this look really professional. You know, make it look like a real rifle. But drilling holes in metal kinda makes too much noise, so I'll have to make do with the gaffer tape and cable ties. It'll still work fine.'

'Have you ever made one before?'

'Oh yeah; learned how to at the DefCon hacking conference years back – Las Vegas, I think. Desert conditions are great for long-distance hacking,' he replied, starting to put the rifle together. 'When it's built, I'll hook it up to my laptop so we can see in real time whatever it picks up.'

Serena watched as John constructed something that, to her eye, looked very like a real rifle except it had a cable linking it to one of his laptops.

'Is he still practising?' asked John.

She looked through the telescope. 'Yes, he's a perfectionist, but you'd better get a wriggle on, just in case he gets tired or something.'

She pulled up a chair to sit behind John and leaned forward, cupping her chin in her hand. 'Bukowski won't notice he's been knocked off the network?'

'I'm only going to do a quick test tonight, to be sure I can do it tomorrow for the launch – timing is everything. For now, I'll be so fast he won't notice and, besides, if he does, he'll think it's just another bloody network glitch.' He looked up at her. 'It's ready. Let's test this little beauty,' he said, moving to the window. He moved the rifle around until he had the antenna pointing at Bukowski's office.

'Serena, can you hold this here? I'll tighten the tripod when I know we've got it right.' John sat in front of the screen. Serena took the rifle with one hand, and with the other, held the telescope to her eye to check on Bukowski. He was thanking the key players. 'Randolph J. Randolph,' she read aloud. 'He's getting near the end.'

'Who?' asked John.

'That's the President of R and D.'

'That can't be his real name?' John asked, smirking.

'Sure is.'

'Parents must have hated him. Can you move the rifle a little to the left?'

She did as she was asked.

'Bingo. Now, can you tighten the tripod so the antenna won't move?'

John cracked his knuckles and placed his fingertips lightly on the laptop's keyboard, like a concert pianist about to perform.

'Okay, let's grab the crypto key first.'

He placed headphones over his ears to shut out the rest of the world. The music must have been loud, as Serena could catch occasional bursts from where she sat. She watched the screen over his shoulder. Bright green numbers, letters and symbols, on a black background, all meaningless to her, flowed down the screen like rain down a pane of glass. She resumed watching Bukowski through the telescope. She breathed a sigh of relief to see him start the whole presentation again.

'Got it,' shouted John after twenty-five minutes. He removed his headphones. 'I'm into the Gene-Asis network. Now I have to find Bukowski. This is the easy bit.' He didn't bother replacing his headphones while he searched.

'Right. Now for the DOS. I've got a 0-day I can try. Gene-Asis uses a software package that's vulnerable to a particular DOS attack and the supplier hasn't patched it. In fact, I don't think this supplier knows about the problem yet. I certainly haven't alerted them, so I'm hoping this could be how I bounce Bukowski off the network.' A minute later, he was punching the air.

'God, I'm good,' he crowed, laughing. 'One shot, one kill! I've knocked him off the network!'

Serena had the telescope pointing at Bukowski. 'He noticed. He's thrown his remote across the room.'

'Shit!' said John, immediately breaking the connection. 'What's he doing now?'

'The presentation is back up. It's all fine.'

'Good; now we wait till Bukowski stops using the projector.'

'That could be a while.'

'Nothing we can do. In the meantime, let's work out where the projector is likely to be tomorrow.'

'The auditorium, on the 119th floor,' she replied. 'I've done some homework.'

Fifty minutes later, Bukowski finished his runthrough and left the office. This time, Serena knew what to do. She moved the antenna to point at the correct floor, until she found the projector. Then she watched John send a test – a Gene-Asis logo – to the projector to demonstrate he had control over it. It worked perfectly.

'If anyone sees this image, they'll just think it's a legit test,' John commented. 'So, that's it! We're in business,' he continued, giving her a big high five.

'We can do better than that,' said Serena, kissing him.

Moments passed before John whispered, 'So that thing about waiting till …'

'Forget about it,' she replied, kissing him again.

Chapter 68

Serena had difficulty waking John. Eventually, he opened one bloodshot eye.

'I need some water. Too much coffee,' he groaned. 'And some painkillers.'

Serena drew back the curtains as John got up. The sky was blue and a weak sun shone, but the roads, pavements and roofs were still covered in snow and ice. Flags on rooftops flapped furiously in the one direction, buffeted by a strong wind. John plonked himself sleepily at the desk, a water bottle in hand. Then he began to repeat the steps he had followed last night.

'What?' he said.

Instantly wide awake, he tapped in a command. The screen remained blank. He scratched his head and then continued to input commands frantically.

'Oh, shit.'

'John? What's wrong?'

He raced to the Wi-Fi antenna and moved it so it pointed at a building, one that was next door to Gene-Asis' HQ. Instantly, a stream of data appeared on screen.

'Fuck,' he said, hitting the desk. 'We're fucked.'

'What's going on? Tell me.'

'Gimme a second … I need to think this through. They must have surrounded the whole building with some kind of RF Shield – it's the only explanation. It wasn't there last night. Shit! They must've turned it on this morning to stop intruders. Fuck, fuck, fuck! Why didn't I think of that?' John paced the tiny room. 'Maybe I triggered something last night or maybe they don't want journos transmitting the Gene-Asis presentation live to their OB units. This RF shield prevents any signals from transmitting into or out of the building.'

'So you can't communicate with Bukowski's laptop or the projector?'

'I can't do a damned thing. We were all set to go earlier – I had complete control of the projector. But now they're shielding emissions, I can't control a thing,' he said, flinging his arms wide.

'John, please sit down,' Serena said, taking him by the arm and leading him to the bed. 'We go to Plan B.'

'No, Serena. That's too dangerous. I'll try emailing it to the journos attending today. Surely one of them will have enough guts to publish it?'

'John, we've been through this. It's not going to happen. What did Tracey say? She couldn't even get *The Post* to print it. I couldn't get Channel One to take the story. They all need Gene-Asis' advertising revenue. It doesn't matter how much the journos want to print it, it's not up to them.'

John rubbed his tired eyes.

'All right then, we put it on *YouTube*. Forget the media. We'll rely on public outrage.'

'It'll be taken off *YouTube* before you know it. Anyway, I want Bukowski to experience the public humiliation first hand. It's got to be at the launch.'

'Then one of us has to be inside the Gene-Asis building and that's far too dangerous.'

'I'm going to get this footage running at the Gene-Asis launch, whatever it takes. Now, tell me what I have to do.'

'God, Serena,' he said, shaking his bent head, 'their security will be impenetrable today. We just can't do it.'

'We can and I'm doing it.'

Serena's lips were clenched and her hands in tight fists. She had a look of grim determination that John recognised.

'You're not going inside,' he said.

'I am. I started this and I'll finish it. And I need you here. You might still be able to breach the shield. You need to stay here and do what you do best.'

'Someone will recognise you. They'll have spy-eyes checking every face entering the foyer, as well as biometric testing for every guest. You'll never get through.'

'How about the back of the building?'

'How do you mean?'

'They've gone all out on the catering for this. They're bringing in some of the top chefs in New York. All the food is made using Supercrop Ultra products. I've seen the invitations. And they've contracted a catering company for their waiting staff called ... what was their name? I was mistakenly copied in to an email about it. Something French, like "Par Excellence". Yes, that's it. So, that's how I get in: I become one of their waitresses.'

'That could work. All the security focus will be on the main entrance where the guests arrive. The caterers won't get anywhere near as much attention.'

'I need you to work your hacking magic and get my name on their waiting staff list for today's event.'

'And what if I say no, I won't do it?'

'Then I'll try another way.'

John shook his head. He took a large gulp of water, hacked into the Par Excellence server and altered the running sheets to include Sarah Bradley as a silver service waitress, and then added some fake references to her file. The sheets told her she needed to be at the catering company's HQ in the West Village at 8.30 am, to pick up her security pass, uniform and instructions.

'I haven't got long,' she said.

'I know. If they say they can't find your social security number, just tell them there's a mistake and you'll sort it out later. The person in charge won't have time to muck about with your pay details.'

'No worries. Now, remind me of the building layout and how to run the documentary.'

In a few seconds, John had the layout of the 119th floor on screen.

'Here is the auditorium, which seats 600 people. Because of the spiral shape of the building, the seating forms a complete circle; a bit like a mini football stadium. In the middle, in the ceiling, is the 3D holographic projector. It will project images in this central space, twelve metres wide by ten metres high. It's awesome technology,' John enthused.

'So where are the controls for the projector?'

'The controls are here in the roof above the auditorium. I hope you're not frightened of heights. You'll need to climb up this ladder into the roof space. When you're up there, you'll be able to walk but only hunched over, as the space is pretty narrow. The floor is solid, so you won't fall through or anything. They might have this ladder guarded but the roof space is our only option, as we need you right next to the projector. If you don't get near enough, the image you project will be very weak and fuzzy, and people may not be able to hear the footage properly.'

'What do I do when I'm in there?'

'Can you pass me your smartphone?' She did so. 'I'll pre-program it to intercept Bukowski's signal and tell the projector to run our doco. All you have to do is turn it on and press this command key.' He pointed.

'Where is the big feast taking place?'

'On the same floor. The other half of the floor is set up for corporate entertainment, with the kitchens over here,' he said, pointing at the screen. 'You'll enter via the ground-floor deliveries entrance, at the back of the building on West 46th. There is a service lift, which will be programmed only to open on the ground floor and the 119th floor, so no one can snoop around.'

'What if something goes wrong and I can't get the handheld to work?'

'It will work, Serena. I promise you. But to ease your mind, we can have a Plan C. I'll copy the documentary onto this memory key. You can always try handing it to one of the journalists, if all else fails.'

John held a silver ring with a rectangular black stone, inlaid with a metallic design.

'That's a memory key?'

'Sure is. See, when I lift the gem off the circular band, it has a metal prong protruding from it. I can plug this prong into the side of my laptop or any smartphone.'

The Genesis Flaw

'You should launch a range of jewellery made from memory keys,' she said, trying to break the tension. She looked at the clock.

'I'd better get ready.'

John took her hand. 'Are you sure you want to do this?'

'I'm sure. I'm shit-scared, but I'm sure.'

'If you don't come out by twelve-thirty, I'm calling the cops.'

Chapter 69

Serena stepped into the bone-chilling wind, her black woollen hat pulled down over her ears. Her thick black coat was done up tightly and her precious smartphone hidden in her pocket. On her way to the subway station, she couldn't resist crossing Broadway and stopping in Duffy Square to look at the Gene-Asis building, already cordoned off. Outside the main entrance lay a massive red carpet and she counted four armed security guards. Through the black glass, she could see nothing of the interior until a woman left the building. The open doors revealed a floor-to-ceiling glass wall about ten metres from the entrance, which stopped people moving any further into the building. This glass wall was interspersed with metal detectors and retina scanners. There were eight of these security barriers, each of which was manned by two armed guards. She failed to register an exterior camera pointing straight at her.

Was she shivering because of the sub-zero temperature or because she felt overawed by her task?

Serena's feet were growing numb, her boots failing to insulate them from the icy cold pavement. She looked around her at the bright colours and lights of Times Square; at the huge billboards, and moving images zooming around buildings and climbing up skyscrapers, like ivy growing up trees. Traffic shunted by in a confusing mesh of crossed lanes; yellow taxis, FedEx trucks, cars of every shape and size, motorbikes. People shuffled along sidewalks, waiting to get the 'green hand' so they could cross the madly busy roads. Cameras flashed as tourists gaped.

The Genesis Flaw

Four blocks away, she saw One Times Square, with five huge billboards and electronic screens clinging to the building. It stood there, a giant wedge between the traffic on Broadway and Seventh Avenue going south. The bottom billboard was for a new movie, *The Tainted*. Above it, bright orange letters whisked around the building on electronic ticker tape, as if following a train track round and round the building. She read the words 'Wall Street Journal' before they disappeared round a corner, replaced instantly by the latest share prices.

Above this, an NBC interview was taking place on the Panasonic screen: with Al Bukowski, grinning confidently. He resembled some dark god, looking down on his people. If anyone wanted to listen to the interview, all they had to do was tune in their smartphones. Above the Panasonic screen, a corporate advertisement for Gene-Asis was running, the screen the height of several floors. And, above this, sat the biggest Cup Noodles she'd ever seen. At the very top of One Times Square, the electronic screen sold Discover Card's benefits like a beacon of light offering salvation to the world.

Serena made her way through the throngs of people to the subway entrance. Stepping down the grit-covered steps, a gust of icy wind ripped into her coat. The draughty ticketing booth, with its varnished wood and brass trimmings, looked like it had been there for many years. Opposite the booth were the turnstiles and, beyond them, the platform.

'Sheridan Square, please.'

Serena handed the attendant a ten-dollar note.

'Other platform.'

Serena couldn't hear her. The woman was sitting way back from the microphone and made no attempt to raise her voice.

'Sorry, I can't hear you.'

Still refusing to move, the woman raised her voice a notch and pointed in the direction of the steps.

'You need to go round the other side. Other platform.'

This side was going north and Serena wanted to go south. Retracing her steps, she noticed an Hispanic man in an unzipped padded jacket and yellow beanie leaning against a ticket machine. He was reading a magazine, as cold gusts flicked around him. He dropped something. The wind blew it along the tiled floor. He stamped on it. For a fleeting second, she glimpsed the person in the photograph. It was a woman wearing a black coat, looking up, her blonde hair peeking from beneath her black hat. It was a photo of Serena outside the Gene-Asis building; the security camera must have taken it. Sprinting up the steps, two at a time, she left the subway station in a hurry. If she were right, that man was either a cop, or working for Gene-Asis. And she didn't fancy meeting either. Spying the entrance for south-bound trains over the other side of the road, she darted through the traffic, a yellow cab narrowly missing her and honking loudly.

Running down the steps, she dropped her ticket into the turnstile machine and moved along the busy platform, weaving in and out of people, until she stood behind a group of teenagers at the farthest end. The Hispanic man raced onto the platform, looking up and down its length. He looked her way. There was an unmistakable look of recognition on his face.

He immediately barged along the platform in her direction. As his jacket opened for a second, she saw the glint of gunmetal.

The next subway train was about to arrive, with another one a minute later. She watched the yellow beanie move through the crowds. He was now about halfway to her. Serena backed into the tiled wall. A shot of adrenaline fired heat through her body. What to do? He was now only twenty metres away and increasing his pace, pushing through the tightly packed crowds on the platform.

Down the black arch of the tunnel, the train's bright lights heralded its arrival before it slowed to a stop. He was now aggressively shoving past people, another man objecting with a 'Watch it, buddy'. The teenagers jostled forward. Serena pushed through them and into the carriage, staking her claim to a position right by the sliding doors. The doors began to close and her pursuer jumped into the next carriage. Just as the doors were about to shut completely she dived through the narrowing gap, back onto the platform.

One carriage down, she saw the man's arm shoot into the narrowing gap. She stared in horror as he forced the doors to open. She ripped an umbrella from a businessman's hand and whacked her enemy's knuckles as hard as she could, and hit them again as the businessman shouted at her. Her pursuer yelped in pain and released the doors as the train moved off. Dropping the umbrella and running down the other end of the platform, she tried to merge with a recently arrived group of English tourists.

What would he do? Would he take the next train back to this station? If Serena didn't get to Par Excellence in the next twenty minutes, she'd blow their whole plan. She had to take the next train.

The doors opened and she leaped on quickly, picking up a discarded newspaper from the floor. Taking a seat, she hid behind its open pages, breathing heavily. She hoped her pursuer wasn't working with anyone else who might have boarded with her. The doors closed. In her carriage was a woman with a baby in a pram, some English tourists, a man listening to music through headphones, and businesspeople. The train rattled through the tunnel. The baby in the pram started to cry and its embarrassed mother rocked the stroller.

At each stop, Serena's heart beat faster. One more to go – Sheridan Square was the next station. Terrified she'd see the Hispanic man waiting for her, she stared through the glass doors but saw only her warped reflection in their curve. The train rattled to a stop and, like a sprinter, she leaped through them and ran. At the exit, she stared confusedly at the busy junction.

She had to be certain she'd lost her pursuer before she arrived at Par Excellence, so she ducked into a women's clothing shop. Spying a pale-blue puffer jacket with a faux-fur-lined hood, she yanked it off its hanger and dived for the changing rooms, locking herself in a cubicle.

'Excuse me, can I check how many items you have?' someone called over the top of her door.

She quickly opened the door and showed the jacket to the shop assistant, who eyed her suspiciously. She locked the door again and sat in the chair. Dripping with perspiration, she removed her black coat, placing the daypack carefully on the floor.

'How you going in there? Can I get you anything?'

'No, thanks,' she called back. 'I'll take this.'

Leaving her black coat behind, she paid for the new jacket. She put it on and pulled the pale-blue hood over her head, almost completely hiding her face. If they were looking for a woman in a black coat, this might help throw them off the scent.

Hurriedly, she walked round the corner to Par Excellence.

Chapter 70

In her crisp black high-collared shirt with gold buttons, and black trousers, Serena wheeled in a trolley laden with neatly folded starched tablecloths. The uniform lacked pockets, so her smartphone was buried deeply beneath the tablecloths.

She was stopped at the Gene-Asis deliveries entrance by two armed security guards, one of whom scanned the security pass hanging around her neck. They then ran a metal detector over her body. When they moved it over the trolley, it beeped loudly.

'Metal trolley,' she shrugged. A spy-eye above the entrance, like an eyeball on a telescopic lens, watched her. Serena kept her head angled slightly down, not permitting the spy-eye a good look at her face. If she were recognised, she was dead.

'Move on,' the security guard said.

She took the oversized service elevator with other Par Excellence staff. The doors opened behind the kitchens on the 119th floor, where the chefs in white hats had been hard at work all morning. Pans clanked, the chefs shouted and the heat was unbearable, but the rich smells emanating from the kitchens were mouthwatering.

She wheeled her trolley to a corner of the massive banquet room, where tables and chairs were already laid out. She checked her watch: it was 9.45 am. The guests would be arriving from midday. The presentation was taking place from 12.15 to 12.45 pm, after which lunch would be served. Serena scanned the ceiling for spy-eyes. They were everywhere, moving every now and again to zoom in on an individual.

Serena had her blonde hair tied back in a neat ponytail and wore a pair of lightly tinted glasses John had lent her. They were very different from the glasses she'd worn at Gene-Asis. They made everything slightly fuzzy but she hoped the tinting might help prevent her being recognised.

She had to find somewhere to hide her handheld because she was about to use all the tablecloths. It was too early to make her way to the projector; her absence would be noticed and the alarm raised. She planned to move into the projector's roof space at the very last moment.

'Lay out the tablecloths and then lay the tables. The cutlery's over there,' her supervisor instructed.

'I'll help,' said a girl, with dark hair in a bun, taking the next tablecloth from the trolley. One by one, the piles of linen got lower and lower. Picking up the neatly folded tablecloth wrapped around the smartphone, and laying another one on top, she told her workmate that they were both stained and she'd get some clean ones. Before the girl could check them, she scuttled off to the kitchens, where a prep chef nearly knocked the phone from her hand as he shot out of the pantry.

'Look where you're going,' he snapped.

She ducked inside. Shelves were stacked high with food, but there were no spy-eyes. Nearest her were boxes of vegetables and fruit, bags of flour, huge tins of food, large sauce bottles, bags of coffee, coffee filters, and ten massive bags of rice stacked in a corner. She wedged the smartphone behind the last rice bag, hoping not all the rice was to be used that morning.

Taking more tablecloths, she returned to laying the tables.

'Smell this,' said the florist, wafting a six-headed tulip under Serena's nose. It looked like Medusa.

'Smells like a rose.'

'Exactly. Amazing what Gene-Asis can do!'

As Serena placed the polished cutlery on the tables, she searched for a valid excuse to go to the auditorium. Toying desperately with a number of equally weak reasons, she hedged her bets and cornered her supervisor.

'I've laid all the tables. Does the podium need any preparation – water or anything?'

'Four jugs of water with slices of lime and eight glasses. Off you go. Shoo!'

Serena prepared the jugs, then ducked into the pantry with a large tray. She laid the phone underneath a white cloth and then placed the jugs and glasses around it. She gingerly entered the auditorium with her heavy burden, and had to hold back a gasp.

In front of her was an enormous 3D holographic image of Bukowski. He was speaking, the image so clear that he appeared solid and real, except for the fact the projection was twice as tall as the man. The technicians were doing a test run.

Serena saw the door at the back of the auditorium. Behind this was the ladder leading up to the projector. There appeared to be no one around but a cleaner. Spy-eyes scanned the area, one already having zoomed in on her static figure at the doorway. She walked forwards, carefully balancing the tray, and placed the water on a table near the podium. Partway through a sentence, the holographic image of Bukowski evaporated, the test over.

Then she heard the click of heels as someone mounted the podium. This was her chance; the spy-eyes moved to focus on the person. The door at the back of the auditorium was not being watched. Serena picked up her tray and casually walked towards the door at the back. The microphone squealed as a voice called out, 'Testing, one, two, three'.

Serena's step faltered. She knew that woman's loud, demanding voice and unmistakable scent. It was Gloria Philladitis, her archrival from the Rooney Agency. Eyes cast down, Serena took another step towards the back of the auditorium, moving out of Gloria's line of vision.

'No, too tinny. Try again,' Gloria said, clearing her throat into the microphone. She gave a little cough.

'Oh, excuse me, can you get me a glass of water?' Gloria called to Serena. The spy-eyes turned onto Serena. She had no choice but to place the tray on a nearby seat and pour her some water. Taking a deep breath, she walked up to the podium, blinking nervously behind her glasses. In her Armani tweed suit and high-heeled brown boots, Gloria stared at the window of the multimedia booth across the auditorium, issuing instructions with the microphone. She took the glass from Serena, giving her only a cursory glance.

'Thank you,' she said. The lights on the podium were blindingly bright and she squinted at Serena. 'Hold on, don't I know you?'

'I don't think so,' Serena replied in her best American accent and turned around quickly.

'No, wait a minute,' said Gloria, stepping off the podium and out of the spotlight.

She pulled the glasses off Serena's face and her red-lipsticked mouth dropped open with surprise.

'Serena Swift. What the hell are you doing here?'

Serena's first instinct was to run, but where? She would get no further than the corridor before she was caught. From the corner of her eye, she could see a spy-eye focused on them. She looked at Gloria's hard-bitten face, her gash of red lipstick and narrowed dark eyes. How could she persuade this woman not to call security?

'Please, Gloria, let me explain.'

'Oh, this I've got to hear. Don't tell me; you've decided to pursue a waitressing career and it's an amazing coincidence that you just happen to be here,' she said, folding her arms across her chest. 'Turn the lights up,' she bellowed at the multimedia booth.

As the light increased, Gloria started to laugh in disbelief.

'What are you up to now, you silly cow? Trying to sabotage the launch? Sore that you got fired?' Gloria sneered, hanging John's reading glasses from her fingers like a hunter's trophy.

'Gloria, I know we haven't got on in the past but I really need your help now.'

'*Me* help *you*? A thieving liar?'

Gloria raised her arm to call for assistance. Serena pulled it down.

'Gene-Asis' products are making us ill, very ill. They'll kill billions of people. Gene-Asis knows it but they're still launching Supercrop Ultra.'

Serena's supervisor popped her head in the door. When she saw Serena holding Gloria's arm, she raced over.

'Is there a problem, ma'am?' she asked Gloria.

'Yes. I need Security, now,' Gloria replied, yanking her arm from Serena's grip. 'Tell them Serena Swift is a security risk and needs to be escorted from the building immediately.'

'Oh my! I don't know how this happened. We always thoroughly vet our …'

'Now!' cut in Gloria and the supervisor shot out of the auditorium.

'Gloria, food trials were done by Gene-Asis in Zimbabwe. They proved eating their GM foods causes deadly viruses and horrific deformities.'

'What is this bullshit, Serena? Their products are tested and safe.'

'No, they're not. I've seen the scientist's research report with my own eyes. I have footage of the suffering caused. Please, Gloria, just forget you don't like me. I'm begging you to look at the evidence and make up your own mind. Tell Security you don't need them. Give me a chance.'

Gloria blinked, seemingly startled by Serena's conviction and not sure how to react.

'We're being lied to. Gene-Asis manipulates scientists, politicians, the media. Gloria, they've killed to keep their dirty secrets,' she said, moving closer.

Stepping back, Gloria yelled at her, 'Stay away from me, you whacko! You're out of your mind.'

Two uniformed security guards charged down the aisle, another man walking slowly behind them. Serena grabbed Gloria's hands. Terrified, Gloria tried to pull them free.

Serena pleaded, her voice low and brittle, 'Gloria, look at this memory key. It shows you I'm telling the truth.'

'Get off me,' she screamed, as Serena pressed the ring into her palm, just as the two guards forced Serena to the ground, winding her.

'Don't move,' shouted one of the guards, pointing a gun at her. The other forced one of her arms behind her back. She squealed in pain, her arm almost pulled from its socket. The guards paused. What were they waiting for?

A big man with one arm in a sling stepped into the light. The arm was encased in what appeared to be a layer of plastic, which fitted like a long glove. Beneath this transparent covering, parts of the arm were red raw. His eyebrows and patches of his hair had been singed away. Serena stared up at her worst nightmare: Ben Hartstone.

'No,' she mouthed in disbelief.

'Hello, Serena. I heard you were in town.' That same raspy, deep voice, seething with subdued fury.

'Please help me,' she sobbed. 'He's going to kill me.'

She tried to struggle free.

'Don't move or I'll shoot,' shouted one guard.

'Aren't you pleased to see me? And I thought we were old friends,' said Ben, moving over to the seat where she'd left the tray. 'I wonder what we'll find here?' he continued, lifting the handheld with his good hand.

'Here, take this,' he ordered the older guard, 'Bring it with us.' He looked at the other guard still pointing his gun at Serena.

'Stand her up, and follow me. I don't want a word of this getting out, do you understand? This never happened. She was never here.'

'Yes, sir.'

'And that includes you too, Ms Philladitis. Mr Bukowski's orders.'

'Of course.'

'Call the police. Please. The police,' she begged as she was pulled to her feet.

'No cops. Mr Bukowski doesn't want any disruption to today's event.'

'Gloria, help me!' Serena screamed, bending her body towards her, struggling hopelessly.

'Perhaps she should be taken to the police? After all, she's committed a crime,' said Gloria.

'Ms Philladitis, you have my word this woman won't come to any harm. The police will be contacted when the show is over.'

'No, he tried to kill me before,' Serena yelled, feeling a sharp stab in her arm. Everything went black as she lapsed into unconsciousness.

As Serena's limp body was carried into a private code-operated elevator, Gloria strode over to the auditorium's multimedia booth. She went in. The spy-eye outside the booth recorded her movements. But there was no spy-eye inside. The technician stared at her for a moment.

'What was all that about?' he asked, his tongue piercing clicking on his teeth.

'None of your damn business! Just get on with the audio checks. We're running behind schedule.'

As the technician did the checks, Gloria opened the palm of her hand and stared at the most unusual memory key she'd ever seen. A ring.

'I've changed my mind,' she said. 'Take five. I need to be alone.'

Chapter 71

Serena opened her eyes. The polished walnut gleamed like a top-of-the-range coffin. Where the hell was she? Her head hung forward and her arm sockets burned. She stared down at pairs of feet and recognised the security guards' black boots. The men were holding her up. Moving one leg, she tried to place her weight on it.

'She's coming round,' said one.

'I can't breathe,' she said, trying to stand straight. The private elevator opened on the floor below the auditorium and she was bundled into a circular room with no windows and no spy-eyes; just a circular desk and eight chairs. It was like being in a giant metallic cylinder designed so that no known spying device could capture the conversations within its perimeter. It was used for Gene-Asis' most secret meetings. Serena was dropped onto a chair.

'Leave us, and take the mobile to Mr Bukowski on the top floor. He'll want InfoSec to take a look,' Ben growled and the guards left, the metallic doors shutting behind them.

Ben leaned over her, his lack of eyebrows making his face look like a mask. Behind his swollen eyelids, his green eyes glared at her with pure hatred. She couldn't bear to see it and looked away.

He grabbed her face and forced her to look at him.

'Thought me dead, didn't you? Huh? Well, you blew me out the ute. Clear of the flames. So here I am to tell the tale.' He circled her as he spoke. 'My arm got the worst of it. Look at your handiwork!' he demanded, pointing at the plastic coating. Then he sniggered. 'Ever seen burns heal this quick? Huh? Gene-Asis are good for some things. The bacteria in here are healing my arm fast.'

Ben took a gun out from his holster and placed it so the cold metal touched her forehead. Her body shook uncontrollably. She clenched her eyes shut and waited for the shot.

'Oh no! Not like that. You put me through hell in that burning ute, you little bitch, and you're going to know what that kinda pain is like.'

If she died now, how would she be remembered? She wanted her family to know the truth. She wanted them to know she loved them. She felt the barrel of the gun leave her forehead and dared to open her eyes.

Transferring the gun to his left hand, Ben took a cigarette lighter out of his pocket and flicked it on. A small white flame sizzled.

'No, a bullet's too easy. It'll be just you and me in a quiet part of New Jersey, with a can of petrol and some matches. I'm going to cook me some pork.'

He sniffed her face.

'Mmmm, smells good.'

Paralysed with fear, Serena watched as Ben tauntingly waved the flame closer to her face. She felt its searing heat, blinking at its nearness. She backed into the chair, desperate to get her face away.

'How do you like that idea?'

Ben was so close she could see his singed eyelashes.

'Don't move now,' he said, placing the gun at her temple. Serena sobbed as she felt the heat of the flame so near her cheeks. She could smell the lighter fuel. She tried to turn her head away, her mouth dry as paper. She heard a click, as the gun's safety catch was removed. The flame was near her neck. Something was burning and she knew it was herself. The repugnant smell hit her nostrils as she heard a crackle like burning twigs. She screamed as her hair caught fire. She screamed as if hell itself had opened. She screamed helplessly, knowing not a soul could hear her.

'Ben!' Bukowski's voice cut through her cries. 'Have your fun and games later. I need to talk to her. Turn off the lighter.'

Ben hesitated, hovering over Serena. Then, like a demon obeying Satan, he shut off the lighter and watched as the flames in her hair burned themselves out. He slunk away from her, slamming the lighter onto the tabletop in protest. He never once stopped pointing the gun at her.

'Patience, patience,' Bukowski directed.

He stood before Serena in a bespoke suit and crisply pressed shirt, not a hair out of place. Shaking his cuff back, he checked his watch: 11.55. Queues of guests had arrived at the main entrance, but Bukowski maintained an unnerving calm.

'Before I hand you over to my friend here, tell me where John Flynn is. I know he's in New York. I've looked at your Tbyte, so I know what you were planning. Only Flynn's got the skill to do this.'

'Go to hell!'

He leaned forward like a cobra attacking, his loss of control so sudden she jumped in her seat. Taking hold of both her shoulders, he shoved her with a thump into the back of the chair.

'I don't have time for this. Answer me or I'll let our flame thrower here continue his games with your face. I can promise you a quick death if you cooperate.'

Serena nodded and he released her shoulders.

'He's in Australia. He programmed the Tbyte before I left.'

He slapped her across the mouth, her head jerking sideways.

'Liar. I know you both flew in last night. What are you calling yourself these days? Oh yes,' he said, reading her name badge, 'Sarah.' He folded his arms. 'Now, tell me, Sarah, what's your back-up plan? What is John up to and where is he?'

'There is no other plan. That's it. I was going to crawl into the roof and trick the projector into running my documentary.'

He frowned, clearly weighing up her story.

'A word,' he said to Ben and they both left, the doors locking behind them.

She could hear and see nothing through the solid doors. She had to get out of there, but there was only one entrance to the room and inside it were no devices to communicate with the outside world.

Serena looked up at the ceiling and spied the smoke detector. She saw the cigarette lighter and a desperate plan formed in her terrified mind. A printed instruction manual was wedged behind the DVD player. Taking it and the lighter, Serena stepped on a chair and then stood on the table. She eyed the door, willing Bukowski and Ben to stay outside a moment longer.

Serena ran her thumb over the lighter's wheel, trying to draw the flame, unable to get it to work. Finally, a tongue of flame leaped up and she set fire to the manual, raising it above her head, holding it directly beneath the smoke detector. The yellow fingers of flame were weak and she feared they would go out. They burned nearer her hand as the manual disintegrated. 'Come on! Go off,' she begged, the flames licking painfully at her fingers. She couldn't bear to hold on much longer.

The noise almost pierced her eardrums. The smoke detector screeched repeatedly every few seconds. Serena dropped the charred remains as Ben hurled himself through the doors. He dived at her, but she jumped from the table, landing on the ground and, toppling forwards, hit her head. Ben yelped in pain as he landed on the table, scraping his barely healed arm.

With a strength she didn't know she possessed, she forced herself to stand and run from the room, the intermittent screech from the smoke detector now accompanied by the ringing of the fire alarm on every floor. Serena glanced at the private elevator and saw it descending to the ground floor. Bukowski must be inside.

Every electronic door in the building instantly opened as people began to stream out.

'Fire escape. This way,' a man ordered.

She raced into the throng of evacuating people as Ben pointed a gun at her back. In the confusion, no one noticed him, because all eyes were focused on the fire exit. As Serena was surrounded by office workers, Ben couldn't fire. He cursed as she dived into the stairwell.

'Oh my God, what if it's a terrorist attack?' a woman yelled behind her.

Serena wove her way past the people already on the stairs. Was Ben following her or would he take the private elevator?

Inside the cavernous concrete stairwell, sound was amplified. People's shoes clicked on the stairs and voices echoed. Serena peered down to the floors below and saw the whole building evacuating. She moved as fast as she could, banging into people, using her shoulders to pass them. The crowd was thickening and her progress slowing as more people joined the march downwards. 'Hey, stop shoving!' a man shouted at Serena.

She was panting now, her lungs burning. She checked the sign: she was only on the 112th floor. She had to find a faster way out of there.

'Can you believe this?' she heard a man say.

'Someone's head's going to roll.'

Serena elbowed her way between them.

'How rude.'

A bottleneck was forming in front of her as a woman in her fifties was being helped down the stairs by two men. Each step seemed painful for her. People could only pass them in single file. She looked behind her again. Was Ben up there? Trapped, she shuffled forward with the rest of the crowd.

'We're going to die, I know it.'

'It's probably just an electrical fault.'

'Just push past her,' someone yelled.

Serena saw people streaming into the stairwell from level 111. She battled her way against the tide and left the stairwell, arriving in a nearly deserted corridor.

'Hey, you're going the wrong way!' someone called after her.

Serena was alone. She jabbed at the elevator button, praying it wasn't programmed to switch off if the fire alarms rang. She watched it rise from the fifty-seventh floor and the doors opened. A recorded voice instructed her not to take the elevator in the event of fire. She ignored its repetitive whine and pressed the button for ground level. The elevator shot down in a few seconds and opened to absolute chaos.

A stumbling mass of people pushed and shoved their way through the foyer to the main entrance. The solid wall of glass that separated the entrance foyer from the elevators had been raised some seven metres above the floor, like a giant guillotine blade hovering over its next victim. The eight security barriers, previously part of this wall, were now flung wide open. People streamed out of the building.

Serena hurled herself into the tightly packed throng, barely able to carve a path for herself. She squeezed into a gap near the wall and let the tide of bodies take her. A hand grabbed her shoulder, wrenching her back so fast she almost fell. She felt something hard on her spine.

'Keep straight ahead of me or I'll kill you right now,' Ben shouted above the screaming mayhem.

'How did you … ?'

'Location finder I planted on your back,' he shouted in her ear. 'I wasn't going to lose you a second time.'

Trapped by hundreds of bodies, she moved with them towards the main entrance, the police outside trying to direct the terrified people away from the building. Traffic had been stopped to allow the thousands evacuating a space to stand. Above the din, Serena heard the honk of fire engine sirens. Ben swore as people banged into him.

'Stay close when we get outside,' he said, breathing down her neck.

Firemen were staring at diagrams of the building's structure, directing others with tanks on their backs. A woman screamed as she tripped over, a cop lifting her to safety. As Serena and Ben stepped outside, it was as if they had walked into a fridge; the temperature was freezing.

Times Square was gridlocked. Drivers stood outside their vehicles, staring around both in confusion and grim fascination. A tourist filmed the commotion on a tiny camera. An ABC News presenter was interviewing an evacuee. People stood between every stationary car, van, truck or cab, staring up at the Gene-Asis building, waiting for something to happen. Others ran away, remembering September 11.

Serena saw Gloria, standing unsteadily on a car bonnet. She was staring back towards the Gene-Asis building, peering into the evacuating crowds. Someone was trying to get her down, and she was arguing with him. Then Gloria spotted Serena and Ben, and pointed straight at them, shouting at her companion.

The cop joined her on the car bonnet. He eyeballed Serena, and then moved a hand to his lapel, speaking into his two-way radio. If he were calling for back-up, he had no chance: the crowd was too packed.

The cop took out his gun and jumped down, disappearing. Was he coming to find them? What had Gloria said? Was the cop going to shoot her?

The Genesis Flaw

'Police!' he shouted, pointing the gun at them. He was only a few metres away and, as he spoke, a space opened in the throng. Even in such a mad panic, people avoided a loaded gun. Ben grabbed her arm, pressing his gun deeper into her back. She froze. One way or another, she was going to be shot dead.

'Put down your gun!' the cop called out.

He was moving closer and Serena could see that the gun was pointed at Ben's head. Not at her. It took her a while to put two and two together: Gloria had sent the cop to rescue her from Ben. She had looked at the memory key's content.

'Officer, I'm Gene-Asis Security. This woman is a terrorist.'

'Help me,' called Serena, her eyes pleading. Ben yanked her arm back and she yelped.

'Shut it,' he said in her ear.

'That may be, sir, but she ain't got the gun. You have. So, put your gun down on the ground, nice and slow, and show me your ID.'

'Listen, you dumbass cop. I'm not letting go of a fucking terrorist.'

'I'm gonna tell you one more time to put the gun down, or I'll shoot,' he said. He plainly didn't like being called a dumbass cop, especially by some foreigner.

'You dumb fucker,' growled Ben, throwing the gun on the icy pavement. He still held Serena firmly.

'Both of you, face the wall and place your hands above your heads.'

Ben groaned with frustration but released her arm. Serena raised her hands, hardly able to believe she'd been saved from certain death. She quickly turned to face the wall. Ben slowly raised his arms. He winced in pain. The cop threw his weight behind him, crushing his face into the wall.

'Who's the dumb fucker now?' the cop said, patting down Ben's clothing. He roughly pulled his arms down to handcuff them. Ben yelled with pain.

'You're not handcuffing me,' he shouted and a struggle broke out, the slighter cop struggling to hold the bigger man.

Serena saw her chance and took it. She shot off into the crowd. The cop could do nothing to stop her: he had his hands full with Ben. As she ran, she found the location-finding device, a small button attached to her collar, and threw it into the gutter.

She needed to hide. She ran out into Seventh Avenue, zigzagging round vehicles, heading in the direction of their hotel. But she couldn't go back there: she might lead them to John. So she followed Seventh Avenue, towards One Times Square. Her breath came thick and fast in the freezing air.

Serena heard a scream, so loud it was like someone had screamed into a microphone at an empty football stadium. It reverberated throughout Times Square. It was a woman screaming in unmistakable agony. Serena stopped in her tracks, as did the people around her. As far as she could see, people turned their heads, searching for the source of the distressing sound.

Serena was standing still on Seventh Avenue, outside the MTV studios, and, at first, she thought the sound was emanating from there. But it was everywhere: all around Times Square. The people next to her raised their mobile phones, staring at them in disbelief. The woman's screams were being transmitted through each and every mobile or smartphone: in fact, every wireless communication device.

A cab driver stared at his car radio, frowning: her screams were coming from his and every car radio. Drivers standing in the street opened their doors to hear better. But it was not just transmitting via car radios and mobile phones. The woman's screams were being transmitted through store radios too. People all over Times Square looked up and around.

'Look. Up there.'

Serena had seen it. At exactly the same moment, every one of the sixty-eight illuminated billboards from one end of Times Square to the other went blank. Completely blank. The brightly lit advertisements were gone, as was the live news coverage. The stock market ticker-tape had stopped rushing around One Times Square and the NASDAQ building walls were their natural grey colour, no longer projecting colourful messages to passers-by.

'Must be a power failure,' said a man in a thick coat.

'Can't be. Power's on everywhere else,' said the man with him.

Then, in unison, every billboard shot into life, displaying exactly the same image.

Chapter 72

On every billboard from One Times Square to Two Times Square, which spans five blocks, appears one image: an African woman wailing in agony, her feverish face filling every screen.

The camera zooms out to reveal the semi-darkness of her impoverished hut. She is laying on a ragged blanket on a mud floor, a man holding her bony hand. The camera pans down her body to her legs, which have swollen like tree trunks. The skin has cracked, forming gaping wounds that weep a yellow pus. A hand swats uselessly at flies hovering above the ruptures.

Next to Serena, a woman raises her hand to her mouth. 'Oh, my God!' A man behind her mutters, 'What the hell is this? What's going on?'

The voiceover, which Serena knows is Tracey's, says simply 'Zimbabwe, Gweru District. A new deadly virus. No cure.'

Next, everyone sees the interior of a run-down hospital, with patchy whitewashed walls and a concrete floor. An emaciated man lies on a bed, shivering with a fever, his dark skin has a yellow hue. His breathing is raspy and his eyes bulge with fear. Tracey's voice says, 'The new hepatitis S virus. No cure.'

The camera pans out, showing men, women and children with that same yellow hue. Some are in beds. Most are on the hospital floor. One woman clutches her abdomen in pain. 'Hepatitis S broke out here before it was first diagnosed in the USA. But the outbreak was kept quiet.'

On each and every screen there is a close-up of a woman's black hands unwrapping a bundle of cloth to reveal a newborn, stiff with rigor mortis. The camera zooms in to show the baby's tiny heart resting on her chest, already fly-blown. Tracey says, 'Born with her heart outside her chest cavity.'

Close to Serena, a woman with two little girls, wrapped in matching woolly hats and scarves, tells them: 'Don't look. This is disgusting. Stop looking, Jemima.'

Then an image of a two-year-old boy, whom his mother hides under a blanket. A voice off-camera speaks in her native dialect, coaxing her to lift the cloth, which she does, exposing her dead baby, its sex indistinguishable. The infant resembles a doll; the area between the legs smooth and flat, having no genitals or anus. 'Died of severe deformities,' says Tracey.

Apart from the occasional murmur and distant noise of a siren, Times Square is hushed. People are staring, shocked and horrified by the images they are seeing. Some shake their heads. Some cover their eyes. Some are crying. Serena hears a woman vomiting. Even the television presenters remain silent; their cameramen are recording everything.

Tracey now focuses the camera upon herself. The sky is bright behind her and her short platinum-blonde hair is combed flat, not spiky as usual, and her pixie-like face looks drawn and tired. She wears a loose white shirt and linen trousers. Behind her are some mud huts with thatch roofs and, to her left, a whitewashed building.

'Who's that?' a woman whispers behind Serena.

Tracey speaks.

'So, who are these people and why are they suffering such terrible health problems? They all live in the Gweru district of the Midlands province of Zimbabwe, and each and every one of them participated in scientific food trials conducted by a well-known biotech company between 2006 and 2011.

'My name is Tracey Pollack and I'm science correspondent for *The Post* in London. This is a true story about 1400 men, women and children who were used as human guinea pigs. Seven hundred were a control group and did not eat any GM food. The other 700 people were used to test the effects of a new range of genetically engineered plant crops, all of which contain the Koch Bottlebrush Virus, or KBv for short. The company carrying out those trials is Gene-Asis Biotech, the world's largest producer of genetically engineered plants and animals.'

A wave of recognition rumbles up and down Times Square. Some turn to look at the looming black building that is Gene-Asis' head office.

'Did these Zimbabweans participate knowingly in this experiment? No, they did not. They were told they were receiving food and agricultural aid. Have they received any financial or medical support from the company that caused them such terrible suffering? No, they have not. Were the results of these food trials ever made public? No, they most certainly were not. In fact, Gene-Asis has done everything in its power to prevent its publication.'

'She's gotta be kidding, right?' Serena hears a cab driver say. A tourist replies, 'How could they!'

'Is this a movie trailer?' a waitress asks, chewing gum.

Tracey continues. 'Let's take a look at the lives of these people before they were experimented upon. Here is some footage taken by a missionary doctor, and his wife, in 2005, in Mutenda village.'

Tracey is gone and in her place is a slightly shaky image of some Zimbabwean women laughing at the camera as they grind grains, using a long, heavy wooden pestle and mortar. Children run around, playing, and when they realise they're being filmed, they stand shyly, staring, huddled together.

A woman picks carrots in her field and proudly holds them up to the camera.

A white doctor with a blond moustache is listening through a stethoscope to the chest of a local boy, who is transfixed by the camera. The boy grins timidly.

'Michael Caldwell, a highly respected American doctor and missionary, worked in the Mutenda Community Clinic. He instigated health checks for each of the 1400 people who later took part in Gene-Asis' experiment. These records are still on file. They are as follows …'

Back on every billboard screen is the image of the woman whose mysterious virus has caused her legs to swell up and weep pus. Tracey's voice says simply, 'Prior to 2006: healthy.'

Then, in a run-down hospital, again the man dying of hepatitis S. She cuts to footage of the same man playing soccer on a dust-bowl pitch in Mutenda, with the voice-over, 'Prior to 2006, this man suffered only from low blood pressure.'

She cuts to a close-up of a woman's hands unwrapping a bundle of cloth to reveal the dead newborn whose heart lies outside her chest. Then she moves to some footage of this same woman, with three other children giggling from behind her legs. Tracey's voice says, 'Her three other children, born prior to the food trials, were all healthy.'

Finally, there is the image of the mother uncovering her dead baby with no genitals or anus. 'Dr Caldwell noted in 2005 only two instances of child deformity in the Gweru district. Today, there are thirty-one. This is a staggering twenty-two per cent of births. Unfortunately for the people, the Caldwells were moved to Ethiopia by their mission in 2006. So, the key question is – what caused these viruses and birth defects, and are they linked? The answer rests in the palm of my hand.'

The camera pans to Tracey's pale hands, which are cupped and through which seeds trickle.

'These are Gene-Asis' wheat seeds. For five years, all their bread was made from this wheat.'

The camera moves to another pair of black-skinned hands, cupping some more seeds.

'These are corn. For five years, they ate only this genetically engineered corn.'

The camera is now pointing at some fields and, as Tracey moves through them, she speaks: 'In fact, every last grain, fruit and vegetable these people ate was grown from Gene-Asis' genetically engineered seeds containing the Koch Bottlebrush Virus. The very same seeds that produce the grains, fruits and vegetables you and I eat every day.'

A murmur, much louder than before, reverberates through Times Square. Feet shuffle uncomfortably. Eyes open wide. More people speak, betraying their concern.

'What? Did she say we eat this stuff?' a FedEx man asks.

'That could happen to us?'

'In an incredible act of corporate greed and a crime against humanity, in 2012 Gene-Asis released for sale these very same seeds to farmers around the world. They are called Supercrop 13, and over three billion people have been consuming them.'

'No way!' someone yells.

'This can't be true. It just wouldn't happen.'

'Oh my God! I'm going to die,' a woman gibbers.

Tracey goes on: 'This begs the question – why has the developed world not yet seen such alarming birth defects? The answer is, we have, but in lesser numbers, because not everyone consumes GM. Hep S? It has killed many thousands worldwide. Because the developed world's diet contains less than fifty per cent GM, there have been fewer outbreaks but this virus is contagious and spreading fast. It is well known that Gene-Asis' stated goal is to make our diet one hundred per cent GM by 2025. If that happens, we could suffer the same fate as the Gweru people.'

'Jesus!' mutters a woman nearby.

'How do we know that Gene-Asis Biotech conducted these trials? I have here a letter from a Mr Waite, an employee of Gene-Asis Biotech, to the regional Bureau of Agriculture in Gweru city, Zimbabwe, confirming the distribution locations of the so-called agricultural aid.'

The camera pans in so that the logo on the letterhead is clearly visible: an indigo-blue image of the earth, as if seen from space, sprouting from the top of which is a tiny green seedling. Behind this shines an orange sunrise. It is indisputably the Gene-Asis logo.

Next appearing on screen is a truck, from the back of which large sacks are being unloaded.

'This is footage taken by an aid worker in July 2008, showing sacks of Gene-Asis seeds being delivered to Mutenda.'

Clearly visible is the Gene-Asis logo on each sack, which stays frozen on screen.

'And I have an audio recording of Dr Fergus McPherson, who was the professor of genetics conducting these food trials in Zimbabwe. He is speaking to his colleague Dr Philip Munroe, the epidemiologist in charge, expressing his grave concern about the research results. At the time, both men were employed by Gene-Asis. Neither Dr McPherson nor Dr Munroe knew they were being recorded. Dr McPherson speaks first:

'This is terrible, Phil. Terrible! Horizontal gene transfer *has* happened in *all* eighty-three of the deceased. KBv has to be the trigger. It's switching on centuries-old viruses. We have no immunity to them. And the birth defects are alarming. Somehow, KBv is screwing with the foetus' DNA.'

'Fergus, you're getting carried away. All we have to do is block the transfer of the foreign genes into human cells. We can find an answer.'

'No, no! This can't be released.'

'Fergus, keep your voice down. You're being alarmist.'

'For Christ's sake, Phil! You've seen the evidence. We have to make Gene-Asis listen. They've got to keep these seeds off the market.'

'Fergus, you don't realise what you're saying. It's like asking Microsoft to stop selling software. They simply won't do it. Microsoft patch their vulnerabilities. That's all we need to do – come up with a patch to prevent horizontal gene transfer.'

'That could take years. And, in the meantime, people suffer. There simply cannot be a Supercrop 13.'

'Good luck, mate, 'cause you'll never win.'

'I'll need your support, Phil.'

'Fergus, I'll verify everything in your report, but if they tell you not to publish it and you try to, then, I'm sorry, I can't afford to lose my job. I've a wife and kids, and expensive school fees.'

'Damn the job. It's immoral. We're not feeding the world – we're poisoning it.'

'Shush. Did you hear that?'

The audio recording stops there and Tracey speaks.

'Dr McPherson tried to persuade Gene-Asis to stop production of GM foods with KBv. He was fired. You are about to see a recording of Dr McPherson at the Mutenda clinic, taken by one of his team. Gene-Asis believed this footage destroyed. The young woman's name is Shoorai.'

The camera is filming inside the run-down hospital. Dr McPherson, in a lab coat, hovers at the side of a young woman. The bed is metal and the mattress bare. She is in labour. A wrinkled walnut of a woman is holding up a blanket to give her some privacy. Shoorai pants a few words at the old woman, who responds with a nod.

The Genesis Flaw

'What are you looking at?' Shoorai snaps at Dr McPherson as she blinks back salty sweat.

Dr McPherson looks down at his palm-sized notebook computer, clearly embarrassed. He continues to take notes, his sweaty hand slipping on the keys.

The girl, barely fifteen, stifles a cry. He steps forward, but the old woman shakes her head, so he steps back. She drops the privacy blanket and hobbles on her emaciated legs to a clay pot of water. Dipping a cloth in it, she wipes the girl's face. Before the rag is removed, Shoorai screams again, panting fast. McPherson says something to Shoorai in her native tongue, but she doesn't respond. He calls for a nurse, who arrives looking tired and dishevelled.

A few moments later, the baby's head begins to appear and with one final push, the infant drops into the nurse's hands. The mother lifts her head, craning her neck to see her child, laughing and gulping back tears. The nurse screws up her face in disgust as she cuts the umbilical cord. She ignores Shoorai's outstretched arms and places the baby on a blanket at the foot of the bed. The nurse backs away.

Catching sight of her child, Shoorai's face freezes, as if she has been mummified. Soon her lips begin to quiver. She stares at her son. Her whole body shakes. Finally, she turns away from him, weeping.

The professor steps closer to get a better look. The young mother releases a sound so hollow, so alien, that he drops instantly to his knees at her side. He hangs his head in shame.

A young man rushes in and, seeing his child, stops, speechless. Wanting an explanation, he stares at each person there. Mouths are open, but no words spoken. Shoorai faces her husband, tears and sweat smeared across her cheeks, imploring him. Reading his expression, she dives for the baby, trying to scoop him up in her arms, but the husband pulls her back.

The camera zooms in on the naked newborn.

From the child's back, something wormlike protrudes. It wriggles. The baby boy has an extended spine, which stretches ten centimetres from his coccyx and is covered in dark skin, forming a tail. The camera travels to the baby's face, to reveal he has no eyes or eye sockets. The skin stretches tightly from his cheeks to his forehead.

The professor puts his hands out to protect the baby but the old woman turns to him. She points a crooked finger and hisses, '*You!* You people did this. Leave us. Go!'

He hesitates and then backs away. She rails at him, screaming and pointing to the baby, spittle dribbling from her toothless mouth.

The camera is jolted violently to one side and then crashes to the floor. The last image is of scuffling feet, which suddenly cuts to black.

Chapter 73

All sixty-eight billboard screens were blank and, for a few seconds, thousands of people in Times Square were silent. Then, grappling for an explanation, they began to look around, asking questions.

'Did you see what I just saw?'

'I saw it. Yeah, we all did. How could anyone do that?'

'Yeah, and what about us? Those sons of bitches have been feeding us this shit. My brother's got that hepatitis disease, and it's all because of them.'

'They've been poisoning us.'

'Oh my God!' called a woman, fainting.

Shaking themselves from their inertia, the news presenters began an almost simultaneous live commentary, the volume rocketing.

'I'm going to sue.'

'Yeah, me too.'

'They're going down!'

'How the hell did she get control of the billboards? That's one clever lady,' said a tourist.

'Yeah, how the hell did she?' one NYPD police officer asked another.

'Get ready for some trouble,' replied his senior officer.

'Gene-Asis must pay!' yelled a man.

'Over there. Get them.'

Serena watched a group near the Gene-Asis building begin to charge forward angrily, recognising the well-publicised faces of some senior executives. But Bukowski was nowhere to be seen.

'We want answers.'

Like dogs at a race day chasing the rabbit, the media raced each other towards the evacuated Gene-Asis building, desperate to record the confrontation. The president of research and development, Randolph J. Randolph, was surrounded by shouting people, his bodyguards and the police fighting hopelessly to keep the hoards at bay.

'Murderers!'

Serena still gazed up at the blank screens above Two Times Square, and smiled. She didn't know how on earth John had hacked into all the Times Square billboards, but somehow he had done it. The Gene-Asis secret was out in the open. The noise was deafening. People talked animatedly, drivers honked their horns, news reporters shouted and jostled for position, police yelled directions, sirens blazed. Everyone was on the move, except for Serena. She remained rooted to the spot, like a tree withstanding the force of floodwaters. She was enjoying the moment. Still facing Two Times Square, she watched as all the billboards winked from their blankness into their many and varied advertising messages, all the brands boldly displayed, the ticker tapes resumed, the NASDAQ lit up once again.

Scuttling down the middle of the street, chased by dozens of news reporters clutching microphones, was Dr Singh, the American scientist who'd worked on the development of Supercrop Ultra. Escorted through the stationary traffic by a Gene-Asis security guard, he tried to hide his face from photographers, who hounded him with the same zeal they would a politician caught with his pants down. Serena wanted nothing more than to be with John, celebrating his achievement. Relishing her anonymity, she wandered through the crowds, alone and unnoticed, towards the Times Tower Hotel.

'Serena, cooeeee!'

Gloria's loud voice carried over the din of the busy streets. She raced after Serena, hands flapping above her head, until she caught up.

'Serena, this is amazing,' she said, gesturing at the billboards above them. 'However did you do it?'

'I didn't. A friend did. But thank you for saving my life. Ben was going to kill me.'

'Serena, I know I've been a real bitch to you, and I'm sorry. I watched the documentary on that funky memory key. That's how I knew you'd been telling the truth. What you did took guts. Real guts. I know I'd never have the courage to take on Gene-Asis. I'm so sorry I didn't believe you.'

'By sending that cop to arrest Ben, you saved my life.'

'I was dialling 911 when the fire alarm went off, and it was chaos. So when I saw you evacuating the building, I told that policeman Ben was a terrorist and you were his hostage. I'm so glad you're okay.'

'I'm fine now,' she said, looking around her.

'You know, I haven't done much in my life that I'm proud of. Until today,' Gloria beamed.

'Me neither,' replied Serena.

Gloria held out John's ring. Serena didn't take it.

'Would you hand it to the police commissioner for me? I'm going to my hotel.'

'What! No, darling, not yet. This is your greatest hour. You did all this and you must take the glory. You've earned it.'

'Gloria, I'm tired. The rest can wait. I want to leave.'

Gloria leaned in closer, her red gash of lipstick slightly smudged at the edges. She took Serena's hand in hers, holding it reassuringly.

'Let me look after you, darling. Let me do your PR. You're going to be famous and I can make you a fortune. And me a teensy-weensy one too. There'll be TV interviews, magazine articles, even a book.'

'All I want is justice. I want them brought to trial and convicted.'

'And I happen to know one of the very best lawyers in New York. I'll get on to him in a moment. But, first, you must make a statement. Look, the world's news media are all around. Pick a channel, any channel, it's all yours.'

Serena looked at the scrambling news crews racing around the Square, and she couldn't face them.

'I don't think …'

'Let me choose for you. Don't worry, Serena, I know what I'm doing here. I'm good at this. Remember?'

L. A. LARKIN

Among all this mayhem, one man stood still, leaning against a lamppost on a traffic island dividing Seventh and Broadway. His black hair glistened in the cold sunlight, not a strand out of place. He had his arms crossed, his head tilted slightly forward, deep in thought. He was not protected by any Gene-Asis security staff and, ironically, for that reason, hadn't been spotted by the news reporters. But his face was well known and it wouldn't be long before he was identified. Despite this, he appeared to display no fear.

Serena froze. The mere sight of him sent her heart rate through the roof. Memory-bites from her assault filled her head. She grabbed Gloria's arm for support.

Gloria followed her line of vision and spotted Bukowski.

'Don't let him bother you. He's going to get what he deserves. Come on, let's find you a big TV station to talk to.'

Gloria tried to steer Serena from him but she didn't move.

'What's the matter?'

Serena dragged her eyes away and looked at Gloria.

'I have something to say to him. Gloria, he tried to rape me.'

'Oh, sweet Jesus! You give him a kick in the groin from me.'

'Can you call for help if I need it?'

Before the speechless woman could reply, Serena had taken her first determined step in Bukowski's direction. 'You'll pay now, Bukowski,' she said.

He looked up and unfolded his arms. There was not a hint of concern in his body language. The 'One Way' sign above his head vibrated.

'I don't think so,' he replied slowly, grinning, displaying his shockingly white teeth.

'You'll be arrested for crimes against humanity and I'll enjoy testifying against you,' Serena said, her voice shaky.

'What crimes?' He shrugged. 'I've committed no crime. My colleagues at Gene-Asis may be guilty of crimes. But not me. I don't know anything about this. It's come as a terrible shock to me,' he said, faking a look of distress.

'No! Nobody will believe that crap. You're guilty as hell and you'll pay for it. How will you like prison, Bukowski?' she asked, deliberately echoing his words to her at Channel One.

The Genesis Flaw

He took a step towards her, and she instinctively backed away. Even surrounded by masses of people, she flinched at his overpowering dark presence. She looked round and saw Gloria watching her closely. It seemed that he sensed her fear and it elated him.

'Don't come any closer. Touch me and any one of these cops will arrest you.'

Bukowski remained where he was, shaking his head.

'Serena, you just don't understand how the corporate game is played, do you? Well, here's how it is: it's all about power. My power to destroy evidence, and anyone who'll try to speak against me. My power to buy the very best lawyers. My power to control the news media. And the power of a few choice words whispered to the police commissioner so I get off with a slapped wrist.'

Shaking her head in disbelief, she asked, 'Have you no remorse? Don't you care how this affects your daughter?'

'Remorse? What for? For running a company to maximise its profits? That's my job. For being loyal to Gene-Asis and protecting its reputation? That's my job. For having some fun with you? That was my pleasure.'

She punched Bukowski so hard that his head jerked sideways with a crack. Her fist had collided with the side of his nose and, as he straightened, blood trickled down his upper lip. Bukowski pulled a white handkerchief from his pocket and wiped it away, raising his eyebrows in surprise, while his eyes flashed angrily, like black marble in sunlight.

'Your father understood. A pity you don't.'

Serena's hand felt as if it were broken but her rage numbed the pain. She yelled at him.

'My dad died of lung cancer because of your toxic canola!'

'He knew what he was doing,' Bukowski said, putting away the handkerchief.

'How could he? He trusted your company. Trusted your seeds were safe to plant. You killed him just like you killed those Zimbabweans, and God knows how many people who died with Hep S. You're despicable.'

'He knew because we paid him to know.'

His words stopped her in her tracks.

'Paid him? What do you mean "paid him"?'

'I mean, paid him. And very well, I might add. We employed him to test GM crops for us; on the quiet, of course. It was never official. He helped us get around all that restrictive bureaucratic red tape.'

'He would never work for you,' she whispered, incredulous.

'So, who do you think paid your university fees and for your first car? For your brother's private medical fees? For your expensive family holidays? You wouldn't have had that successful career if we hadn't paid for your education.'

In that instant, it all made sense. How else had a small-time arable farmer like her father paid for all that? Neighbouring farms in Orange had struggled to make a profit, yet her dad always seemed to have money. Bukowski was telling the truth for once – her beloved father, the man she had always revered, had worked for the very company that killed him. She leaned forwards, her hands on her knees, barely able to stand.

'But your canola caused his cancer.'

'Yes, we're still working on that one. Can't get it quite right.' He shrugged. 'You know it took us a couple of days to work out who you really were. It's ironic, isn't it? Imagine my surprise when you turn out to be the daughter of an employee who helped develop the very varieties you have so misrepresented today.' He gestured towards the big screens. 'You must understand now why your father didn't want you taking us to court.'

She groaned, recalling his protestations, which she had mistakenly thought were because he'd wanted to end his life peacefully.

'Serena, are you all right?' asked Gloria, placing a protective arm around her.

'It's been fun, Serena, but I have things to do.'

'Go to hell, where you belong,' said Serena, as he walked away.

Chapter 74

Bukowski smiled broadly and strode towards a CNN news team that was hounding the police commissioner. He tapped the attractive news presenter's shoulder. She swung round to find him smiling charmingly at her.

'Hey, aren't you … ?'

'Yes, I am, and I would like to make a statement.'

'You would? Jesus, Larry, over here! Forget the police commissioner. This is Al Bukowski.'

'Okay, let's run with it,' she said. Then, smiling into the camera, she began. 'This is Tina Mudgeway from CNN, with an exclusive coming to you live from Times Square. With me is Al R. Bukowski, global CEO of Gene-Asis. He would like to make a statement about today's events.'

Bukowski looked straight into the camera: immaculate, unflustered and solemn.

'Firstly, I wish to speak to you from the heart, not in my capacity as CEO of Gene-Asis. The images we saw broadcast just now have moved and upset me greatly. Who would not be disturbed by such harrowing images of pain and suffering? If the allegations made in the documentary are true, I will be the first to speak out against those who participated in such heinous crimes.

'In my role as global CEO, however, I must point out that, at this stage, we have no idea of the validity of that documentary. It may, indeed, turn out to be some sick prank, the result of a vendetta against the company, or an attempt at extortion. We simply don't know.

'What I can tell you is that I was never made aware of any problems with these food trials in Zimbabwe, and I never saw any documentation that raised concerns. I was, to the contrary, informed that Supercrop 13 had proved safe for human consumption. If there had been the slightest doubt as to its safety, I would never have allowed its release.

'And let me say finally that I will be cooperating fully with the investigating authorities. I, more than anyone, want to get to the bottom of this. Thank you.'

He attempted to step away but was now surrounded by baying reporters.

'Mr Bukowski,' said Tina, 'you can't seriously expect us to believe that? A man in your position would know your products were unsafe. It's your job to know.'

'Tina, I'm only as good as the information I receive, and I never received such information.'

Like worker bees swarming around the queen bee, reporters fired questions at him, clambering to get near. In the midst of the buzzing media, Al R. Bukowski stood calmly, answering their questions. He was in his element.

Serena watched his performance with abhorrence. She could see his charm working its magic on the faces around him and realised that her earlier elation had been premature. They'd opened the can of Gene-Asis worms, but now its contents had to be untangled. In fact, Serena and John were only at the very beginning of a long and difficult investigation into Bukowski and the other senior executives. She knew it would take many years of gruelling legal work before the case against Bukowski reached the International Criminal Court. She thought of her father and how he had fallen into Gene-Asis' trap, to give his children the kind of start in life he had not had. Serena vowed she would correct her father's mistake. She'd use that Gene-Asis-funded education to see the legal process through to the bitter end.

'Serena, don't let that smarmy piece of shit bother you. Your story is the one everyone wants to hear,' said Gloria, forcing Serena back to reality. 'You're not going to let him win, are you?'

'Oh no,' she replied. 'I'm taking this man down. Find me a journalist, Gloria.'

'Will do,' she replied excitedly.

Within minutes, a camera crew and reporter came through the gridlocked traffic towards them. Serena saw the BBC World Service logo on the side of the camera. A ruddy-complexioned man put out his hand and shook hers enthusiastically.

'Hi, I'm Paul Weil from the BBC. I know Tracey Pollack very well, and I hear from Gloria you worked together on this amazing exposé.'

'I did the groundwork, that's all. She made the documentary and John Flynn ran it on the billboards. Have you heard from Tracey? Is she still alive?'

'She's fine. We've been in contact with the British Consul and she's turned up over the border in Botswana. She's under the protection of the British Embassy.'

'Thank God!'

'Serena, I can only imagine the hell you've been through to uncover this crime. We'd like to hear your story, and I'd be proud to do the interview.'

She carefully looked at Paul, studying his face.

'Let's do it.'

'Just tell it exactly how it was.'

And she did. Paul let the camera run and she told her story uninterrupted. When, through sheer exhaustion, Serena could speak no more, and the cameras were off, he spoke above the hubbub of shouting news crews that had descended upon them.

'You're a very brave woman, Serena Swift.'

Serena was surrounded by cameras, microphones and bodies surging at her, pushing and shoving to get closer. Cops were trying to control them, with little success. The BBC crew attempted to protect her from being crushed and, gasping for air, she looked up at the clear blue sky. Standing on the roof of the US Army Recruitment cabin, only ten metres away, was John, his eyes sparkling, waving at her with his arms high in the air. She laughed with the joy of seeing him.

'Can you get me to that man?' she asked Paul.

'Sure can. But this mob will follow, I'm afraid. Make way!' Paul shouted as he and his crew pushed a path through the sea of microphones. He lifted Serena onto the cabin's roof, and into John's arms. Cameras flashed.

'You did it,' said Serena, hugging him.

'*We* did it,' he replied, 'and thank God you're safe.' He reluctantly pulled away from her, but still held her hand. 'There's someone who wants to speak to you,' he said and gave her the phone.

'We're bleeding famous,' screeched Tracey.

'Tracey! Are you all right?'

'I'm fine. Being pampered by a very spunky bloke at the embassy. I think it's love,' she joked.

'I know the feeling,' Serena said, squeezing John's hand. She could hear Tracey squealing on the other end of the line, but ignored her and directed her next statement to John. 'And this time, I'm not going to let you slip through my fingers.'

Some distance away, Bukowski looked up at her on the roof. The police were escorting him from Times Square. Did she see a moment's fear in his dark, cold eyes?

Yes, she did.

'Let the battle begin,' she said.

Author's Note

I have created a fictional world in which genetic engineering goes horribly wrong, threatening the survival of the human race. While I have taken great pains to research the science behind genetic engineering of food – interviewing world-renowned geneticists and virologists – the biotech company and genetically engineered products and processes in the book are all my invention.

During the course of my research, I learned a great deal; some of it shocked me and all of it I found fascinating. I hadn't realised how much of our food contains genetically modified organisms (GMO) – some estimate as much as seventy per cent of processed foods in the US. I discovered that debates rage about GMO's safety and that claims of bigger crop yields have been challenged, that parts of viruses can be used in transgenes, and that some scientists believe gene transfer from plant to human gut bacteria is possible.

The Genesis Flaw has passed through many hands and each time it has become a better story. I would like to take this opportunity to thank Michael for his encouragement and unwavering support. I am indebted to Gaby Naher, my agent, for championing my novel and for her invaluable guidance. My publisher, Colette Vella, has helped me grow as a writer, and I thank her for her insight and enthusiasm. All three of you have changed my life.

The team at Pier 9 has worked incredibly hard to deliver this book and has been a joy to work with. In particular, I cannot thank enough the sales and marketing team. Every bookshop I have been to has sung your praises and what better praise could there be?

Many geneticists and experts in their field have assisted me. In particular, I would like to acknowledge Professor Joe Cummins, Professor Emeritus of Genetics at the University of Western Ontario, whose generosity with his time enabled me to fine-tune the deformities and illnesses described in the story. Jeffrey M. Smith, Executive Director of the Institute of Responsible Technology and author of *Seeds of Deception*, your list of 'What could go wrong?', gave me a feast of ideas for this story. Jeremy Rifkin, Dr Arpad Pusztai, Greenpeace Australia's John Hepburn, and all the geneticists and virologists who gave up their time to answer my questions, but who prefer to remain anonymous, I salute you.

I want to give a special thanks to Dean Carter, information security guru and the inspiration for my hacker character. Dean swept me up into a world of hackers' jargon and chat rooms, data and identity theft, and even took me along to the Ruxcon hackers' conference. I should make it very clear that he does nothing illegal and works for an organisation paid by companies to hack their own systems. He's a good guy. Dean, I couldn't have done it without you.

Lastly, thank you, Mum. I learned from you the value of an independent and questioning mind and the importance of standing up for what you believe in.

If you would like to read some of the research that inspired *The Genesis Flaw*, please go to my website: www.lalarkin.com